TREASURES
of
ANCIENT DEVON

John Allan and Simon Timms,
with contributions from John Cherry,
Alison Hopper-Bishop and
Norman Shiel

Photographs by David Garner
with contributions from
Plymouth City Museums
and James Ravilious

DEVON BOOKS

First published in Great Britain in 1996 by Devon Books

Copyright © 1996 Devon Books

ISBN 0 86114 909 2

British Library Cataloguing in Publication Data

A CIP record for this title is available from the British Library

DEVON BOOKS
Official Publisher to Devon County Council

Halsgrove House
Lower Moor Way
Tiverton, Devon EX16 6SS
Tel: 01884 243242
Fax: 01884 243325

Printed in Great Britain by Culm Print Ltd, Tiverton, Devon

CONTENTS

ACKNOWLEDGEMENTS

The idea for this book arose from the joint Devon County Council–Exeter City Museums exhibition of 'Treasures of Ancient Devon' which was displayed at the Royal Albert Memorial Museum, Exeter from December 1996 to February 1997. This exhibition drew together objects from museums, libraries and archives across Devon and thanks are due to the following organisations for their support:

The Beaford Centre; the Trustees of Dartington Hall; the Devon Libraries Service; the Devon Record Office; English Heritage; the Exeter City Museums Service; Exeter Guildhall; the Museum of Dartmoor Life (Okehampton); the Museum of North Devon (Barnstaple); the National Trust (Devon Region); the Trustees of the North Devon Athenaeum (Barnstaple); the Plymouth City Museums Service; the Teignmouth Museum and Historical Society; the Torquay Natural History Society; and Messrs Watts, Blake, Bearne and Co. plc.

The help of the following individuals is also gratefully acknowledged: Mr T. Browne, Peter Child, Christopher Currie, Cynthia Gaskell-Brown, Frances Griffith and Mr D.J. Nicholls. All photographs have been specially taken by David Garner unless otherwise credited.

BOOKS OF INTEREST

In addition to the books and articles mentioned in the main text, readers may find the following general books of interest. They can all be found in local bookshops or are obtainable from local libraries:

Peter Beacham (ed.) 1990 (reissued 1995), *Devon Building* – essays on the county's traditional buildings.

Bridget Cherry and Sir Nicholas Pevsner 1989, *The Buildings of England: Devon* – the definitive architectural survey of the county.

Aileen Fox 1964 (revised 1973), *South West England* – pioneering work on the archaeology of Cornwall and Devon.

Frances Griffith 1988, *Devon's Past – An Aerial View* – over 100 sites illustrated and described from prehistoric times to the present century.

W.G. Hoskins 1954 (reissued 1992), *Devon* – the magisterial and highly readable account of the county's history.

Malcolm Todd 1987, *The South West to AD 1000* – overview of the archaeology and early history of the region.

INTRODUCTION

Devon is an ancient place. People have farmed its land for over 5000 years, and the earliest human activity can be traced back more than a quarter of a million years to the Old Stone Age.

Devon's great antiquity can be seen all around us – in the patterns of medieval farms, woods and fields, along Roman roads and through prehistoric hillforts and burial mounds which often still survive as local landmarks today.

Devon's history is also witnessed by the wealth of artefacts, books, documents and photographs that are conserved and displayed in museums, archives and libraries across the county. This book highlights just 26 of them. They cover the prehistoric (Nos 1–6), Roman (Nos 7–9) and medieval (Nos 10–16) periods and also items from our more recent past (Nos 17–26).

Only a few can be classified as 'treasure' in the strict sense of being made of gold or silver, but they are all surely treasures of our common past by virtue of their rarity, antiquity, craftsmanship and beauty. As we marvel at them, let us remind ourselves that our lives today are but a brief moment in the long history of Devon – both past and future.

DISCOVERING DEVON'S PAST

On 22 August 1978, Mr Cyril Cole was ploughing a field on his farm at Rose Ash in North Devon when a large stone became caught in his plough. Pausing to cast the stone aside, he saw that it had covered a small circular pit which had opened up in the ground. He reached in only to come up with a handful of ash and burnt bone. Mr Cole reported his discovery to the Reverend Christopher Tull, Vicar of Mariansleigh with Rose Ash, who in turn contacted W.G. Hoskins, the eminent landscape historian then living in Exeter. Professor Hoskins passed the news on to Simon Timms, the Devon County Archaeologist.

The end result was that, over that August Bank Holiday weekend, Dr Geoffrey Wainwright and his team of archaeologists from England's Central Excavation Unit excavated Mr Cole's pit with an appreciative group of local people looking on. They found that the pit contained a Bronze Age clay urn in which the cremated remains of one of our prehistoric ancestors had been laid to rest 3000 years ago. Once the urn had been safely excavated, it was taken to London for study and conservation, and subsequently, by agreement of Mr Cole, acquired by Exeter City Museums with the support of Devon County Council. The urn is now part of the Museums's permanent collection.

Such stories of archaeological discovery have been repeated, in one form or another, across the length and breadth of Devon. Artefacts that are hundreds and even thousands of years old and which have long lain buried beneath our fields and settlements have been discovered through such activities as farming, mining, and building works – and of course through archaeological survey and excavation. But this is only part of the story for, as Mr Cole's urn shows, once found, an object has to be carefully conserved and stored so that it is available for public display. This is where museums come in. Among their wealth of material, museums across Devon care for and display an astonishing range of artefacts relating to the county's past. Old or not so old, rare or everyday, traditional or exotic, they are all 'the real thing' – and often evidence of high levels of art and craftsmanship. And they act as a direct link with our common past and all the generations that have trod this land before us.

In Devon we are fortunate to possess a plethora of museums which come in all shapes and sizes and contain items of national and even international importance. Indeed Devon has more recognised museums than any other English county. Large museums at places such as Exeter, Plymouth and Torquay house the principal collections, whilst there are also dozens of small community museums ranging from Ilfracombe in the north and Kingsbridge in the south to Budleigh Salterton in the east and Okehampton in the west.

Many of these smaller museums are in the hands of local societies and charitable trusts made up of volunteers, whilst the city and district councils look after some of the larger ones. At the heart of the museum world today is the Museums and Galleries Commission's scheme of National Museum Registration which means that Ashburton Museum can become officially registered alongside the giants such as the British Museum. Behind the scenes the specialist staff of the Area Museum Council for the South West provide valuable support and advice. Devon County Council too lends a helping hand with grant aid and through its heritage services such as education, archives, libraries, tourism and conservation. Its Devon Learning Resources service offers museum education opportunities to schools across the county.

But perhaps with all the conflicting demands of modern life, the value of museums to society can sometimes be overlooked. To some they may be seen as no more than the dustbins of our past and their cultural, community and – yes – economic contribution to the life of Devon is ignored. One way of explaining this lack of recognition is to realise that they remain among the unsung glories of Devon. And it is to encourage readers to marvel at their glories that this book has been written. If it tempts you to visit a Devon museum, it will have done its job!

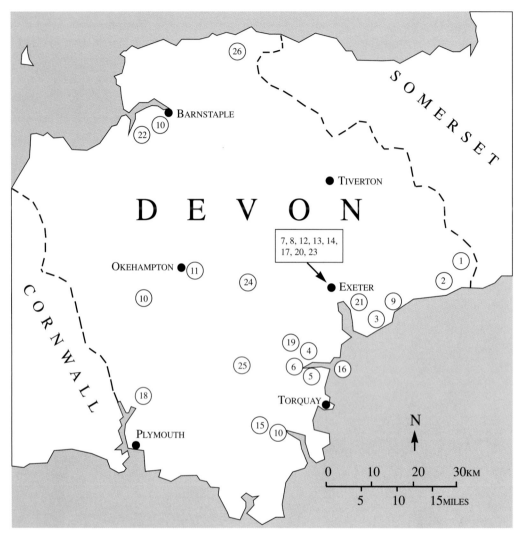

Location map showing find-spots or places associated with objects described in the text.

Devon: an ancient land. Photographed by James Ravilious.

9

┌─────┐
│ 1 │
└─────┘

PREHISTORIC HAND-AXES
FROM THE AXE VALLEY
Mainly *c.* 250,000 – 200,000 years ago

From the collections of Exeter City Museums

Devon lay on the edge of the inhabited world of the hunters and gatherers of the Palaeolithic period (the Old Stone Age), and finds of Palaeolithic date are restricted almost entirely to the south and east of the county. Hand-axes form the most distinctive and prolific artefacts of this period, and have been found on some 40 sites in Devon, mainly in ones or twos. The major series of more than 2500 hand-axes recovered from the gravels of the River Axe at Broom on the Devon/Dorset/Somerset border is thus exceptional, and must reflect the repeated seasonal use of this favoured area on the edge of the Axe. Many of these artefacts, which are among the oldest tools used by our humanoid predecessors, were discovered during gravel working in the nineteenth century.

Hand-axes in Britain can be roughly divided into two shapes – pointed and ovate (egg-shaped). At some sites one or other type will predominate. At Broom, however, there is a mixture of the two, and also great variety in size and condition. Some are fresh, others have evidently been rolled by river action from occupation sites further upstream. Most are of brown chert, but some are of flint.

Reading

W.S.M. D'Urban 1878 'Palaeolithic Implements in the Valley of the Axe', *Geological Magazine* **5**, 37-8.

D.A. Roe 1981 *The Lower and Middle Palaeolithic Periods in Britain.*

R.A. Shakesby & N. Stephens 1984 'The Pleistocene Gravels of the Axe Valley, Devon', *Report and Transactions of the Devonshire Association* **116**, 77-88.

2

A PREHISTORIC CUP FROM FARWAY
c. 2000 – 1500 BC

From the collections of Exeter City Museums

Small cups made of precious or exotic materials are rare but important elements in rich burials of the Early Bronze Age, both in England and on the Continent; their function is unknown. Examples are known in gold, silver and amber; this cup, which is less than 10cm in height, is the best-preserved of such vessels made in black shale and is one of two examples to have come from Devon. The raw material almost certainly comes from Kimmeridge in Dorset.

It was found in 1868 during the excavation of a barrow at Broad Down, Farway, in east Devon, by the Rev. Richard Kirwan, the rector of the local parish of Gittisham. The barrow displayed an interesting sequence of funerary practice which Kirwan interpreted as follows: first, a levelled platform of flints had been laid on the old ground surface; it displayed signs of burning (probably of burnt brushwood or furze). Above this was a bed of charcoal which Kirwan saw as a funerary pyre. This contained nodules of red ochre and iron pyrites 'which occurred in a quantity suggesting deliberate collection', and on which a deposit of calcined human bone had been placed. The cup must have been placed in the mound after the cremated bone; it lay close to it, but slightly higher in the mound. It is unburnt. A large barrow was then erected over the deposit.

Cups such as this are little masterpieces of Bronze Age craftsmanship. The Farway vessel has long been believed to have been made on a lathe, but recent experimental production of a replica has demonstrated that it could have been made with quite simple hand tools. The late Dennis Sloper demonstrated this by making a replica in about 120 working hours.

Reading

David Clarke, Trevor Cowie & Andrew Foxon 1985 *Symbols of Power at the Time of Stonehenge.*

Richard Kirwan 1868 'Memoir of the excavation of three barrows at Broad Down, Farway, near Honiton', *Report and Transactions of the Devonshire Association* **2.2**, 619–49.

Dennis Sloper 1989 'The Experimental Production of a Replica of an Early Bronze Age Shale Cup from Farway Down', *Proceedings of the Devon Archaeological Society* **47**, 113–17.

THE PREHISTORIC GOLD HOARD
FROM COLATON RALEIGH
c. 1000 – 650 BC

From the collections of Exeter City Museums

The hoard consists of three gold bracelets, accompanied by a small folded sheet of gold. The bracelets are of two sorts. Two are formed from flat bands of metal, the terminals simply being folded over. The third is worked from a rod of gold of D-shaped section, with expanded terminals. Both types are characteristic of Late Bronze Age finery; they are datable to *c.* 1000–650 BC.

The hoard is the only surviving find of prehistoric goldwork from Devon (an amber dagger pommel inlaid with gold pins from a Dartmoor barrow was destroyed during the Plymouth blitz). Comparable hoards of Bronze Age gold are, however, known from Cornwall. The Colaton Raleigh find was discovered by chance in 1986 when a man collecting firewood spotted them protruding from the ground beside a path near Colaton Raleigh in east Devon. He took the bracelets, which he found to be packed one within the other, to Exeter Museum, where they were identified as a hoard of Bronze Age gold-work, an opinion later confirmed by the British Museum. At a coroner's inquest in July 1986 they were declared Treasure Trove (i.e. Crown property), and the finder was award-ed an *ex gratia* payment. The hoard was bought from HM Treasury by Exeter City Museums with the support of Devon County Council in 1987.

Upon close inspection faint vertical ribbing and minor areas of raggedness can be seen on the inner faces of the flat-sectioned bracelets, suggesting that these remain unfinished. The presence of a small folded fragment of gold might also indicate that this is a smith's hoard. A small excavation on the site of the find showed that the original burial place of the hoard had been disturbed in antiquity.

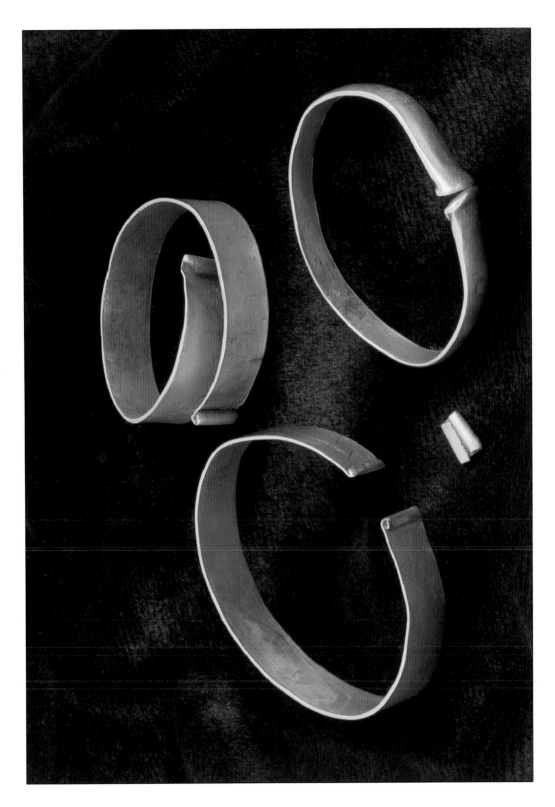

THE PREHISTORIC WOODEN FIGURE FROM KINGSTEIGNTON
c. 426 – 352 BC

Loaned to Exeter City Museums
by Messrs Watts, Blake, Bearne and Co. plc

Prehistoric wooden figures are great rarities in the British Isles; only seven examples survive, spanning a period of more than 2500 years. This example, which was found in 1867 by workmen digging ball clay at Zitherixon, Kingsteignton, is owned by Messrs Watts, Blake, Bearne and Co. plc, who have deposited it on loan in Exeter City Museums. According to one nineteenth-century account the figure was discovered 'in a standing position 23 feet below the surface against a black oak tree which was embedded in mud, sand and gravel and lying on the deposit of large stones which overlies the clay here'.

The figure, which is 34cm tall, is carved from the centre of a branch of oak. It is clearly male with stubby legs, long body and very long neck. A horizontal hole through the neck may once have held detachable arms. Professor Bryony Coles of Exeter University has recently undertaken a study of this figure and the other wooden figures surviving elsewhere in the British Isles. There has been great uncertainty about their date, so Professor Coles initiated a programme of radiocarbon-dating at Oxford University, taking tiny samples from each figure. The Kingsteignton sample was datable to *c.* 426–352 BC.

In examining the formal characteristics of these figures, Professor Coles noted features common to several of them, such as sexual ambiguity, a tendency to asymmetry and scoring of the left side of the face. These are not characteristics of the Kingsteignton figure, whose purpose remains unknown. It is tempting to see it as having some symbolic significance; it was found against the remains of an oak tree, and we know that trees and woodlands were objects of veneration in the prehistoric period.

Reading

Bryony Coles 1990 'Anthropomorphic Wooden Figures from Britain and Ireland', *Proceedings of the Prehistoric Society* **56**, 315–33.

William Pengelly 1883 'Discoveries in the more recent deposits of the Bovey Basin, Devon', *Report and Transactions of the Devonshire Association* **15**, 368–95.

THE COFFINSWELL HOARD OF PREHISTORIC 'CURRENCY BARS'
Probably second or first century BC

From the collections of Exeter City Museums

This magnificent hoard of 'currency bars' (so-called because Julius Caesar in his *Commentaries* observed that prehistoric British tribes used iron bars as well as coins for currency) is one of the most remarkable archaeological finds in Devon in recent years. It was discovered in 1990, after a farmer at Coffinswell had ploughed up a number of rusty iron bars. He reported the find to local metal detectorists, who in turn contacted Torquay Museum. A small excavation was carried out in 1991 to recover the hoard, since it would obviously suffer further damage if left *in situ*. The excavation, which was supported by Devon County Council, revealed a corroded mass of iron bars packed tightly into a small pit. It was therefore decided to lift it entire and transport it to Exeter City Museums, where Alison Hopper-Bishop of the museum's conservation department undertook the lengthy and laborious process of conservation and cleaning. Her work revealed that the hoard contains about 80 bars; the original deposit must have included 100 or more. They were arranged in eight tightly-bound bundles, each of between eight and eleven bars, whose twine wrappings could be discerned by careful cleaning. The bindings proved to be stems of fern, and further vegetable matter around the edge of the hoard indicated that organic material, possibly bracken, had been used to line the pit.

The bars are all plain rods, beaten at one end into a socket shape. The process of forming the rounded end requires a surprisingly high degree of smithing skill, and can only be achieved with high-quality malleable iron. The sockets, then, may have served to show off the high quality of the iron. In fact modern experimental manufacture of similar bars using traditional technology shows that the production of a single bar of this sort would require a great deal of work – 50 or more working hours.

This is one of the largest currency bar hoards ever recovered in Britain. Of some 49 finds in Britain, one exceptional find contained nearly 400 bars and three had around 150, but most finds are considerably smaller. The only other find from Devon was made by Sir Bourchier Wrey's gamekeeper whilst rabbiting in Holne Chase in 1870; not recognising their significance, he let them be used by the gardener as frames for growing cucumbers and it was only later that their remaining fragments were recognised and deposited in Torquay Museum.

Richard Hingley's recent study has emphasised that most hoards have been recovered in circumstances which suggest their deposition was strictly controlled and was part of an act of ritual, for example on the boundary of an important prehistoric settlement. This emphasis on the ritual or social purpose of currency bars is in contrast to the more traditional explanation of bars as units of wealth or pieces of raw iron ready to be worked into iron tools.

Reading

P.F.S.Amory 1906 'Supposed currency bars found near Holne Chase Camp', *Report and Transactions of the Devonshire Association* **38**, 370-76.

Richard Hingley 1990 'Iron Age "Currency Bars": The Archaeological and Social Context', *Archaeological Journal* **147**, 91-117.

S.J. Simpson 1991 *Excavation of a Hoard of Iron Currency Bars in South Devon. Archive Report*, Exeter Museums Archaeological Field Unit Report **91.44**.

THREE PREHISTORIC BRONZE ANIMAL FIGURINES FROM MILBER
c. 100 BC – *c.* 50 AD

From the collections of Torquay Museum

These three small figurines of bronze were found during excavations carried out at Milber Down hillfort near Newton Abbot by the Devon Archaeological Society in 1938. The hillfort has three concentric and widely-spaced ramparts; the bronzes were found in the upper ditch fill of the middle rampart.

The figures, which are about 6cm long and up to 3.5cm high, are a bird, a stag and a duck. The bird has a long tail and detached wings; the stag is prostrate, with a raised band extending across its body; the duck is swimming, with a little cake in its mouth. In the published report of the excavation, Sir Cyril Fox, then the doyen of Celtic art studies, wrote as follows:

> *The stag and the bird shew just clever naturalistic modelling – nothing Celtic about them, whereas the duck is* essential duckery *expressed in the simplest terms, and is of the same order as the Hounslow boars, the Harpenden ram or the Felmersham fish head. It represents a specific British-Celtic contribution to art and is timeless and unique. But this exquisite creature is more than a duck; it is a duck swimming. The double lines are slightly broader in front and behind; the duck's movement – I have watched it so often in St James' Park – creates a double bar of light and shade along its side, stronger in front and lapping up when the tail is lowered. I expect that there were ducks kept on the sacred pools of the Celts such as that in which the* Aurum Tolosanum *was hidden, and fed by the priests; and watched lovingly by craftsmen and others, as we sit and watch the ducks in our parks.*

These are most unusual objects, and it has been suggested that they served some religious or ritual function. They might for example have been mounted on a ceremonial staff, vessel or casket.

Reading

Devon Archaeological Society 1987 *Field Guide No. 1: Milber Down.*
Aileen Fox 1996 *Prehistoric Hillforts in Devon.*
A. Fox, C.A.R. Radford, E.H. Rogers & A.H. Shorter 1949–50 'Report on the excavations on Milber Down, 1937–8', *Proceedings of the Devon Archaeological Society* **4**, 27–66.

A ROMAN *AUREUS* FROM EXETER
AD 75 – 79

From the collections of Exeter City Museums

Roman coins are one of the main clues for tracing the history of Roman conquest and settlement in Britain following the invasion of AD 43. Large numbers of Roman coins have been found in Exeter. W.T.P. Shortt, who lived in Heavitree in the mid nineteenth century, was one of the first people to collect them as they were found on building sites in the city, and many of his finds are now in Exeter City Museums.

The gold *aureus* was the most valuable denomination of Roman coinage so it is not surprising that very few have been found in Exeter. This example is one of only four known from the city. Norman Shiel, classics teacher at Exeter School, writes:

This aureus *of Vespasian is a fine example of Flavian portraiture showing the rugged features of the soldier emperor who had emerged victorious from the turmoil of the Civil War which followed Nero's suicide in AD 68. Vespasian reigned as emperor from AD 69-79 and brought order and stability back to the Roman world. During his reign, the Second Augustan Legion left the fortress base which it had established in Exeter (and from which the early town of* Isca Dumnoniorum *developed). Much earlier in his life Vespasian himself had been the commander of this same legion during the emperor Claudius's invasion of Britain in AD 43. His biographer tells us that he led this legion into the southwest of Britain where he encountered heavy resistance from the British tribes occupying hillforts in the area and had to fight many battles.*

The aureus, *made from almost pure gold, represented very considerable wealth and few have ever been found save in hoards. So far only four have been found in Exeter, which was occupied continuously by the Romans from the 50s AD. At the time of issue an* aureus *represented about six week's earnings for a legionary soldier. Anyone who lost one would make every effort to find it again.*

The reverse of the coin depicts Ceres holding ears of corn and a sceptre. Ceres was a Roman corn goddess, symbolic of good harvests, whose name has given us our word 'cereal'.

Reading
Norman Shiel 1980 'Another Exeter *aureus'*, *Proceedings of the Devon Archaeological Society*
38, 124-5.

Roman aureus from Exeter, depicting on the obverse (above) the emperor Vespasian, and on the reverse (below) the corn goddess Ceres.

A ROMAN PORTRAIT HEAD FROM EXETER
Late first century AD

From the collections of Exeter City Museums

Although Exeter was occupied by the Romans for over 300 years (being first the site of a Roman legionary fortress, and then of the town of *Isca Dumnoniorum*, the regional capital of this part of Roman Britain), finds of Roman sculpture are very rare from the city. This fine miniature sculpted head measuring only 7.5cm in height was found during the excavations directed by John Collis in Goldsmith Street in 1971 in advance of the construction of Exeter's Guildhall shopping centre. It was found in a mid or late fourth century context, but in fact dates to the late first century AD. Dr Roger Ling in his study of the head writes:

A realistic portrait of a man in late middle age, bald on the dome of the head, with bushy hair round the temples and the back of the neck. The fracture at the neck is flattish and worn smooth, but the head is presumably broken from a complete statuette (or a bust). In style there are clear signs of the 'veristic' manner favoured for middle-class portraits of the late Republic and early Empire, and taken over in modified form for portraits of the emperor Vespasian. The features of this style are a dry and often unflattering realism with much use of sharply cut facial creases. Our head shows such creases running across the forehead above the eyebrows, rising on either side of the bridge of the nose, and sloping down from the nostrils to the corners of the mouth. In addition there are traces of laughter-lines at the outer corners of the eyes and pouches below the eyes; and the cheeks are hollowed, with folds of loose flesh falling beneath the jaw. Further signs of individuality are the highly domed head, the bulging brows, and the deeply set eyes. At the same time the mouth is turned down at the corners and deeply cut with the drill so as to produce an expression of pain or suffering reminiscent of some work in the Hellenistic tradition. If the general style suggests a late Republican or early Imperial date, further precision may be offered by the remains of drill-holes in the hair round the back of the head and above the ears. This technical feature begins to appear in the Flavian period when it was used for the honeycomb effect of fashionable female coiffures and also, more discreetly, in certain portraits of Titus and Domitian... . It is possible therefore to suggest a Flavian date for our piece too.

The marble is a fine semi-translucent white stone almost certainly from a Mediterranean source, so the portrait was either imported ready worked from the Mediterranean world or carved in a piece of imported marble in Britain by a sculptor versed in the styles of Romano-Italian ateliers. Its purpose must remain uncertain: the tiny scale is unusual for a marble portrait. The most plausible explanation, suggested by Professor J.M.C. Toynbee (in a letter dated 2 August 1971), is that it came from a memorial bust set up in a private house or in a tomb.

Reading

Roger Ling 1991 'Sculptural finds' in Neil Holbrook & Paul Bidwell, *Roman Finds from Exeter*, Exeter Archaeological Report **4**, 230-31.

9

A ROMAN BRONZE FIGURE OF ACHILLES AND THE CENTAUR FROM SIDMOUTH
Probably second century AD

From the collections of Exeter City Museums

This battered and abraded figure shows Cheiron, a Centaur of Greek mythology, with the Trojan War hero, Achilles, on his back. It is perhaps one of the most evocative images from Devon, combining as it does Greek myth with Devon's Roman past.

The group shows the young Achilles equipped with bow and quiver, riding on his tutor Cheiron, who has the Centaur's body of a horse and trunk and head of a man. Cheiron raises his left arm to his face, as if searching for some distant quarry, but as he does so a wild beast snaps at one of his forelegs. The group sits on a long rectangular plate, below which descends a rod of roughly rectangular profile.

The group, which is 18cm high, was found by fishermen on Sidmouth beach close to the mouth of the river Sid in 1840, hence the piece's abraded condition. It was recognised as a Roman object by the local antiquaries Peter Orlando Hutchinson and N.S. Heineken and was presented to Exeter Museum by the Rev. Heineken in 1871.

The group was long believed to be the top element of a Roman legionary standard, and early studies of the piece linked it to the advance of the Second Augustan legion. This interpretation is no longer tenable: the group in fact comes from the top of an elaborate Roman folding tripod. Such furnishings had three uprights, each topped with a group of figures, connected to each other by diagonal bars. Flat trays, bowls or basins could be held within. Such an expensive and elaborate house-furnishing, no doubt an import from abroad, is a surprising sign of the adoption of Roman household customs in rural Devon.

Reading

W.T.P. Shortt 1842 *Collectanea Curiosa*.

P.O. Hutchinson 1857 *A New Guide to Sidmouth*.

M.V. Taylor 1944 'The Sidmouth Bronze: Legionary Standard or Tripod?', *Antiquaries Journal* **24**, 22-6.

SAXON PENNIES OF THE BARNSTAPLE MINT
c. AD 979 – 1086

From the collections of the Museum of North Devon
and the North Devon Athenaeum

Prior to the Norman conquest of AD 1066, the kings of Late Saxon England operated a quite remarkably complex and sophisticated monetary system, many of whose intricacies have emerged only through recent scholarship. Following the monetary reform carried out by Eadgar in 973, the coinage took the form of a series of national types issued for a restricted period – at first of six years, later of only three. Each type displayed the royal portrait and titles on the obverse while the reverse design was divided into quarters (marking where the coins should be cut if they were to form halfpennies or farthings) and bore the name of the mint and moneyer. The striking of coins was carried out in as many as 90 Saxon towns scattered throughout the country, whose output was broadly proportional to their economic importance. The basic unit of currency was the penny, made of sterling silver (92.5% silver), whose quality was maintained by close regulation. Most of the coins of these types have been found in Scandinavian hoards, reflecting the fact that much of the Saxon coinage served to pay *Danegeld*, the levy demanded by Viking armies from the English king on their raids across the North Sea.

Devon had four Saxon mints – Barnstaple, Exeter, Lydford and Totnes. Barnstaple was among the smallest mints in England, so its coins are amongst the rarities of the late Saxon and Norman series. The collection of 15 Barnstaple coins now held in the Museum of North Devon is a splendid series of the mint's issues, with some of its great rarities. This selection includes the following coins: 10a. Aethelred II, First Hand type, struck by Alfhelm, *c.* 979–985. 10b. Aethelred II, Second Hand type, struck by Byrhsige, *c.* 985–991. 10c. Aethelred II, Crux type, struck by Alfsige, *c.* 991–997. 10d–f. Aethelred II, Long Cross type, struck by Byrhsige, *c.* 997–1003. 10g. Edward the Confessor, Hammer Cross type, struck by Aelfric, *c.* 1059–62. 10h. William I, PAXS type, struck by Seword, *c.* 1083–6.

Reading

Michael Dolley 1970 *Anglo-Saxon Pennies*.

Bror E. Hildebrand 1881 *Anglosachsiska Mynt* (Anglo-Saxon coins in the Royal Swedish Cabinet of Medals at Stockholm).

Sir Ian Stewart 1975 'The Barnstaple Mint and Its Moneyers', *Catalogue of the R.P.V. Brettell Collection of Devon Coins: Barnstaple* Glendining & Sons.

Eight Saxon pennies from the Barnstaple mint. Obverses (above) and reverses (below).

SAXON PENNIES OF THE MINTS
OF LYDFORD AND TOTNES
AD 959 – 975

From the collections of Exeter City Museums

These two coins are great rarities. The Lydford penny is the only known coin of the mint of Eadgar's reign and the earliest issue of the Lydford mint. The Totnes piece is one of two such pennies known; both were found far from Devon – in a hoard at Chester in 1950. This one was acquired by Exeter City Museums with the support of Devon County Council in 1990.

10i. Eadgar, Reform Issue, *c.* AD 973–5, struck at Lydford by the moneyer Aethered.

10j. Eadgar, Bust Crowned type, *c.* AD 959–73, struck at Totnes by the moneyer Burhstan.

A Saxon penny from the Lydford mint. Obverse (left) and reverse (right).

A Saxon penny from the Totnes mint. Obverse (left) and reverse (right).

A SCULPTED STONE HEAD FROM OKEHAMPTON CASTLE
Mid – late 12th century AD

From the collections of Plymouth City Museums

This sculpture takes the form of a head with sunken cheeks, narrow chin, bulging almond-shaped eyes, open mouth and crudely scratched hair. It projects on a long neck from a block of stone which would have been embedded in a wall. It is 24cm high.

The sculpture was found during English Heritage's programme of excavation in the 1970s at Okehampton Castle, which is recorded in Domesday Book (AD 1086), when it was held by the Sheriff of Devon. The head was found with other remains of demolished stone buildings which had been used to backfill the motte ditch of the Norman castle prior to a major new building campaign of *c.* 1300.

In his published study of this find, Jeffrey West interpreted the stone as the keystone, spandrel stone or label from an arch or pair of arches. He associated this sculpture with work in various churches in North Devon and North-East Cornwall, such as Parkham, Buckland Brewer, Shebbear and Morwenstow. These belong to the mid and late 12th century, the probable date of the Okehampton Castle find, which has been part of the display of finds from the castle excavations in the Museum of Dartmoor Life at Okehampton.

Reading

Jeffrey K. West 1982 'Two Romanesque Stone Carvings' in R.A. Higham, J.P. Allan & S.R. Blaylock, 'Excavations at Okehampton Castle, Devon; Part 2, the Bailey', *Proceedings of the Devon Archaeological Society* **40**, 79–82.

George Zarnecki 1979 *Romanesque Arches Decorated with Human and Animal Heads*, Studies in Romanesque Sculpture, No. **6**.

$$\boxed{12}$$

THE EXETER PUZZLE JUG
c. AD 1300

From the collections of Exeter City Museums

The Exeter Puzzle Jug is perhaps the most celebrated example of medieval imported pottery found in England, and one of the most extraordinary pieces of medieval ceramics to have been discovered anywhere in northern Europe.

The jug was probably made around 1300. It was found in fragments in South Street, Exeter, in 1899 and restored at the British Museum in the 1930s at the personal expense of Dr Ralegh Radford. The vessel's fine white fabric and painted decoration are typical of the potteries of the Saintonge region of western France, an area which supplied much tableware to the ports of medieval England. The elaborate plastic modelling of the upper part of this vessel, however, is unparalleled. Such an elaborate jug may have been made for use in feasts - presumably for serving wine.

'Puzzle jugs' are so-called because they were made as trick jugs, designed to pour their contents over the unsuspecting drinker. Despite its intricate appearance, the Exeter example is not strictly a puzzle jug since it lacks the concealed holes which caused the liquid to spill out. In this example liquid would be poured into the upper chamber, flowing down through the hollow handle into the bottom chamber, allowing it to be drunk without spills.

The subject of the openwork tower which supports the upper chamber is of comic interest. Within the tower are two bishops. They wear mitres and hold croziers but do not appear to be clothed. Young ladies disport themselves from the windows, whilst musicians play below. The scene pokes fun at the morals of the medieval clergy.

Reading
Gerald C. Dunning 1933 'Inventory of Medieval Polychrome Ware found in England and
    Scotland', *Archaeologia* **83**, 126-34.

THE SEAL MATRIX OF PRIOR THOMAS DENE
OF ST JAMES'S PRIORY, EXETER
c. AD 1419

From the collections of Exeter City Museums

Found in Southernhay, Exeter, in 1822, this silver seal matrix with its chain is a fine illustration of the craftsmanship of a medieval goldsmith and a particularly handsome example of a medieval prior's seal. It is therefore a surprise to find that the man for whom it was made was the prior of a very small Devon monastery, where there were at times only two or three monks.

The seal, which is 4.5cm long, depicts St James of Compostella with hat, staff and bag below an elaborate canopy. The surrounding inscription reads *S fris thome dene prior exonie* (i.e. the seal of brother Thomas Dene the prior of Exeter). Dene had become prior of St James at Exeter in 1419, and that is probably the date of the seal. St James's Priory belonged to the Cluniac order, owing its origins to the great house of Cluny in Burgundy which placed emphasis on elaborate liturgy and architecture.

The priory stood beside the River Exe, a little more than a mile downstream from the walled city of Exeter on a site at the foot of Salmonpool Lane where Abbey Court now stands. It was dissolved in 1444 and none of its buildings stands today, but various architectural fragments, including Norman scalloped capitals which probably derive from its cloister, have been recovered from the site.

Reading

John Cherry 1983 'The Silver Seal of Thomas Dene, Prior of St James in Exeter', *Proceedings of the Devon Archaeological Society* **41**, 138-9.
George Oliver 1846 *Monasticon Diocesis Exoniensis.*

ONE OF THE EXETER WAITS' CHAINS
Late 15th century AD

From the collections of Exeter Guildhall

The four chains of the waits of Exeter are highly unusual survivals of medieval regalia and striking testimony to the importance of ceremonial in the early life of the city.

The waits were the city's paid musicians. The first record of a wait was in 1362; there were two before the end of the 14th century, three by the 1420s and four by the 1520s. John Hooker, Exeter's Elizabethan historian, records a veritable orchestra of instruments kept by the city in his day, which the waits were to play – three Hoyboyes (oboes), four recorders, a cornet, a kind of bassoon called a curtall, and an instrument which he called a lyserden – apparently a serpent. The term 'wait' probably derives from the musicians' duty to accompany those who kept watch or wait in the city in the winter nights between Halloween (October 31) and Candlemas (February 2). They also performed at festivals and elections.

The chain displayed here is one of the three attributable to the 15th century. Two of these are each composed of 40 links, the other of 38. They display alternately the letters X and R – presumably for Exeter – with a central shield engraved with a castle, the symbol of the city. The chains are believed to be those recorded in 1476–7 when 14 shillings was spent by the city in remaking the 'colors' (collars = chains) with shields for the waits. In 1494–5 a further 10 shillings was spent repairing the three waits' chains, and their regular use necessitated fairly frequent subsequent repairs. Sadly the Exeter waits were finally disbanded in 1815. Nowadays these chains are worn by the city mace-sergeants and form part of Exeter's rich collection of civic regalia.

Reading
H. Lloyd Parry 1936 *The History of the Exeter Guildhall and the Life Within.*

A SILVER GILT PIN FROM DARTINGTON HALL

15th-16th century AD

From the collections of the Trustees of Dartington Hall

According to Bridget Cherry and the late Sir Nicholas Pevsner, Dartington Hall 'vies for pre-eminence with Haddon Hall and Wingfield Manor in Derbyshire as the most spectacular domestic survival of late medieval England'. Since 1993 Christopher Currie has been carrying out a summer excavation each year on the site of the south court to provide evidence for the future conservation of the outstanding gardens, and also to train students in the techniques of garden archaeology. His 1995 excavation season uncovered this remarkable pin, which a Treasure Trove inquest in 1996 determined to be the property of the Trustees of Dartington Hall with the recommendation that it should be given to Exeter City Museums on permanent loan for public display. John Cherry of the British Museum writes:

The silver gilt pin found at Dartington Hall Devon was submitted to me in 1995. It has been cleaned in our Department of Conservation and analysed in our Department of Scientific Research. This analysis shows that the pin contains approximately 95% silver. It weighs 14.35 grams which corresponds to a silver bullion value of £1.60. The present length of the pin which has a bent shank is 9.3cm.

The pin consists of two parts – the gilded head and the ungilded shank. The head of the pin is hollow and consists of two hemispheres soldered together. Each hemisphere has six raised bosses surrounded by a double wire strand. On the upper hemisphere there is an applied knob of silver above, and three smaller beads between each boss surrounding a smaller wire circle between the larger circles. This is reversed on the lower hemisphere. The top of the head is surmounted by a knob. Between the head and the shank is a protruding loop. The silver shank is bent at present though how far this reflects the original arrangement is uncertain.

The pin was used for the adornment of dress in some form. The style of manufacture of the spherical head in two parts and its decoration with knobs and wire appear to link this pin with three pins found in post-medieval contexts in Norwich (see Sue Margeson 'Norwich Households', East Anglian Archaeology 58, (1993) p. 10). The Dartington pin is likely to be of late medieval/early post-medieval date i.e. dating from the 15th or 16th century.

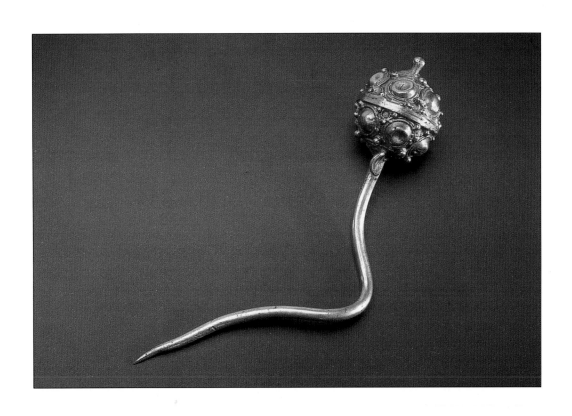

CANNON FROM A WRECK
OFF TEIGNMOUTH
16th century AD

From the collections of Teignmouth Museum

Historical documents record numerous shipwrecks along Devon's coastlines, and many more as yet undocumented sites doubtless await discovery. Some of the most significant Devon wreck sites have been the subject of systematic archaeological survey and are officially designated as 'historic wrecks' under the Protection of Wrecks Act. Of these, the site off Teignmouth has attracted national media attention (it was the subject of a Channel Four *Time Team* investigation in 1995) and has produced numerous finds which form the focus of a special display in the town museum run by the Teignmouth Museum and Historical Society.

The wreck site was discovered in 1975 by Simon Burton, a thirteen-year-old schoolboy, who spotted what he thought to be an old pipe sticking out of the seabed just off Teignmouth beach. This object turned out to be a large cannon some 3.5 metres in length of a type known as a 'saker'. Further survey of the wreck site produced five more guns (some loaded ready to fire), more than 120 cannon balls, numerous small objects and timbers forming part of the ship's structure. No historical documents clearly identifying the name of this ship have yet been found, but ongoing research at Teignmouth Museum has revealed exciting clues pointing to it having been a wreck from the Spanish Armada of 1588.

Among the six guns recovered, there are two outstanding specimens of a type of cannon known as a 'minion'. The well-preserved minion raised in 1981 now takes pride of place in the Simon Burton gallery at Teignmouth Museum. It is 2.74 metres in length and is decorated with a shield and the initials 'S A'. These initials have been linked to Sigismundo Alberghetti, whose family operated a foundry in Venice in the sixteenth century. The same initials are found on the second minion and on a saker which has been put on display by English Heritage at St Mawes Castle in Cornwall.

The investigation of the Teignmouth wreck site follows a Devonian tradition reaching back over 200 years for Newton Abbot was the home of John Lethbridge who invented a famous 'diving engine' which he used for salvage work on wrecks as far afield as the West Indies prior to his death in 1759.

Reading

Austin C. Carpenter 1993 *Cannon*.

Richard Larn 1996 *Shipwrecks of the Devon Coast*.

Teignmouth Museum and Historical Society 1992 *The 16th century Bronze Guns of Teignmouth*.

A sixteenth century minion from the Teignmouth wreck with a detail showing the shield decoration and initials 'SA'.

JOHN HOOKER'S MAP OF EXETER

AD 1587

From the collections of Exeter City Museums

Devon ranked among the foremost two or three counties in England in terms of wealth and population in the middle of the sixteenth century. Exeter was then, as now, the centre for much of Devon's life and this map of the city, which was commissioned by John Hooker, embodies the civic and commercial pride of the time.

Hooker (1525–1601) was born into an Exeter family and seemed destined for an academic life. He put down his failure to live up to his early promise to the fact that he chose to get married! Academia's loss was Exeter's gain as he went on to serve as City Chamberlain and as its MP. Hooker's official duties included acting as custodian of the city records and he is now regarded as Devon's first local historian, having written a *Synopsis Chorographical* of the county. His works also included histories of the city and of the lives of the Bishops of Exeter.

This map, which measures 50cm by 35cm, gives a bird's-eye view over the walled city and is rich in details of buildings such as the cathedral, the castle, and the medieval bridge across the Exe. It has two inscriptions in Latin. The title at the top of the map reads: 'Isca Damnoniorum, in British *Kaier penhuelgorte*, in Saxon *Monketon*, in Latin *Exonia*, in English *Exeancestre* or *Exestre*, and now commonly called *Exeter*: a very ancient city and a very famous port'. At the bottom of the map is the inscription: 'By the labour and expenses of John Hooker, Gent. and the City Magistrate, Remigius Hogenberg engraved this map AD 1587'. Only three original versions of Hooker's map have survived, this version being known as State C (the others are in the British Library and in private ownership). It was acquired by the City of Exeter in the 1950s and is kept on deposit in the Devon Record Office.

Reading

Kit Batten and Francis Bennett 1996 *The Printed Maps of Devon – County Maps 1575–1837.*

K.M. Constable 1932 'The Early Printed Plans of Exeter 1587–1724', *Report and Transactions of the Devonshire Association* **64**, 455–73.

William Ravenhill and Margery Rowe 1992 'A Decorated Screen Map of Exeter based on John Hooker's Map of 1587' in Todd Gray *et al.* (eds) *Tudor and Stuart Devon – Essays presented to Joyce Youings*, 1–12.

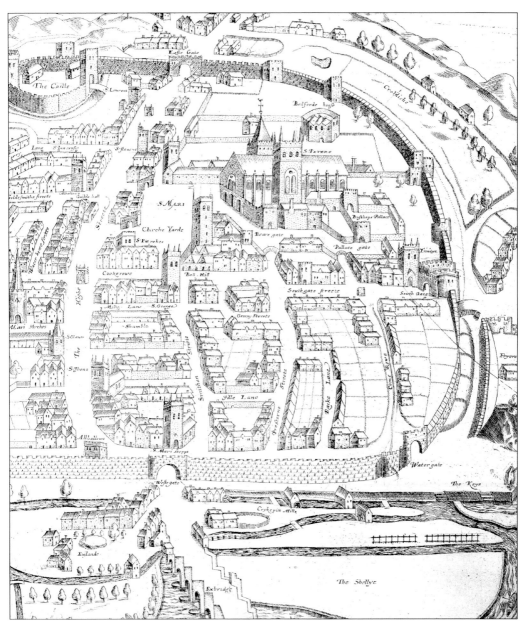

A detail from John Hooker's Map of Exeter, showing the cathedral, the castle, the medieval bridge over the Exe, and buildings within the city walls.

THE 'DRAKE CUP' FROM BUCKLAND ABBEY
c. 1596 AD

From the collections of Plymouth City Museums

Born near Tavistock in *c.* 1540, Sir Francis Drake, the first English sea-captain to circumnavigate the world, is Devon's best-known historical figure and one of England's greatest heroes. This magnificent gilt silver cup captures the spirit of Drake and the Elizabethan era of exploration. It stands 51cm high and has at its centre an engraved globe based on Mercator's World Map of 1587. Geographical details on the globe (such as the coasts of South America and China, and the depiction of the Solomon Islands) indicate that it was probably engraved in *c.* 1596, the year of Drake's death.

The exact links between this cup and Drake are rather unclear. The exchange of elaborate gifts was a custom of Elizabethan court life and we know that Drake once presented Queen Elizabeth with a gold globe. He may have given this cup to Sir Anthony Rouse, his Cornish friend and neighbour. Another possibility is that it was bequeathed to Thomas Peter of Exeter, whose descendants owned in until the twentieth century.

The 'Drake Cup' was purchased in 1942 by the National Art Collections Fund, which subsequently presented it to the City of Plymouth in recognition of her connections with Drake and her part in World War II. It is now displayed alongside Drake's Drum at Buckland Abbey, Drake's Devon home, now a National Trust property. The photograph is by Plymouth City Mueums.

Reading
Cynthia Gaskell Brown 1995 *The Battle's Sound – Drake's Drum and the Drake Flags.*
National Art Collections Fund 1984 *Catalogue of the Grosvenor House Antiques Fair.*
National Trust 1991 *Buckland Abbey.*

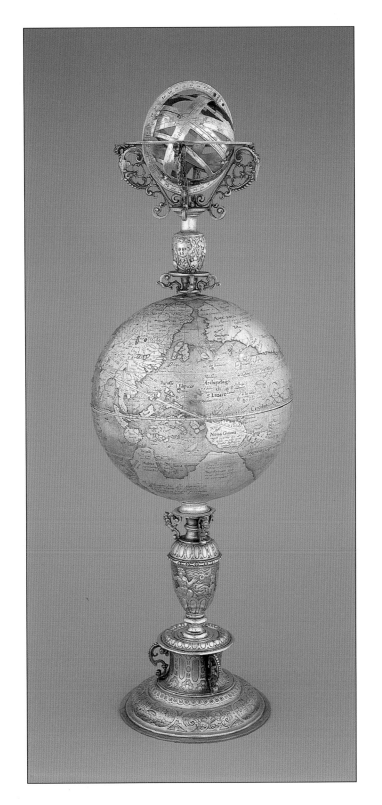

THE HOARD OF GOLD UNITES FROM CHUDLEIGH
AD 1604–18

From the collections of Exeter City Museums

The gold unite, valued at £1, was introduced into the English coinage in 1604 to celebrate the union of the crowns of England and Scotland under James I. It showed a royal portrait and titles on the obverse, with the new Royal Arms on the reverse surrounded by the legend *FACIAM EOS IN GENTEM UNAM* – 'I shall make them one people' - a biblical quotation from the Book of Ezekiel.

This hoard of gold unites was found by metal detectorists near Chudleigh in 1986. The coins must have been concealed in a hedgebank, where some remained; others had fallen from their original position and were found redeposited in soil below it. They were declared Treasure Trove in 1987.

All seven coins were struck at the Tower of London. Their date is indicated by mint marks (small symbols which precede the legend on each face of the coin): lys (1604–5), tower (1612–13) and cross (1617–18). The hoard was probably concealed around 1620.

At a time when the wages of a weaver for a full year would total £10 and those of a master carpenter or mason around £20–25, failure to recover the hoard would have represented a very considerable loss.

A SERIES OF SILVER CROWNS FROM THE EXETER CIVIL WAR MINT
AD 1643–5

From the collections of Exeter City Museums

At the outbreak of the Civil War in 1642 the isolated West Country army of Charles I needed payment, but Parliament controlled the national coinage at the Tower of London. King Charles therefore commissioned Sir Richard Vyvyan, a Cornish Royalist, to set up a mint to coin money to help pay his troops. Truro was first chosen, but with the capture of Exeter in 1643 the mint was soon moved there; production continued until 1646. Its site was apparently in Mint Lane, off Fore Street.

A range of denominations was struck, from the handsome gold pound to the tiny silver penny, but the bulk of the mint's output was of silver crowns (25p) and half-crowns. These coins make up a selection of the crowns struck at Exeter. A crown represented two days' pay for a cavalryman or seven and a half days' pay for a footsoldier. Characteristically they are of rather irregular shape, reflecting the simplicity of equipment used at the Exeter mint. Each shows on the obverse an equestrian portrait of Charles I, surrounded by the royal titles. The reverse shows the Royal Arms, surrounded by the legend *CHRISTO AUSPICE REGNO* (I reign by Christ's favour). Each coin bore mint marks – small symbols placed in the legend which indicated the place of issue. The coins illustrated show the various Exeter marks – first the Westcountry rose, later an EX or the tower mark also employed on Exeter silver.

Reading

Edward Besly 1992 'The Exeter Mint, 1643–1646', *Proceedings of the Devon Archaeological Society* **50**, 91–115.

Edward Besly 1992 'The English Civil War Mints at Truro and Exeter', *British Numismatic Journal* **62**, 102–53.

A PLASTER OVERMANTEL FROM GREAT MOOR FARMHOUSE, SOWTON
Late 17th century AD

From the collections of Exeter City Museums

Internal plaster decoration, often depicting heraldic or religious themes, is one of the glories of Devon's traditional buildings, particularly those dating to the 17th century. This lively plaster panel formerly stood over the fireplace of the best (eastern) bedroom of Great Moor Farmhouse on the outskirts of Exeter. It depicts the sun within an ornamental surround, flanked by a pair of winged cherubs. It belongs to the late 17th century. Its simple homely manner contrasts dramatically with the other plasterwork of Great Moor – the splendid and refined ceiling of the parlour which comprised a central oval flanked by rectangular panels bearing sprays of oak leaf and laurel.

Most unfortunately, Great Moor, a listed historic building, had to be demolished in 1971 as a result of fire damage as its conservation and reuse were being considered as part of the overall development of the Sowton Industrial Estate beside the M5. It formed one of a group of historic buildings in Sowton parish which was the focus for a pioneering study by Nathaniel Alcock in 1962.

Reading

Nathaniel Alcock 1962 'Houses in an East Devon Parish', *Report and Transactions of the Devonshire Association* **94**, 185–232.

Michael Laithwaite 1971 'Middle Moor, Sowton: a Re-Assessment', *Report and Transactions of the Devonshire Association* **103**, 77–83.

John Thorp 1990 'Wall-painting and lime-plaster decoration' in Peter Beacham (ed.), *Devon Building*, 129–49.

A NORTH DEVON HARVEST JUG
AD 1703

From the collections of Exeter City Museums

The pottery industry of North Devon in the late 17th century and early 18th produced one of the most vigorous folk art traditions of its day to be seen in England. Alongside rough kitchenware for common use, the local potters made a range of slip-wares of red earthenware dipped in white slip with sgraffito (scratched) ornament. Jugs of this type are commonly called 'harvest jugs' because of their links with the North Devon farming community.

This jug is an example of the traditional craft at its best. On the globular body a hunts-man and his four hounds pursue a rabbit. Above the long-winded inscription two floral bands ornament the neck. The vessel is lead-glazed. Its freehand style, here supple-mented with bands of punched dots added with a comb, is characteristic of the years *c.* 1660–1705. Few examples of North Devon pottery with this quality of decoration survive intact today but thousands of fragments have been excavated from the sites of the potteries at North Walk, Barnstaple, with other finds from the various Bideford potteries. They were exported to South Wales, Ireland and the American colonies; a famous series of dishes in this style was excavated at Jamestown, Virginia.

Reading
Alison Grant 1983 *North Devon Pottery: the Seventeenth Century.*

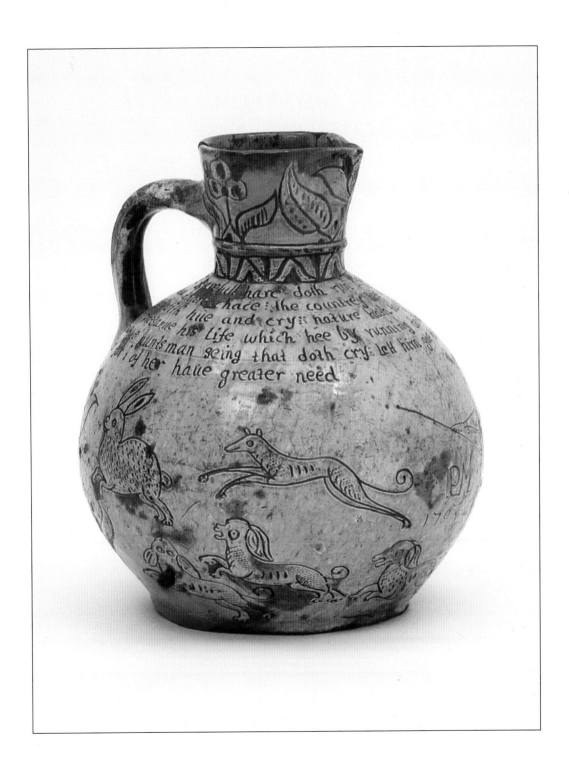

COAT OF ARMS FROM EXETER CUSTOM HOUSE
AD 1702–1714

From the collections of Exeter City Museums

The Exeter Custom House is the oldest custom house in England and served this purpose for over 300 years from its construction in 1680–1 until its closure in 1989. The major importance of the customs as a source of revenue to the Crown is reflected both in the solid quality of customs buildings and in their well-made fittings.

This wooden coat of arms was kept before 1989 in the Long Room of the Custom House, to which it had probably been removed in the early 19th century. It shows the Royal Arms of England of the time of Queen Anne with lion and unicorn supporters. It was erected, no doubt on the pediment of the Custom House, at the time the city reached the height of its commercial prosperity. It makes a telling contrast with the coat of arms which replaced it in 1820, and which hangs on the pediment today. The arms of Anne are well carved, with spirited and well-proportioned figures. By the early 19th century, as Exeter rapidly became a backwater, the new arms commissioned for Exeter were of much poorer quality, the figural work comparatively ham-fisted.

Reading

John Allan 1990 'The Custom House' in *The Exeter Area, Proceedings of the 136th Meeting of the Royal Archaeological Institute 1990.*

DANIEL AND SAMUEL LYSONS' *DEVONSHIRE*
AD 1822

From the archives of the Devon County Record Office

The tradition of compiling histories of Devon, which can be traced back to John Hooker of Exeter, gathered pace in the eighteenth and nineteenth centuries. The efforts of the Lysons brothers, published in 1822 in two volumes running to more than 1000 pages, represent local history on a grand scale and still make a valuable contribution to our knowledge of Devon today.

Daniel (1762–1834) and Samuel (1763–1819) were strangers to Devon, the former being a Gloucestershire clergyman and his younger brother Keeper of the Royal Records at the Tower of London. Together they devised the idea of publishing a history of every English county under the title *Magna Britannica, being a concise topographical account of the several counties of Great Britain.* Fortunately for us, they embarked on their mission by studying the counties in alphabetical order, Devon being the sixth and last that they were able to complete due to the death of Samuel in 1819.

In keeping with the times, their published history dwelt on the great events and leading historical figures of the county but they also ventured into the realms of natural history (e.g. they record the fact that a meteoric stone fell on an orchard at Ermington on 10 January 1623). Samuel Lysons was an accomplished draughtsman and their *Devonshire* contains some valuable illustrations including topographical maps of Dartmouth and Plymouth, and detailed drawings of archaeological sites such as Spinsters Rock, the prehistoric megalith on the eastern flanks of Dartmoor, and the post-Roman memorial stones from West Devon, which are among the oldest christian monuments surviving in Devon.

The second volume of the Lysons' *Devonshire* is of particular interest as in it they adopted the format of brief histories of individual Devon parishes set out in an alphabetical gazetteer. W.G. Hoskins followed a similar approach in his pioneering study of *Devon* published 132 years later in 1954. Professor Hoskins acknowledged the debt that he and other local historians owed to Daniel and Samuel Lysons. Coincidentally, his *Devon* was written as an early volume in his publisher's *A New Survey of England,* a series which, like the Lysons' *Magna Britannica,* faded away after only a few counties had been covered.

Reading
W.G. Hoskins 1954 *Devon.*
Daniel and Samuel Lysons 1822 *Magna Britannica Volume Six – Devonshire.*

The sketch beneath is from an accurate drawing, made by my brother, in 1807.

On the opposite page are representations of three ancient inscribed stones, from drawings made by my brother. Mr. Polwhele mentions another in Yealmton church-yard, of which I have no note, with the word Toreus inscribed on it.

No. 1. is at Buckland Monachorum, at the corner of a blacksmith's shop; it is seven feet two inches in height, fourteen inches wide at the top, and one foot six inches in the widest part.

No. 2. now forms a sill under the door of Lustleigh church. It is four feet in length, and 14 inches wide.

No. 3. is at Tavistock, on the site of the abbey. It stands seven feet above the ground, is 11 inches thick, and 21 wide.

Numerous tumuli, or barrows, occur in various parts of the county, on Haldon and other downs, particularly in the north of Devon. Many of them are of stone, which are sometimes called kairns : a few of those on Haldon have been opened; urns were found in them [t], and in one some Roman coins; fragments of urns were found in one that was opened in the parish of Moreton, and Roman coins, &c. in one in East Worlington.

[t] The great tumulus on the highest part of the east side of Haldon, 200 feet in circumference, and about 10 feet high, which is a conspicuous object from a great distance, was opened in 1780 by Mr. Tripe, and was found to contain, within a stone cell, an inverted urn, containing the burnt bones of a small size and ashes.

Crosses.

A page from Lysons' Devonshire *illustrating Spinster's Rock,*
one of Dartmoor's most impressive prehistoric monuments.

25

SABINE BARING GOULD'S
FOLKSONG COLLECTION
AD 1892

From the collections of the Devon Libraries Service

The Rev. Sabine Baring Gould (1834–1924) was squire and parson of the west Devon parish of Lewtrenchard for over forty years. He is today best remembered for giving us the words to the hymn, *Onward Christian Soldiers*. Less well-known are his efforts to collect and publish traditional Westcountry folksongs.

Baring Gould started collecting folksongs as a result of a conversation over the dinner table. He was concerned that the oral folksong tradition, by which words and tunes had been passed on by memory for generations, was dying away. Thus he spent hours listening to local singers, such as James Parsons, 'the Singing Machine', and transcribing their words.

These efforts led to the publication, just over one hundred years ago, of his large collection of folksongs under the title, *Songs and Ballads of the West*. But the published version is only part of the story. Fortunately he also presented his detailed working manuscripts to the Plymouth Public Free Library. These manuscripts come in two main parts; first there are some fourteen volumes of rough drafts of words and music which were made in the field. Secondly, Baring Gould prepared a hand-written volume (dated 1892) containing fair copies of 202 folksongs.

Widecombe Fair appears as Song No 16 in Baring Gould's fair copy manuscript. He sets down the words as sung to him by W.F. Collier of Horrabridge in July 1888, and also gives several variants of the tune collected from singers at Horrabridge, Kingsbridge, Merrivale Bridge, Two Bridges, and from Miss F.J. Adams 'as sung by her mother in 1822'. This indicates that he was hearing different versions of the song; indeed his rough field notes name Tavistock, and not Widecombe, as the site of the fair this song has now made world-famous!

Reading
Sabine Baring Gould and H. Fleetwood Sheppard 1895 *Songs and Ballads of the West*.
W.E. Purcell 1957 *Onward Christian Soldier – a Life of Sabine Baring-Gould, Parson, Squire, Novelist, Antiquary etc 1834 –1924*.

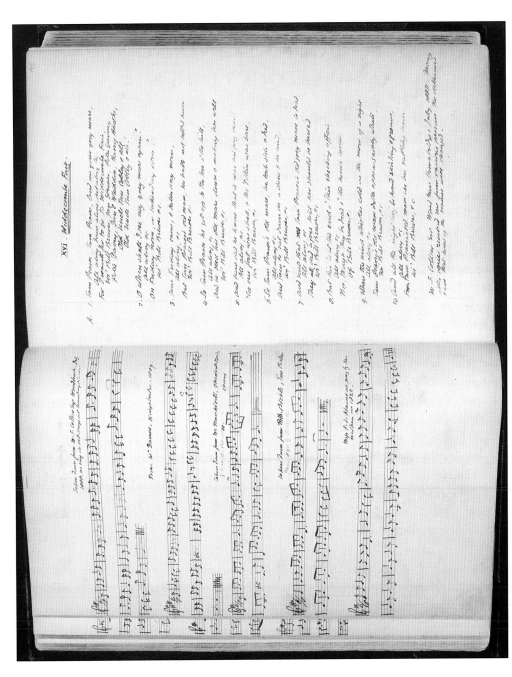

Widecombe Fair from the fair copy volume of Sabine Baring Gould's folksong manuscript.

61

JAMES RAVILIOUS'S *STANDING STONE* ON *MATTOCKS DOWN*
AD 1996

From the collections of the Beaford Archive

Photographers have been recording the changing Devon landscape for nearly 150 years, and the value of Victorian photos for studying the social history of the county has long been recognised. Collections of historic photographs can be found in the Devon Record Office, in the Westcountry Studies Library (and other reference libraries) and in museums all over Devon. In addition, a number of community photographic archives have been established in recent times to store copies of old photos owned by local people. The Beaford Archive in particular has built up a unique collection of photographs of North Devon life and landscape since it was founded thirty years ago. The Archive is now housed in the North Devon Record Office in Barnstaple.

It is not just Victorian photographs that help to bring Devon's past to life. Photos from the early twentieth century also serve as vivid record of places and life-styles that have sometimes changed beyond all recognition. The historians of the future will look back at the photographs we take today as valuable evidence of the late twentieth century.

The value of contemporary photographs is highlighted by the work of James Ravilious, who worked at the Beaford Centre for seventeen years making a unique photographic record of the rural traditions of North Devon. From his Chulmleigh home he continues his work, which has been widely acclaimed and is to be the subject of a touring exhibition by the Royal Photographic Society.

James Ravilious photographed *Standing Stone on Mattocks Down* in November 1996 at the request of Devon County Council. His view serves as a record of the damage caused to this prehistoric North Devon monument after it received a direct lightning strike on 25/26 October 1996. Shattered fragments of the massive stone were thrown as far as 20 metres away from the surviving fragment, which still stands some 2 metres high.

Writing in 1630, the Devon historian Thomas Westcote recorded that there were two massive standing stones and a further 23 smaller stones forming a prehistoric stone row on Mattocks Down. Today, this single stone is all that remains to be seen; the site is protected as a scheduled ancient monument of national importance.

Reading
L.V. Grinsell 1970 *The Archaeology of Exmoor*.
James Ravilious 1995 *A Corner of England – North Devon Landscapes and People*.
James and Robin Ravilious 1980 *The Heart of the Country*.

James Ravilious's Standing Stone on Mattocks Down.

MUSEUMS IN DEVON

Devon has a wealth of museums and heritage attractions highlighting the county's history. For museums, the government supports a National Museum Registration Scheme designed to ensure that museums in the hands of local authorities, charitable trusts and voluntary societies follow recognised guidelines. The following museums in Devon have been Registered or are working towards Registration, for which the Area Museum Council for the South West acts as adviser.

Allhallows Museum, Honiton.
Ashburton Museum.
Axe Valley Heritage Museum, Seaton.
Beaford Archive, Barnstaple.
Bishopsteignton Museum.
Braunton and District Museum.
Brixham Museum.
Burton Art Gallery and Museum, Bideford.
Coldharbour Mill Working Wool Museum, Uffculme.
Combe Martin Museum.
Cookworthy Museum, Kingsbridge.
Dartmouth Museum.
Dawlish Museum.
Devonshire Collection of Period Costume, Totnes.
Elizabethan Museum, Totnes.
Exeter Maritime Museum.
Exeter City Museums Service:
    Royal Albert Memorial Museum.
    St Nicholas Priory.
    Underground Passages.
    Exeter Guildhall.
    Quay House.
    'Connections' Discovery Centre.
Exmouth Museum.
Fairlynch Arts Centre and Museum, Budleigh Salterton.
Finch Foundry, Sticklepath.
Henley Collection, Dartmouth.
High Cross House, Dartington.
Holsworthy Museum.

Ilfracombe Museum.
Lyn and Exmoor Museum, Lynton.
Morwellham Quay Open Air Museum.
Museum of Dartmoor Life, Okehampton.
Newcomen Engine House, Dartmouth.
Newton Abbot Town and Great Western Railway Museum.
North Devon Maritime Museum, Appledore.
North Devon Museums Service, Barnstaple:
    Museum of North Devon.
    St Anne's Chapel and Old Grammar School.
Park Pharmacy Trust, Plymouth.
Plymouth City Museums Service:
    City Museum and Art Gallery.
    Buckland Abbey.
    Elizabethan House.
    Merchant's House.
    Plymouth Dome.
    Smeaton's Tower.
Salcombe Maritime and Local History Museum.
Sidmouth Museum.
South Molton Museum.
Tavistock Museum.
Teignmouth Museum.
Tiverton Museum.
Topsham Museum.
Torquay Museum.
Torre Abbey, Torquay.
Torrington Museum.

About

C000224747

Annie West has devo[ted...] charismatic heroes w[ho...] the lives of their hero[...] locations for roman[ce...] encampments and f[...] eastern Australia with her hero husband, between sandy beaches and gorgeous wine country. She finds writing the perfect excuse to postpone housework. To contact her or join her newsletter, visit annie-west.com

Chantelle Shaw enjoyed a happy childhood making up stories in her head. Always an avid reader, Chantelle discovered Mills & Boon as a teenager and during the times when her children refused to sleep, she would pace the floor with a baby in one hand and a book in the other! Twenty years later she decided to write one of her own. Writing takes up most of Chantelle's spare time, but she also enjoys gardening and walking. She doesn't find domestic chores so pleasurable!

Pamela Sadadi Yaye has a bachelor's degree in Christian Education and her love for African-American fiction prompted her to pursue a career in writing romance. When she's not working on her latest novel, this busy wife, mother and teacher is watching basketball, cooking or planning her next vacation. Pamela lives in Alberta, Canada with her gorgeous husband and adorable, but mischievous son and daughter.

Bachelor Bosses

Bachelor Bosses:
Boardroom
Antics

ANNIE WEST

CHANTELLE SHAW

PAMELA YAYE

MILLS & BOON

First Published in Great Britain 2022
By Mills & Boon, an imprint of HarperCollins*Publishers*, Ltd
1 London Bridge Street, London, SE1 9GF

www.harpercollins.co.uk

HarperCollins*Publishers*
1st Floor, Watermarque Building,
Ringsend Road, Dublin 4, Ireland

BACHELOR BOSSES: BOARDROOM ANTICS © 2022
Harlequin Enterprises ULC

Undone by His Touch © 2012 Annie West
Secrets of a Powerful Man © 2013 Chantelle Shaw
Seduced by the CEO © 2014 Pamela Sadadi

ISBN: 978-0-263-30567-8

UNDONE BY HIS TOUCH

ANNIE WEST

To two inspirational women, Miranda Lee
and Emma Darcy,

with thanks.

PROLOGUE

'You can't save us!' The hoarse cry echoed in Declan's ears and he tore his gaze back to Adrian, dangling below him on the rope. 'It's going to give way!'

They were suspended a hundred metres above an isolated canyon. The wind was rising and his brother's nerves were shot. Already Adrian's panic had dislodged one of the pitons securing them to the cliff.

'Hang on,' Declan gasped. His lungs hammered from his last attempt to haul them up.

Craning his neck, he looked up to where they'd fallen. A cascade of crumbling rock splattered his face. His throat shredded raw with each breath.

If only he'd called Adrian's bluff when he'd threatened to climb solo. But Adrian had seemed so brittle, Declan hadn't pushed. He'd hoped to regain their closeness and persuade Adrian to open up while they climbed.

Now their survival hung in the balance.

'Steady, Ade. It'll be OK.'

'OK?' Adrian's voice rose. 'Don't lie, Declan.'

Declan shot him a reassuring look. 'I almost made it last time. Third time's the charm. You'll see.'

Setting his jaw, he grabbed the rope and hauled, blocking out screaming pain as the rope lacerated hands already raw. His shoulders and neck locked in agony as he took their combined weight. It felt as if his spine might snap or his shoulders dislocate from the strain.

'You'll never do it. It's impossible.'

The words washed over him. He had no wind for speech.

'You know, it's not so bad.' Minutes later Adrian spoke again, his voice barely audible over the thundering of Declan's blood. 'A fall will be quick, at least.'

'Won't...' Declan fought to dredge up words in a throat scoured dry '...fall.'

'I've thought about it. One turn of the wheel in front of an oncoming truck and it'd all be over.'

The words slurred, warped by the frantic throb of Declan's pulse and the searing pain in his hands. Sweat blurred his vision.

'It's not like there's anything to live for.' Adrian's voice was so soft Declan wasn't sure if he imagined it. Could pain make you hallucinate?

'I've lost her. She wants someone rich and successful like you, not a failure. She dumped me!'

'Dumped?' Declan's voice was a husk of sound.

He needed to stop before his arms wrenched from their sockets. The world narrowed to the line that wore his hands to the bone, the wrenching strain and the eddying sound of Adrian's voice. A shiver of anxiety snaked through him at his brother's tone, but he was too exhausted to respond.

The wind picked up, swaying them.

The salt tang of blood burst on his lip. Two metres...

'I can't go on. I've tried, but she's the only woman I ever loved and she betrayed me. This is for the best.'

Best? The rope jerked unevenly. Despite the sweat streaming over Declan's sun-baked body, an icy finger slicked the back of his neck.

'Ade?'

Readjusting frozen neck muscles, he managed to look down. Familiar grey eyes met his. This time they held no panic, only an odd calm that made Declan's heart plunge.

'This way one of us might survive. I can't go on without her.'

Declan gasped in horror as he looked lower to where Adrian sawed at the line that bound them.

'Adrian! No!'

'Goodbye, Declan.'

Suddenly the dragging weight on his shoulders disappeared. There was no scream, no sound. It seemed a lifetime before Declan heard the muffled crunch of branches below and lost sight of his brother.

CHAPTER ONE

THE stack of towels was thick and soft in Chloe's arms as she nudged open the laundry door and headed for the pool house.

She dipped her head and inhaled the scent of sunshine and lavender: one of the special touches she prided herself on when the weather was good enough to use the drying hedge rather than the industrial-sized drier.

Concentrating on such small things, resuming her routine, had seen her through this difficult first morning back at Carinya.

She refused to let memories spook her. Her job was too precious and she needed the financial security more than ever. Besides, she had nothing to fear now.

So she'd ignored the anxiety feathering down her spine when she'd entered her housekeeper's quarters and remembered the last morning she'd been here. And again as she'd started work and imagined a dark-haired presence watching from the shadows as he had so often watched before.

That was in the past. He'd gone for ever. That knowledge helped banish the shadows.

Turning the corner of the house she slowed, hearing the sound of someone in the pool.

The sight of a familiar dark head emerging from the water with each stroke slammed her heart against her ribs. She faltered to a stop, not believing her eyes.

But he's gone!

This was impossible!

Transfixed, Chloe watched him execute a perfect racing turn, coming up metres from the end of the pool. The strenuous butterfly stroke, one she'd never been able to master, looked easy as that long body cleaved the water. The scoop of out-thrust arms accentuated the impressive length of tanned limbs and the power in his shoulders.

Chloe sagged against the wall, her throat tight, heart pounding as she tried to make sense of what she saw.

But he's dead... Dead. The words ran, a bewildered mantra, through her brain.

Yet for one lap of the pool Chloe was caught in nightmare, transfixed by the return of the man she'd come to fear.

Another turn and this time he swam freestyle, powering down the metres as if he had a record to break.

It was only then that her stunned eyes saw beyond the shreds of memory and noticed anomalies. This man looked bigger, though it was difficult to tell in the water. He swam differently, as if propelled by an unseen force that supercharged him through the crystal depths. He was like an efficient machine, each stroke smooth and economical, yet with a raw strength that seemed almost brutal.

Chloe couldn't imagine this man doing a lazy lap or two then loafing away an afternoon at the pool-side with a tray of drinks and his mobile phone.

Even now, turning again and beginning another lap, his speed didn't diminish.

Driven: that was the word that came to mind.

The man she remembered had been many things but driven wasn't one of them. *At least, not until he'd turned his attention to her.*

Chloe clanged that door shut in her mind. She refused to go there.

The swimmer reached the far end of the pool and in one supple movement heaved himself out. Water streamed down, bright sunlight burnished bronzed, water-slicked skin, from the bunch of muscles in his arms and back to the tight curve of bare buttocks.

Chloe sucked in her breath, her dazed brain registering his nakedness at the same time it assured her this couldn't be *him*. The shape of the head was different. The height. The breadth. His sheer imposing *maleness*.

He half-turned and she averted her eyes, but not before she saw a long scar ripping down one powerful thigh.

Relief, the return to normality after those frozen moments of disbelief, made her light-headed. Sanity returned with a rush of embarrassment as she realised who she'd been staring at.

Hurriedly, she straightened away from the wall and stepped out briskly towards the pool house.

'Who's that?' The deep voice was sharp but he didn't turn around, merely reached for his towel on a nearby sun lounger. He wrapped it casually round his hips with all the nonchalance of a man supremely confident in his own nakedness. And the fact he owned the whole multi-million-dollar estate.

Reluctantly Chloe detoured towards the clematis-draped pergola where he stood, putting on sunglasses.

It wasn't the way she'd have chosen to meet her employer at last.

Housekeepers were supposed to be discreet, unobtrusive, not intruding on their boss's privacy.

The image of firmly toned masculine flesh flashed before her eyes and a tingle of unfamiliar heat stirred.

She faltered, taking a moment to identify the sensation she hadn't experienced in years. When she did, shock brought a gasp to her lips.

'I'm waiting.' The words weren't curt, but his languid tone barely concealed impatience.

Chloe stepped forward. Now was not the time to dwell on the fact she'd just felt a spark of arousal for the first time in six years. At the sight of her naked employer.

'It's your housekeeper, Chloe Daniels.' She waited for him to turn. When he finally did she hefted the towels higher on one arm and extended her right hand. Tried to banish the memory of how she'd stood, gawping like some sex-starved miss at the sight of him.

Sex-starved she might technically be but she was no simpering miss.

He stood four-square before her, wearing nothing but reflective sunglasses and a towel. He exuded an air of authority that befitted a man of his commercial stature.

Right now it was his physical stature that pole-axed her.

Chloe had to tilt her head to meet his eyes. Despite her self-discipline and the compelling need not to ogle her employer, it took far too much effort to keep her gaze from that broad chest and ridged abdomen.

Standing this close, she realised Declan Carstairs was bigger, tougher, more imposing than the man she'd known. Only the hair colour and loose-limbed grace were the same—family traits.

His jaw was shadowed, not with sculpted designer stubble, but with several days' growth that made him look more like a lumberjack or pirate than a corporate tycoon.

A sensation like swirling treacle low in her belly unnerved her. She had a sudden mental picture of him swinging across a tall-masted ship, a woman on his shoulder.

Maybe it was the scar that conjured the notion. Long and not yet silvered with age, it carved an uncompromising groove up one cheek, curling in towards his eye.

Chloe shivered as she thought of the long matching wound on his leg.

'We haven't met before,' she said in the efficient housekeeper's voice she'd perfected over the years. She was grateful for it now as her pulse hammered. 'I've been—'

'Away.' He paused, watching her, yet giving no answering smile. His forehead pleated in a frown and his dark eyebrows slashed down as if in disapproval.

By now she felt gauche with her arm extended towards him. When it became clear he wouldn't give her the courtesy of a handshake, she dropped her arm, disappointment adding to her discomfort. Maybe arrogance ran in his family.

'A family emergency, wasn't it?' he surprised her by asking.

She hadn't expected him to know that, especially since they'd never met. His personal assistant had hired her, explaining his boss was often away for months at a time. Carinya had been his family's spectacular Blue Mountains retreat for generations but he lived a couple of hours east in Sydney when he wasn't travelling.

'That's right, Mr Carstairs. A family issue.'

Not that she'd known that the morning she'd fled this house. She'd simply packed her bags and caught the first train out. It was only later she'd discovered that in a weird coincidence of fate she faced not one but two crises. At least one of them was over.

'But we can count on your continued presence now?' One eyebrow arched above sleek designer glasses.

'Of course.' She'd been grateful when her sudden request for leave had been granted, but now she felt a spark of resentment at his attitude. 'I moved back in a couple of hours ago. I'll be on hand whenever you need me.' She forced herself to smile up into his stern face.

If she'd expected a glimmer of friendliness she was disappointed.

The way he stood, staring, no answering smile or nod, should have unnerved her. But Chloe was used to standing up for herself, proving herself again and again. Her self-confidence had been forged in a hard school.

She met his gaze squarely, trying to read his face.

Most people gave non-verbal clues to their thoughts. Not Declan Carstairs. Maybe that was how he'd taken his inherited fortune and turned it into something astronomical—by playing his cards close to his chest.

Yet this was something more. Was that disapproval she read in his set jaw and tense mouth? Anger, even?

Her skin tightened as she recalled standing frozen, eyes glued to his naked form, well after she'd realised who he was. There'd been a distinct element of appreciation as her gaze had slid over his virile form.

Had he caught her staring? Heat washed her throat and cheeks.

'I'm sorry for interrupting you just now. I hadn't realised you were here in the pool.'

Or that you were naked.

'Mr Sarkesian left a message saying you'd both be working in your study this morning and he'd brief me after that. I'd never intentionally...'

A dismissive gesture silenced her. 'David had to leave on unexpected business.' He paused and she had the impression of tension clamping his big frame rigid. 'Was there anything else?'

'No, nothing.' She'd been waiting for *him*. 'I'll just take these to the pool house. Unless there's anything I can get you?'

He shook his head. Chloe fought not to notice the way tiny droplets of water eased over his shoulders to track down across the solid musculature of his chest.

Her mouth dried and the heat in her face notched up to scorching.

She was doing it again!

She didn't ogle attractive men. Yet the sight of her boss's half-naked body and don't-mess-with-me jaw conjured feelings Chloe had all but forgotten. How could it be?

Even the dreadful scar seemed to accentuate the earthy sexuality and power of his strong-boned face.

Inwardly she cringed, hoping he was oblivious to her thoughts tumbling out of control.

That black eyebrow climbed again. 'Well. What are you waiting for, Ms Daniels? Don't let me keep you from work.'

That was what he paid her for. She had no trouble reading his dismissive tone.

'Of course, Mr Carstairs.' Chloe tamped down annoyance

and embarrassment as she turned away. She kept her pace even and her shoulders back, projecting a calm she was far from feeling.

Yet she reeled in shock. First had been the horror of thinking the man who haunted her nightmares had returned. Then there'd been that rush of relief, so strong she'd trembled with it. And finally the punch-to-the-gut reaction to Declan Carstairs.

Despite the scarring, he had the body of a male pin-up. More than that his sheer, sizzling intensity resonated like a force field, sucking the air from her lungs.

She was horrified to register a jiggle of response in that secret hollow place deep within. It had been years since she'd felt sexual awareness. On the contrary, she'd been accused of chilling indifference, of being an ice princess.

The recollection twisted her lips. She'd promised herself never to dwell on that again.

Now to feel a spark of attraction for her boss? Impossible!

In twenty-seven years there'd only been Mark, just one man to make her feel the blaze of desire. It was unthinkable that Declan Carstairs, rich, ruthless and disapproving, should re-ignite such feelings.

Pursing her lips, Chloe set about stripping the pool house of used towels.

Halfway back to the house, the sound of shattering glass made her spin towards the pergola.

Declan Carstairs stood, frozen in tableau, one arm stretched towards the table. On the ground before him lay the splintered remnants of a glass.

Curiously it was his stillness that snared her gaze rather than the broken glass so dangerously close to the pool. Too late she caught herself staring at those broad, straight shoulders a little too avidly.

'It's all right, Mr Carstairs, don't you bother with it. I'll fetch a brush and pan.' Chloe hurried back to the laundry, dumped the towels and scooped up her equipment.

Strangely, on her return he hadn't moved, as if he was waiting to make sure she did the job properly.

She'd worked for wealthy people before, some demanding and others so relaxed they barely noticed what went on around them. None would have questioned her ability to do such a simple task. Yet his stillness and the furrow of concentration on his brow told her he had other ideas.

Chloe crouched before him, brushing up the shards.

'I'll just be a moment.' Yet her usually brisk movements seemed slow, her limbs heavy as his silent presence loomed close. Deliberately she turned from the sight of those strong sinewed feet planted wide on the flagstones.

Ridiculous that even the man's naked feet looked sexy. He disapproved of her, was checking on her. She didn't want to feel anything for him.

'Thank you, Ms Daniels.'

Chloe bit down on a bubble of laughter. Such formality when her mind buzzed with unsettling images of his bare body. Just as well he couldn't read her thoughts.

If only he'd move and leave her to get on with this.

Thinning her lips, she concentrated on locating shards that had spread further than the rest. 'I think that's almost— No! Watch out!'

Too late she saw his heel come down on a splinter as he turned.

A single, low oath blasted from his lips as bright scarlet bloomed and spread across the flagstones.

'Wait, there's another one.'

Chloe scuttled across to pick up the shard. 'There, that's all. You can move to the chair now.'

Above her he stood still as a bronze god, though in the silence she heard the hiss of his indrawn breath. Blood streamed from the gash at his heel.

Finally he spoke. 'Perhaps you'd help me, Ms Daniels.'

Frowning, she got to her feet, put the brush and pan aside

and moved closer. What did he want her to do? Surely he had the strength to hop the short distance to the chair?

'You want me to support you?'

Something like anger flashed across his face and his nostrils flared. 'Nothing so dramatic.' He spoke through gritted teeth. 'Just give me your hand.'

Bewildered, Chloe complied, slipping her hand into his, absorbing the heat and sensation of hard strength surrounding her work-roughened fingers. She registered the ridges of scar tissue across his palm. A shiver of sensation skated up her arm and shoulder, raising the fine hairs on her nape.

She ignored it and looked into his face. This close she read the tiny lines bracketing his mouth as if he spent more time compressing his lips than smiling.

His features were stiff and the scar stood lividly on his taut cheek. Fierce energy hummed through him and into her, like a power source without a safety valve, inexorably rising. Tension twisted as she waited for him to speak.

Her eyes were at the level of his mouth and she watched, fascinated, as his sensuously sculpted lips thinned into a pained line.

'You need to sit down so I can get the glass out. It won't hurt so much then.'

His bark of laughter, rough and raw, echoed across the flagstones, jerking her gaze up to those impenetrable dark glasses.

'The pain doesn't bother me.'

Chloe frowned. If he wasn't in pain, then what…?

He exhaled slowly through his nostrils, his fingers tightening around hers. When he spoke there was resignation as well as an undercurrent of anger in his words. 'Just lead me to a chair, will you?'

'Lead…?'

'Yes, damn it. Haven't you realised you're talking to a blind man?'

CHAPTER TWO

THE silence pounded with the beat of blood roaring in his ears. He held his breath with anticipation, waiting for the inevitable gush of sympathy.

It was all he could do not to fling away from her.

He didn't want sympathy. He didn't want company. But he couldn't afford the luxury of managing for himself. He'd probably end up with a foot full of glass, or, having lost his bearings completely, a black eye from walking into the pergola.

Almost he didn't care. Yet he retained enough pride not to want to make a complete fool of himself before her. He did that often enough when he was alone.

Frustration surged and his muscles tightened as he thought of his frequent tumbles, his inability to do half the things he'd always taken for granted.

'Of course,' she murmured. 'I apologise. I hadn't realised you couldn't see.' Her words were the same as before, cool, crisp, not a shred of syrupy sympathy and for a moment he stood, startled.

Then she lifted his arm, wrapped hers around his torso and wedged her shoulder beneath his armpit. 'If you lean on me it will be easier.'

She might have been a nurse with her brisk practicality. If he was reasonable he'd be grateful for her no-nonsense attitude.

But the soft press of her breast against his side, the cushioned swell of her hip against his thigh, the sudden scent of vanilla and sunshine as her hair tickled his bare chest and arm, made him anything but reasonable.

How long since he'd held a woman close? Would he ever again?

'No!' Declan yanked his arm free, shoving her aside rather than feel the teasing brush of that rounded feminine form. 'I can do it myself. Just show me the way.' His other hand tightened around hers as frustration rose.

'Very well.'

Without another word she stepped forward, leading him. Declan put his weight on his good foot, and then supported himself on the ball of the injured one.

She didn't go too fast. Nor did she shilly shally and ask if he could keep up. It had taken him weeks to cure David of that and David was the best PA he'd ever had.

'There you are. The chair is to your left.' She took his left hand in hers and pulled him gently forward till he touched metal. 'There's the arm of it.'

She said no more but waited till he manoeuvred himself round and down into the seat.

'If you wait a few moments I'll go and get the first-aid kit.'

'I've got nowhere else to go.'

There was an almost inaudible huff of sound, as if he'd surprised a laugh out of her. Then she was gone and he was alone.

He should be used to it now, this sense of isolation. Sometimes it grew so intense it morphed into a crawling fear that one day he'd be left so completely alone in the dark he'd never be with others again. A childish terror, but one that still woke him in the middle of the night, chest heaving and heart pounding as he reached out, clawing at the inky darkness that enveloped him.

Declan reminded himself that solitude was what he'd always come to the mountains for. A change from the hectic pace of his overloaded schedule. His usually overloaded schedule.

No longer. He'd had to delegate more to keep up, despite David's assistance.

Anger, his ever-present companion, snarled in his veins— till he reminded himself he'd been the lucky one.

Instantly the familiar fog of regret and guilt enveloped him. His stomach twisted. He should be thankful to have survived. Yet he couldn't convince himself it was for the best. His failure made this prison of blankness even more unbearable. If only he'd...

'Here you are. I've brought the first-aid supplies.' That voice again, cool and clear, yet with a richness that made him wonder what her singing voice was like.

'You had no trouble finding me, then?' Sarcasm was poor repayment for her assistance, but the caged beast that raged and growled inside demanded outlet. Declan's usual means of using up excess energy—skiing, climbing and sex—were denied him.

Sex was possible, he supposed. He'd have to get someone like this efficient housekeeper to find and dial the numbers in his private directory. For a moment he diverted himself, wondering how she'd react if he asked her to ring his ex-lovers. Would she sound so prim and proper then?

But he couldn't stomach the thought of sympathy sex. For that was what it would be.

Scorching anger churned in his belly. What woman would want him now?

He refused to be the object of anyone's pity, grateful for the crumbs they deigned to dole out now he was so much less than he'd been. Even the doctors played that game, holding out the possibility his sight might return, though never guaranteeing it.

'Your foot must be paining you after all.' He heard her put something on the paving stones.

'You know that for a fact, do you?' He'd got tired in hospital of the staff dictating what was best for him and how he should feel. Till he'd discharged himself early and come here to recuperate in private.

'I'm guessing. You're cranky, but I'm giving you the benefit of the doubt in thinking there's a reason for your tone.'

To his surprise, his mouth lifted in a twist of amusement that pulled unused muscles tight. He couldn't remember smiling since the accident.

'Where's your sympathy for the poor maimed invalid?'

'Probably the same place your manners are.' She paused and lifted her foot carefully to place it on something cushioned. A towel on her lap? For some reason he rather enjoyed the idea of her kneeling at his feet.

'Besides,' she said as he felt gentle fingers touch his heel, 'You're not an invalid.'

Declan's mouth tightened and his hands curled into fists. Great, just great: another happy-clappy optimist. Just like the last rehab worker.

'What do you call this, then?' he jeered, jerking a hand in the direction of his glasses.

'Just because you can't see doesn't mean you're an invalid. The man I saw doing lap after lap in the pool was fitter and more agile than most people I know.' Her hold on his foot changed. 'This may hurt a little.'

It hurt a lot, but Declan was used to pain now. Getting walking again on that bad leg had taken more guts and determination than anything he'd ever done. It had been harder even than turning his back on family connections when he was a kid determined to build a business his own way.

'Most people can see what they're doing.' Was she deliberately obtuse?

'Are you looking for sympathy?'

'No!' Not that. Just…

Hell. He didn't know what he wanted. Just that he was tired of do-gooders telling him to look on the bright side.

'Good.' She pressed something to his heel. 'This is just to

stop the blood. I don't think it needs stitches but I'd like the bleeding to slow before I dress it.'

'You're one tough cookie—is that it?' For the first time he wondered what sort of person his housekeeper was. What had made her so cool and capable in the face of a growling employer who wasn't fit company for anyone? 'Are you trying to prove yourself to me?'

'I'm simply trying to help so you don't get an infection in this foot.' Not even a hint of impatience in that controlled tone. For an unsettling moment Declan was reminded of his kindergarten teacher who'd had a way of quieting rambunctious little boys with just a look.

'What are you smiling at?'

'Was I smiling?' He firmed his mouth into its habitual line. 'This may hurt.'

Good. It might focus his straying mind.

Pain sliced through him as she applied antiseptic.

'What do you look like, Ms Daniels?'

For the first time she hesitated. *Intriguing.*

'Average,' she said firmly.

'On the tall side,' he amended.

'How do you know?'

Declan shrugged. 'The way you fitted under my arm.' He paused. 'What else?'

'Is this really necessary?'

'Indulge me. Think of it as the job interview I never gave you.'

'You're saying my job's in doubt?' For the first time a hint of emotion coloured her voice. Panic?

He shook his head. 'I'm not that unreasonable, just curious.'

He heard a huff of exasperation and then she was winding a bandage around his foot with deft movements that assured him she knew exactly what she was doing.

'I've got light hair, light eyes and pale skin.'

'Freckles?' Why he bothered to tease when he couldn't see her reaction he didn't know. But despite her calm responses

Declan *felt* her disapproval. It shimmered around him. Tired as he was of his own company and his limitations, even that was preferable to solitude.

How pathetic could he get? Taunting the woman because he was bored, bitter and defeated by the guilt that clung like a shadow.

'Yes, as it happens. A few.' Her voice dropped a little and he caught a husky edge as she snapped shut the first-aid kit.

Declan surged to his feet. 'Thanks. Now, if you'll just lead me to the edge of the pergola, I can find my way from there.'

Chloe stopped in the open doorway to the vast book-lined library. It had been updated with a state-of-the-art computer on the antique cedar desk and a phone that looked like it could hold conference calls to several countries simultaneously. Hand raised to knock, she paused at the sound of Declan Carstairs' voice.

'OK, David. There's no help for it, you'll just have to stay there. Don't worry about it.' Her employer thrust a hand back through his hair in a gesture of clear frustration. 'No, *don't* send one of the junior staff in the meantime. I don't want anyone here gawping and…' He hunched his shoulders. 'Never mind.'

He turned and she caught his expression. His face was drawn with weariness. Lines etched the corners of his mouth and furrowed his brow. Then she caught a glimpse of his eyes and wondered with a jolt if it was tiredness or something akin to despair that shadowed his face.

The notion surprised her. He'd seemed so vibrant, so arrogantly in control just half an hour ago. Even as he'd been dependent on her to lead him and remove the glass from his foot, there'd been no question but that he'd been the one calling the shots, and not just because he paid her wages. The force of his personality made him dominate any situation.

'No, I'll just have to wait till you—'

He broke off and lifted his head as if scenting the air, his head swinging round inexorably to where she stood in the doorway.

Dark eyes fixed on her with an intensity that was unnerving.

Even knowing he couldn't see her, Chloe had to resist the urge to straighten her neat skirt and blouse or lift a hand to ensure that flyaway curl hadn't escaped again. Heat trickled through her veins and her skin flushed.

'Call me later, David, and update me.' He disconnected the call and stepped towards her, his eyes never wavering.

Was it an illusion that his gaze connected with hers? It had to be. Yet Chloe felt a strange breathlessness facing that hard, handsome face, as if he saw her with a clarity no-one else ever had.

'Ms Daniels. How long have you been there?' His voice dropped to a velvet-soft murmur that signalled danger.

How did he know she was there? She hadn't made a sound. The hairs rose on the back of her neck at the idea he'd somehow sensed her presence.

'Not long. I was about to knock but I didn't want to interrupt your conversation.'

His mouth firmed and his nostrils flared as if with impatience. 'In future make your presence known immediately. Given my…impairment, I like to know when I'm not alone.'

'Yes, sir.'

'Especially when I'm discussing business. I have a particularly delicate negotiation underway at the moment and I prefer to keep the details private. Understood?'

Chloe's mouth pursed, holding in indignation. Did he think her a potential corporate spy?

'Of course.' Stung at his assumption she'd tried to eavesdrop, Chloe hastened to explain herself. 'I came to find out if you'd like lunch soon.'

His mouth twisted. 'What have you got planned for me? No, let me guess—coddled eggs and toast. Or soup. Soup is always good.'

Chloe frowned, her mind racing through the contents of the pantry and what she could make quickly from scratch.

'If you like soup I could manage that.'

'I *don't* like,' he growled, pacing towards her, close enough to block her view of the room and fill her senses with his presence. 'I'm sick of bland food and being fussed over. The housekeeper the agency sent in your absence thought I needed cosseting to build my strength. If she'd had her way I'd have lived on omelettes and junket.' He shook his head, lifting a hand to rub his stubbled chin.

Unwillingly Chloe's eyes followed the movement, noting the hard, intriguing angle of his jaw and the line of his powerful throat. A faint citrus scent teased her nostrils and she wondered if he'd lathered himself with lemon soap in the shower. She swallowed. He hadn't buttoned his shirt. It hung loose, revealing glimpses of taut golden skin and a smattering of dark hair.

Her breath stilled as she recalled him emerging from the pool: naked, wet and virile. Her mouth dried.

Horrified to find her gaze following a narrow line of dark hair to the top of his faded jeans, Chloe yanked her attention back to his face, her cheeks glowing.

Anyone less in need of building up she had yet to meet. He was all hard-muscled energy and husky, powerful lines. She'd never met a man so vibrantly alive. So confrontingly masculine. Her stomach gave a strange little shimmy just being close to him.

'I hadn't thought in terms of…building up your strength.' Again her gaze strayed and she firmly yanked it back to his face.

Despite her embarrassment, amusement rose at the idea of trying to cosset this man like a child. The previous housekeeper must have had her work cut out trying to feed him invalid food. Had she *really* tried to serve him junket? Chloe wouldn't have dared.

'What was that?' His brows arrowed down ferociously as if he'd heard the laugh she stifled.

'Nothing, Mr Carstairs.' She paused. 'I'd planned chicken tikka-masala burgers with cucumber raita and lime pickle for lunch. But if that doesn't suit…'

'It suits perfectly. Suddenly I'm ravenous.' For a moment the shadow of a grin hovered on his lips and Chloe had a shocking glimpse of how irresistible he must be in good humour.

If ever he *was* in good humour.

'Clever too,' he drawled. 'Far easier for a blind man to handle.'

That observation, the little sting in the tail, robbed his earlier praise of warmth and left her deflated.

Was there anything wrong in trying to take his limitations into consideration? To realise it must be difficult chasing unseen food around a plate?

He made her consideration seem like condescension.

Her boss was frank to the point of rudeness, bad-tempered and graceless. He was nothing like his charmer of a brother.

A shiver whispered down her spine and she stiffened.

Chloe knew which brother she'd rather deal with. Declan Carstairs might be arrogant but…

'I'll have it ready in half an hour, then.'

'Good.' He turned away, took three uneven paces and put his hand down to the corner of the desk as if to reassure himself he was in the right place. It was a subtle move she wouldn't have noticed except that her brain was busy cataloguing everything about him.

Instantly she felt a pang of sympathy. How hard it must be for an active man to adjust to a world he couldn't see.

Perhaps his temper was understandable.

'Before you go, Ms Daniels.' She paused in the act of turning away. 'Tell me, you did sign a confidentiality clause with your contract of employment, didn't you?'

'I did.'

'Then you know the severe penalties for revealing private

information about anything you see or hear in the course of your work.'

Chloe drew a deep breath, telling herself he was within his rights to check, just as he'd been to insist she sign such a clause before working for him. It had nothing to do with her personal integrity.

'I understand that.' Nevertheless her fingers curled tight.

'Good. Keep it in mind. Because I'd have no hesitation in suing an employee who betrayed my trust if, for instance details of this current deal, or personal information about my life, were to appear in the press.'

Chloe's hackles rose. Did he distrust all his employees on principle or just her?

That fragile stirring of sympathy withered, replaced by a belligerent determination to keep out of Declan Carstairs' way. She didn't need to listen to his provocation. She had enough on her plate with worry about Ted's health and meeting the cost of his rehabilitation.

'I've worked for celebrities in the past, Mr Carstairs. People hounded by the paparazzi every time they stepped outside.' Her tone, more frigid than cool, implied they were far more newsworthy than he, despite the fact he was one of the country's richest men. 'None of them ever had complaints about my discretion.'

'Really?' One dark eyebrow arched provocatively.

'Really. Now, if you'll excuse me, Mr Carstairs, I'll get on with lunch.'

Chloe immersed herself in the routine of keeping the house in tip-top condition. A magnificent sprawling place, it dated from the nineteenth century. Her favourite feature was the wide veranda with its vista of manicured gardens. The gardens led to the cliff edge that dropped sheer to the blue-green valley, which spread into the distance.

Built at a time when a rich man included a ballroom in his country retreat, the place was a pleasure to work in. Especially as a wing had been added with a modern kitchen and house-keeper's suite.

She loved the gracious old home and didn't mind that it took a lot to maintain. That gave her reason to avoid the corner study where Declan Carstairs spent his time.

Occasionally as she crossed the lobby she heard his rich baritone on the phone or chatting to his PA, David Sarkesian, who'd returned from Sydney. The sound of her employer's deep voice made her quicken her pace lest he accuse her of eavesdropping for saleable gossip.

That insinuation still burned.

As did the suspicion that she enjoyed listening to the smooth rhythms of his voice for too much. The tingling awareness she felt in Declan Carstairs' presence disturbed her. It reminded her that, contrary to everything she'd learned in the last six years, her libido hadn't died with Mark.

She wished it had. She didn't need that hot, edgy sensation low in her stomach when Declan touched her hand reaching for a plate. Or the breathless anticipation that caught her lungs when he spoke to her.

She even enjoyed the verbal wrangling that seemed to be part of daily life working for him. He never let an encounter go by without challenging, probing or teasing till she almost suspected he looked forward to provoking her responses.

At least it prevented her dwelling on memories of the last time she'd lived here, when her dream job had turned into a nightmare.

'It's over now. You need to put it behind you,' she told her reflection in the bathroom mirror.

Easier said than done when fragmented nightmares still shattered her dreams. That was why she'd forced herself to come in here, to what had been Adrian Carstairs' suite.

Better to face the past squarely.

She'd learned that when she lost Mark years ago. The shock of grief, the unfairness of it, had kept her in denial for ages, trying to cling to a life that was past. It was only when she accepted the devastating blow that had stolen their dreams that she was able to move on.

Chloe swiped a cloth over the vanity unit.

'The past is gone.'

When she lost Mark those words had been a lament. Now there was relief that the trauma of Adrian Carstairs' frightening obsession was over. No matter how much she regretted his death, she couldn't help feeling a sense of freedom that he'd never stalk her again. That his dangerous fixation was over.

She picked up her cleaning supplies and turned, only to walk into a wall of naked male muscle.

She was soft, lithe and warm as his arms instinctively closed around her. The unexpectedness of contact momentarily stunned Declan, but a second later his body was responding to the intimate contact.

Predictable, he supposed, since he hadn't had a lover since well before the accident.

Yet why did his grip tighten when she moved to pull away? Surely not because he enjoyed the feel of her slender hand splayed across his bare chest? The gentle, almost phantom caress of her breath near his collarbone?

'Ms Daniels, I presume?' He forced himself into speech, covering his abrupt loss of control.

'Mr Carstairs, I didn't expect to see you here.'

There was a slightly breathless quality to her usually crisp voice as if he'd caught her out in some way.

He liked it.

Just as he liked the firm yet enticingly soft curves pressed against him.

This was Chloe Daniels, his sharp-tongued, no-nonsense housekeeper? She sounded young, but he'd supposed her voice was misleading. She was nothing like those sturdy, slightly frumpish women who'd staffed the various Carstairs properties in his childhood.

This woman was slim but curved in all the right places.

'Luscious' was the word that sprang to mind. His fingers tightened.

A familiar surge of frustration hit him: impatience that he couldn't see her for himself. Anger at this disability. Damn his blindness! Would he ever be whole again? He'd been curious about her so long and now, holding her, he had more questions than ever.

'I didn't expect to find you here either. I thought I heard voices.'

No need to say the muffled sound of conversation from Adrian's room had hit him like a sledgehammer blow to the heart. He'd dropped the shirt he'd taken off as he reached the head of the stairs and hurried here, nerves strung tight.

He wasn't a fanciful man but to his guilt-ridden conscience, the sound of talking from Adrian's suite had seemed portentous.

'I was talking to myself.' She sounded defiant rather than defensive, as if challenging him to make an issue of it. He was intrigued at this facet of his ever-practical employee.

'Indeed?'

'I'm sorry I disturbed you. I was just doing a quick clean.'

'No one will be using the suite.' He'd lost his taste for company the day he'd lost his brother.

'I understand.' She paused then added, her voice low, 'I'm sorry about your brother, Mr Carstairs.'

'Thank you,' he said tersely, dropping his hands.

Familiar guilt swamped him—that he was here, alive, experiencing a surge of sexual interest for this woman, when Adrian was dead. He'd failed his younger brother.

He should have been able to stop him.

His stomach lurched sickeningly. They'd been close, despite their recent geographical separation. He'd been Adrian's biggest supporter, the one Adrian had turned to when their parents had been busy with their business and charity interests.

But that counted for nothing. All that mattered was that last, irrevocable failure.

How had he let himself be persuaded by Adrian's upbeat assurances? He should have come here sooner, not relied on phone and email during that vital phase of his new project. How could he not have *known* Adrian was in such despair?

'Is there anything else, Mr Carstairs?'

Declan plunged a hand through his shaggy hair. He wished there was something else—something to distract him.

Work was no solace. It couldn't ease the weight of remorse.

Nor could the search for the woman who'd used his little brother then tossed him aside when she found he'd lost his wealth. Her betrayal had driven Adrian to suicide. Any doubts Declan had about her guilt had been obliterated by the scrawled note David had found jammed in Declan's desk. As soon as he'd recognised Adrian's handwriting he'd told Declan, who'd insisted he read it aloud.

Neither had spoken of it since but the words were engraved in Declan's memory: desperate words that confirmed Adrian's unnamed girlfriend, the woman he'd been seeing those last weeks, had pushed him to the edge.

Yet the private investigator had turned up no clue to her identity. Where had she vanished to?

Declan's mouth tightened. Adrian had always been the more sensitive one and, he realised now, more vulnerable. Declan felt impotent, unable to find the woman who'd destroyed his brother and make her face what she'd done.

He gulped down bitter regret, concentrating instead on the burning hate that sustained him when the burden of guilt grew unbearable.

Self-hatred for not saving his brother.

Hatred too for the woman with red-gold hair and come-hither green eyes in the photo his brother had shown him so proudly. A photo so candid it was obvious he'd taken the shot in bed. The woman had lain sprawled in abandon, as if sated from love-making. Golden light had bathed her, giving her the aura of a languid sex goddess inviting adoration.

And Declan had felt a shot of pure, unadulterated lust blast through him at the sight of her.

Remembering made him sick to the stomach, as if he'd betrayed his brother with his response to the woman Adrian had loved. The woman who'd driven Adrian to fatal despair.

Between them they were responsible for Adrian's death.

CHAPTER THREE

HE NO longer touched her, yet Chloe burned as if still pressed against him.

Shivers trembled down her spine. She had to lock her knees to stand firm. But nothing, not all her willpower, could prevent her dragging in the scent of citrus and man, spice and warm musk, that tickled her nostrils. Her gaze strayed to his half-naked form.

She'd never seen anyone like Declan Carstairs—his powerful, beautiful body and his larger-than-life aura. Unshaven, hard-jawed and scarred he looked more then ever like a pirate. The sort who thrived on danger and the pleasures of the flesh.

Chloe tried to recall Mark's generous smile, the twinkle of encouragement in his hazel eyes and, to her horror, conjured only the weakest of images. Could she have forgotten in just six years? Or was Declan Carstairs clouding her thoughts? The idea appalled her.

Eyes wide, she retreated a step and put down her bucket of supplies, crossing her arms defensively.

'Mr Carstairs? If there's nothing else I really should be getting on.'

A flicker of movement stirred his features as if he'd only just recalled her presence. Why did he look so grim?

'Actually there is something, Ms Daniels.'

He flexed his hands, drawing her gaze to the sinewy strength in his forearms.

What would it be like to be held by him? Not supported impersonally after bumping into each other, but embraced?

It felt like betrayal of her past even to wonder. Yet she couldn't prevent the niggle of curiosity.

'You were working here when my brother came to stay, weren't you? While I was in China?'

Instantly alert, Chloe darted a look at his face.

'Yes. I'd been here some time when he arrived.' Anxiety jiggled inside. Just the mention of Adrian Carstairs gave her the jitters.

How could one brother fascinate and reawaken long-dormant female awareness when the other had left her cold?

'Tell me, did he bring anyone to stay with him?'

She shook her head, remembering too late that Declan needed to hear her response. 'No, he came alone.'

'But there must have been visitors.' Dark eyes fixed at a point near her mouth, as if focused on her words. She sensed an intensity in her employer she hadn't encountered before, even when he'd quizzed her about confidentiality.

'There were no overnight guests.'

'But for a meal perhaps?'

'No, not that I recall. Your brother ate alone.'

Except for the days he'd turned up in the big kitchen and insisted on sharing a meal with her.

At first Chloe had welcomed him. Then, when he had grown more intense—his gaze fixing on her hungrily, his moods unstable—she'd taken to eating early in her room or finding an excuse to be away at meal time.

But she couldn't say that to his brother. There was nothing to be gained by sharing the fact Adrian Carstairs had made her life hell those last weeks. Declan had enough to deal with without her dumping that on him.

'I see.' Yet still he frowned, his brows bunched. 'But it's possible he had a visitor you didn't know about?'

'It's possible,' she said slowly. 'Though not likely.'

Increasingly Adrian had spent his time within sight of her

until she'd had to resort to subterfuge to escape him. She'd
have been grateful then for visitors to distract him from his
fixation on her.

'He didn't mention anyone?' The urgency of her boss's tone
surprised her.

'I… Not that I recall.'

'I see.' Declan's head sank slowly, as if weighted. The vibrant energy that was so much part of him dimmed and she
sensed despair.

Impulsively she lifted her hand to him, then let it drop. She
could imagine his sharp rejection of unwanted sympathy.

'I'm sorry I can't help.'

His lips curved in a twist that might have passed for a smile
if it weren't for the grim lines creasing his cheek and pulling
his scar tight.

'No matter.' He lifted a hand to thrust back a lock of dark
hair from his brow. 'But if you recall seeing a woman with gold
hair—a friend of Adrian's—you'll let me know? I'm trying to
contact her. It's…important.'

'Of course.'

Chloe frowned. Adrian had never mentioned a girlfriend.
He'd seemed a loner.

'Good.' For a moment longer Declan stood, as if wanting to
prolong conversation. Then he turned and paced stiffly away,
arm out in front of him till he reached the hall door and disappeared towards his room.

'I have a favour to ask.'

Chloe spun round to find her employer leaning against the
doorjamb as if he'd been there for ages, watching her.

Her pulse accelerated. Though he clearly hadn't been watching, she was unsettled by the notion he'd been there, listening
to her potter in the kitchen, humming under her breath.

Yet even as the thought surfaced, she realised it wasn't anxiety she felt. Not like when his brother had stalked her, silently
watching with an intensity that had given her the creeps.

No, this was different—a spiralling drop of excitement that drew her skin tight and clenched her stomach muscles in awareness. It had everything to do with her inability to blot Declan Carstairs from her brain.

His charismatic presence had banished the last shadows of anxiety she'd felt about returning to Carinya.

At least now her dreams weren't all nightmares, she admitted with a grimace. The last few nights she'd woken hot and shaken by vivid fantasies featuring Declan in glorious, nude detail. An insidious little tremor shot through her at the memory.

'Yes, Mr Carstairs?' She injected her tone with a brisk efficiency she was far from feeling.

He straightened and stepped into the room, turning to the sound of her voice.

'I have a meeting in Sydney and I want to be rid of this beard.' He lifted one hand ruminatively to his chin and Chloe heard the scratch of bristles.

For one insane moment she was tempted to lift her hand so they rasped against her palm. She could almost feel the rough pleasure of that tickle on her skin.

The realisation hit her like a hammer blow, robbing her of speech.

How had she grown so desperate for this man? Just imagining the scrape of his unshaven skin made her insides liquefy. How could that be? They weren't friends or anything like lovers. She barely knew him! With Mark, desire had grown with liking, with love. By comparison this was a smash-and-grab raid on her senses.

'David's gone on ahead so I wondered if you'd oblige. I can just about get by with an electric razor but it's pretty haphazard.'

'Of course, Mr Carstairs. I'm happy to help. But I should warn you, I've never shaved anyone.'

'Then I'll be your first.' His mouth widened in a slow smile that snagged her heart mid-beat. 'A first for us both.'

Not once in these last weeks had he smiled at her properly. Chloe wished fervently he hadn't decided to begin. She sagged against the worktop, her hand to the pulse trembling in her throat. Just as well he couldn't see her.

Even blind and scarred the man was devastating. What would he be like if he set his mind to seducing a woman?

She should be grateful for his usually brusque manner. It was a buffer to what she guessed could be formidable charm. His rare smile set her heart hammering.

'Shall we say my bathroom in five?'

Though she'd lived with Mark for almost a year, Chloe hadn't realised how intimate shaving a man could be.

Standing between Declan's splayed knees as he sat on the bathroom stool, jammed between the basin on her right and the wall at her back, she felt hemmed in. Not by the room, but by his proximity.

Her breathing shallowed as she slid the razor over his foamy cheek, too aware of the soft puff of his breath against her shirt and the heat of his legs around hers.

Her hand trembled and slowed.

'Like this.' His hand closed on hers, guiding her. She tried to concentrate on the shape of his jaw, the need to be careful. Yet her mind kept straying to the way his long fingers encircled hers.

'Got it?' His hand dropped and she sucked in a breath.

'I think so.' She cleaned the blade then made herself lean in, stoically ignoring his citrus scent and concentrating on the next stroke of the blade.

He sat statue-still and she told herself this would get easier. Except she made the mistake of looking into his eyes between strokes, intrigued to find they weren't blank as expected. Even unseeing they fascinated her. Deepest brown, so dark they hinted at blackness, yet rayed at the centre with a rim of golden shards.

'Chloe?' The question in his voice focused her wandering thoughts.

'Yes, Mr Carstairs?' This time she dared to tilt his chin for better access, telling herself the faster she got this done the sooner he'd leave and she'd be alone, safe from these unsettling feelings.

'Just checking,' he murmured. 'Given the circumstances, you can drop the "Mr Carstairs". It sounds too formal when you're holding a razor to my throat.'

Chloe rinsed off the razor and tilted his head further to the side, trying to ignore the fact his face was bare inches from her breasts. And that her nipples puckered flagrantly against the lace of her bra.

'You *are* my employer,' she protested, clinging to formality to counter the rising tide of utterly inappropriate feelings. She looked down, registering the way his jeans clung to solid, muscled thighs and felt a jab of longing deep in her belly.

'So, if I don't mind you calling me Declan, there's no reason to refuse.'

Silently she shook her head and ventured another stroke down the hard line of his cheek. The scrape of the blade against his skin was curiously sensuous. There was something intriguing about revealing the strong contours of his face with each careful stroke.

'Do it, Chloe.' The words feathered the bare flesh above the top button of her shirt and a line of tingling fire ran from her tight breasts to her groin.

'Sorry?'

'Say my name.'

'I really don't think…' It was stupid to refuse, but at some instinctive level she knew she'd be crossing into dangerous territory from which there'd be no retreat.

'Are you contradicting me?' His deep voice slid like silk across her skin.

'Are you ordering me?'

She watched his mouth lift at one corner.

'How did you get this job when you're so unwilling to comply with reasonable requests?'

It was on the tip of her tongue to say that calling him Declan wasn't reasonable. That it might reveal the pent-up longing she'd been trying so hard to repress, the very unprofessional thoughts she'd been able to hide only because he couldn't see.

'If that's what you want,' she said grudgingly.

'I want.'

His eyes lowered. Did he realise he appeared to be looking straight at her breasts? Was that why a smile flickered at the corner of his mouth? She made to step back, only to find his thighs imprisoned her. A pulse of sensation throbbed low in her body.

'As you wish.'

'Out loud, Chloe.'

She drew a deep breath, telling herself she was making a mountain out of a molehill.

'Declan.'

There. It was done. The word was easy and she sounded confident.

So why did she lick her lips as if she'd just tasted a forbidden delicacy? Why the jitter of excitement at the echo of his name on her tongue?

'Good. Now, stop delaying. I know it must look appalling but it's just dead skin.'

For a moment Chloe stared, uncomprehending. Then finally she realised. His scar. She'd stopped before shaving there. He thought she was wary of touching it.

Carefully she rinsed the razor.

'It doesn't look appalling.' The words emerged, a hoarse whisper, before she knew they'd even formulated in her mind.

'Don't give me that!' The lingering trace of amusement died and his lips thinned in a cruel, hard line. 'I don't need lies to keep me sweet. I know I look like the very devil.'

'No.' The choked protest welled from her.

That long, mobile mouth twisted in a sneer. 'No?' His nostrils flared as he dragged in a breath that pumped his whole torso. 'Then what, pray tell, does it look like?' Cynicism skeined through his words like silk.

The venom, the strength of his anger, was a vibrant, living force, pulsing from him in waves. Instinctively Chloe stepped back, or tried to. His thighs, iron-hard and unmoveable, trapped her. Something hot twisted low in her belly.

'Come on, Chloe,' he taunted. 'I deserve to know.'

Her mouth flattened at his baiting tone, even as she realised his fury stemmed from issues that had nothing to do with her. That he was still coming to grips with the legacy of the accident that had blinded him.

'I didn't say it's beautiful.'

'Ah, at last, something like the truth!'

Her hands fisted as she stared down into his grim face. 'But it's not as bad as you think. It gives you…character.'

No way could she be frank enough to add that the way it followed the natural line of his cheek complemented his strong features. Or that she'd come to appreciate the asymmetrical cast of his face that saved it from being too dauntingly perfect.

It made him look dangerous and sexy and far too intriguing.

'Character!' A jeering laugh burst from his lips. 'That's a good one.'

'It's true.' The fire inside, the heat of unwanted arousal, twisted and morphed into a dangerous mix of distress and anger.

He shook his head, his hands clamping on his thighs as if to restrain himself from pushing her aside and shooting to his feet.

'I do not need your sympathy.' Each glacial word dropped with the pinpoint accuracy of a precision bomb, designed with lethal intent.

A shiver sped up Chloe's spine and her skin iced. She hunched her shoulders.

'No, but you need to stop feeling so sorry for yourself.'

The words burst into echoing silence.

The razor clattered, unheeded, into the sink and Chloe found herself standing, arms akimbo, staring furiously down into eyes that darkened to ebony. A pulse jumped at his temple and the air throbbed with a surge of dangerous power.

Silence stretched till her nerves were taut with expectation. She couldn't believe she'd answered back that way. He was her boss. The man who paid her wages.

Yet she cared about him. Cared enough, it seemed, to risk the sack to tell him the truth.

The unnerving realisation froze her while the ramifications played out in her mind.

Abruptly he raised his hand, fumbling in front of him till long fingers touched her hip. She told herself she imagined the imprint burning through her skirt. But she didn't imagine the burst of heat when his fingers found hers, locking them hard and tight in his hold.

He yanked her hand to his face, to the point beside his eye where the scar ended.

A tremor hit her as he pressed her finger on the damaged flesh so she felt the ridge of healed tissue. But her overwhelming impression was of heat and excitement—an illicit thrill that skirled in her abdomen, clenching muscles.

Slowly, oh so slowly, he dragged her hand down, her fingers to the scar, her hand dwarfed by his.

Through the shaving cream, centimetre by centimetre the skin-to-skin contact continued. It was a punishment, a challenge, yet to Chloe it had the force of a caress. Potent, provocative, drawing out hidden longings and exposing them, raw and unvarnished, to the light of day.

His warm skin scent was inside her; his heat infused hers. The prison of his long legs evoked a delicious, terrible thrill she fought and failed to conquer.

Now her hand was beside his mouth, pressed there, feeling the supple skin stretch as he spoke.

'You have the gall to call that *character*?'

She opened her mouth but before she could speak he dragged her hand away. A blob of shaving cream fell from their joined fingers.

Did he know he held her so tight that the sensation bordered on pain?

'Or this?' He slammed her hand, palm down on his thigh, right up near his hip.

Chloe's heart galloped high in her chest as she looked at her fingers splayed under his, moulding the wide muscle of his upper leg. Her breath came in raw, shallow gasps at the intensity of the contact.

At his fury. His frustration. Her regret, sorrow and still, through it all, the unrepentant hum of sexual energy that furred her nape and drew her breasts tight and full and heavy.

Under his guidance her hand slid down over soft denim that covered hot flesh and uneven scar-tissue.

The wound was long and jagged.

'What would you call that, Chloe?' The jeering note had faded from his voice, replaced by a weariness that betrayed the effort it took to face the world as if it was his for the taking.

These last weeks she'd marvelled at his confidence, his ability to adapt within mere months to his life-changing injuries. His ability to stride without pause through the open French windows of the study, unerringly cross the flagstones and dive without hesitation into the pool. To run a multi-national company despite his impairment.

He even had time to parry and riposte verbally whenever their paths crossed, as if drawing her into conflict was a challenge that afforded him pleasure.

Now, feeling the tremors running through his thigh, the fierce clench of his hand, she glimpsed a fraction of what it cost him to appear in control.

Her heart missed a beat as another protective layer crumbled. Soon there'd be nothing left to keep her safe.

'Well, Chloe?' His voice dropped low, reverberating right

through her. 'Is that full of character too? Should I be *grateful* for the accident that blinded me?'

'Maybe it sounds trite, but there are lots of people worse off than you.' Chloe drew a slow breath, refusing to be cowed by his anger. 'You have your health. You're mobile. You have the satisfaction of running your own business. You have enough money to live in comfort. Millions of others aren't that lucky.'

She spoke from experience. Her own foster father, Ted, had been an active, energetic man whom nothing could daunt. Now, still grieving the loss of his wife, he was confined to a rehabilitation clinic, recuperating slowly from the stroke that had immobilised one side of his body and robbed him of speech. And then there was Mark. His death at twenty-two had been fate at its cruellest.

'You're right,' he snapped. 'It does sound trite.'

'I'm sorry.' Not for speaking the truth, but that he obviously wasn't ready to hear it.

His sightless eyes glittered with barely leashed emotion.

'Do you have any idea how infuriating it is to be lectured about looking on the bright side? About how *lucky* I am? To have false hope of recovery held out like a holy grail?'

'No.' She stood stiffly.

'No.' His expression was grim. 'How could you know?'

Abruptly he stood, making her shuffle a half-step into the corner to give him room. Still, he held her hand and she wondered if he'd forgotten it.

But then, with a sudden, unerring accuracy, he lifted their joined hands to her cheek. Together they stroked the contour of her cheekbone and her skin came alive at the incredible intimacy of their joined touch.

'You're whole,' he said, so low it was like a vibration rather than a sound. 'Your life hasn't turned upside down so that everything you took for granted—*everything*—is now exponentially more difficult if not downright impossible.'

Their hands traced down to the corner of her mouth and a ripple of awareness shook her.

'You're not dogged by regret over what you *couldn't* do, that you failed the one person who above all relied on you.'

He was talking about Adrian, she realised, and her heart squeezed. She wanted to tell him she knew the guilt that came with loss. She'd spent so long bedevilled by guilt because she hadn't recognised the signs of meningitis early enough to save Mark.

But it was too soon for Declan to listen to reason. His fury was too fresh, too raw.

Perhaps she shouldn't have stood up to him. He was still coming to grips with his changed lifestyle and his loss.

Suddenly he loosened his hold and let her hand fall. It tingled as blood rushed back.

Yet he didn't move away. His tall frame crowded her into the corner, making her acutely aware of how her wayward body responded to him. Even tipping her head up to look into his face shot a tiny thrill through her.

He was her employer. Feelings of this sort were totally inappropriate.

That didn't stop anticipation swirling through her.

His hand settled on her face, fingers spreading to mould her jaw.

Chloe sucked in a startled breath as he slid his hand over her, cupping her chin and circling her cheek almost as if he could picture her face through touch.

Each stroke reinforced the urgent, eager need for more. It was all she could do to stand still, not tilt her head into his hand.

Her response scared her.

With Mark there'd been fun, shared joy, respect. She couldn't remember anything like the visceral urgency she felt when Declan Carstairs merely brushed his hand over her skin in the questing gesture of a blind man.

'How old are you, Chloe Daniels?' His voice hit that low, rich note that made something curl inside her.

'Twenty-seven.' She straightened and tilted her chin higher, only to find his hand dropping to her throat as if she'd invited his feather-light caress there.

Had she?

Whorls of lazy heat eddied at his touch and her head eased back.

She gulped, desperately trying to regain her composure. 'How old are you?'

Long fingers stroked her lips, cajoling her into silence.

'Thirty-four.' His head tipped towards her as if, even blind, it was important that he look her in the eyes.

'Thirty-four, blind and scarred. Not the man I was.'

His voice was an indictment, as if he saw himself as less a man than before.

He leaned towards her and her breath caught.

'And you, Chloe, are smooth and young and unscarred.' He paused while his hand traced her nose and returned with heart-stopping intent to her mouth. Her lips felt swollen and pulsing, as if waiting for more than the touch of his hand.

Fire sparked in her veins and she found herself straining towards him.

'You're whole,' he murmured. 'And I'm…'

He shook his head, his mouth grim, even as he framed her face with his fingers, letting them slide through her hair. Tremulous delight filled her at his gentle massaging pressure.

Then, with an abruptness that floored her, his hands dropped and he stepped back, his shoulders stiff, his face a forbidding mask not even the smear of shaving cream could humanise.

'I don't want you here.'

The statement, so simple, so unambiguous, stuck in her dazed mind as if he spoke in a foreign tongue.

When she didn't move, his brow pleated in a ferocious scowl. His hands curled into tight fists.

'Get out of here, Chloe.' Words spat from him like bullets. 'Now!'

CHAPTER FOUR

DECLAN paced the empty boardroom his staff had scurried to leave. The pace of the China project was too slow and he hadn't minced his words.

He felt so bloody powerless, managing from a distance. Unable to see the figures for himself, view the footage of the site, read the faces of the consortium partners during the video hook-up.

He spun on his foot and strode down the room, registering the faint heat from the long windows beside him. They gave a spectacular view over the Domain and the no-doubt sparkling waters of Sydney Harbour, right to the Heads where the sea swell surged in from the Pacific.

A multi-million-dollar view he'd never see again despite the doctors' talk of possible recovery. They said there was no lasting physical damage to keep him blind.

As if he *chose* not to see!

He shoved back the hair flopping over his forehead and turned to pace. At least with the room's simple layout he wasn't going to trip over furniture and make himself a laughing stock.

Maybe he should be grateful for *that* too.

Chloe's words rang in his head—that there were people worse off than himself.

Did she think he didn't know that? There was barely a minute ticked by when he wasn't acutely aware that Adrian was dead, not merely maimed and blind.

Or that Declan was the one who'd failed to save him.

How dared she accuse him of feeling sorry for himself?

Who was she to lecture him? To talk in platitudes about something she didn't understand?

She was young, too young surely for the responsible job of running Carinya. Her skin still had the smooth, taut texture of youth. Unblemished and perfect.

Declan clenched his fists, recalling the pulse of need that had shot through him as he'd traced her features, learnt the high curve of cheekbones and delicate point of her chin. Her silk-soft hair, pulled back from her face. Her neat nose and soft, plump lips.

Damn! His fist pounded the toughened glass window with a dull thud that did nothing to ease the turbulent roil of emotions churning his gut.

Anger—yes.

Impatience—that was a given.

Frustration—that word had taken on a whole new meaning since Chloe Daniels had entered his home. Before that he'd been frustrated merely with his blindness, his incompetence in this world of darkness, his inability to find and punish the callous woman who'd driven Adrian to his death. That failure ate like a canker at his soul.

Now Declan's frustration had the keen edge of sexual hunger. The ever-present hint of Chloe's vanilla-sunshine scent in his home tantalised his nostrils and fed the gnawing hunger in his belly.

For too long his dreams had been haunted by Adrian's fall. Now they'd changed, waking him nightly, sweating and with his heart pounding.

He could barely make himself face it but those dreams featured not just Adrian, but the woman in his brother's treasured photo—the lover who'd betrayed him. Yet, instead of hatred, it was lust that sizzled through Declan as he dreamed of her, sprawled and voluptuous.

His fist pounded futilely on the glass and he hung his head, shame washing him.

Bad enough to feel that instantaneous spark of interest when Ade had shown him the photo. Far worse to dream of her and imagine she had Chloe's clear voice, her quick mind, her impossibly soft skin.

It was as if he betrayed both his brother and the woman he employed. The woman who'd done nothing wrong but stand up to him rather than kowtow like most of his staff. Who'd unwittingly provided comfort and company with her gentle presence when he most needed it.

She sparked a sense of life and energy in him with her independent, almost combative attitude. She drew him back from the dark maw of despair that hovered close. He'd even taken to finding excuses to seek her out.

Until the day he'd left Carinya.

He'd been within a breath of grabbing her, had been perilously close to losing control. If she hadn't left at his command, he'd have had her hard and fast against the bathroom wall. His groin throbbed just remembering that dangerously charged atmosphere, the way her voice had turned husky as his blood had thrummed with desire. He'd wanted her with a desperation that scared him. A desperation that would have terrified his prim and proper Ms Daniels if she'd known.

With an oath he turned and strode to the door. He needed to find David and get to work. Anything to stop thinking too much.

Halfway to the door he collided with a chair that hadn't been pushed back to the conference table. His momentum hurtled him forward. When he grabbed the chair it slid sideways. He tumbled to the carpet, his bad knee a sear of burning pain and his dignity in tatters.

He lay there, winded.

A bitter laugh escaped.

Back at Carinya he'd allowed himself to fantasise that Chloe had felt that quake of connection too: the heart-in-mouth desire that turned him weak at the feel of her body heat or the hint of her vanilla-and-woman scent in his nostrils.

He was a fool.

What woman would want him like this?

'Mr Carstairs?' Chloe prided herself on her cool, professional voice as she paused at the study door. Yet her pulse beat faster at the prospect of seeing him.

Declan had been like a bear with a sore head since his Sydney trip. She hoped it was because of business problems instead of that scene in his bathroom—the day she'd almost flung her arms around his neck and kissed his cynical, sensuous mouth with all the passion building inside her.

She shivered at how close she'd come to making herself a laughing stock. She could imagine the poised, beautiful women Declan spent time with. Even blind he wouldn't want a house-keeper with practical shoes and work-roughened hands.

It stunned her that she wanted him to notice her. As if she liked living on a knife-edge of excitement.

'Yes?' His tone was brusque, reinforcing his status as ty-coon employer and hers as paid underling.

It was the reminder she needed. She and her employer had nothing in common except their address. And yet…

'I just took a call from David… Mr Sarkesian.' She glanced across to the desk where the phone was off the hook. Was his mobile switched off too? Lately Declan spent too much time brooding, or so it seemed to her.

It bothered her that she cared quite as much as she did. Enough to want to comfort him.

He wouldn't appreciate that.

'I know who he is.' It was an impatient growl, as if she'd in-terrupted him in the middle of important work. Yet he'd been staring sightlessly towards the window.

She tried to ignore her heart's abrupt lurch of sympathy. Despite his wealth and power, he was so very much alone.

Declan shunned the possibility of anyone supporting him through his grief and recuperation.

Chloe stepped further into the room, refusing to shout across the vast space. Unerringly his head turned towards her as if he could pinpoint her exact location even after she crossed from the polished floor to the heirloom carpet.

The uncanny movement made her falter. Despite logic, despite all the rules, there *was* more between them than boss and servant.

She'd only ever been intimate with Mark, the man she'd married. Yet her connection with Declan felt intimate in ways she didn't understand.

'Well?'

She thinned her lips, refusing to respond to his terse tone. 'It's bad news, I'm afraid. David has just been to the doctor. He's got chickenpox.'

'You're kidding! He's thirty. Only kids get chickenpox.'

She shrugged. 'Apparently it can be more severe in adults. He didn't sound well. The doctor advised he'd be off work for a couple of weeks.'

'A couple of weeks?' Declan's expression froze.

'He asked if you wanted one of the junior staff to come and help with the current projects and any other matters…' Her voice trailed off. David was Declan's guide, the pair of eyes he no longer had. Those 'other matters' involved helping Declan with day-to-day tasks when he grew impatient with his own efforts.

Declan's face turned stony. Instantly she recalled his expression when she'd shaved him. Heat burst out of nowhere and coiling tension swirled deep inside, undermining her effort to remain professional.

How could she go on like this?

'I'll call him myself.' Declan sounded subdued, not like the arrogantly assured man who drove her crazy with his strong opinions and certainty he was right.

She opened her mouth to offer to dial the number then stopped. The merest whiff of sympathy was anathema to him.

'Then I'll get back to my duties.'

'Not so quickly.'

'Yes, Mr Carstairs?'

His lips thinned. 'Declan, remember?'

Oh, she remembered all right. Remembered so well her nipples tugged into hard peaks just thinking of that scene in his bathroom. His proximity, the touch of his skin, had fed a shocking hunger that time hadn't assuaged.

'Is there anything else I can do for you?' Chloe focused on his evident displeasure that she hadn't used his name. It was better than letting her mind stray to the things she'd like to do for him.

Heat suffused her skin. She couldn't remember ever feeling so overwhelmed, so wanton. Selfishly, she was glad he couldn't read her face. One look and he'd know her weakness for him. Sex, she told herself. That was all it was. Physical attraction. All she had to do was keep out of his way and eventually it would fade.

'Come back in an hour. I need someone to check my emails. Normally David would read them to me, but now...' He shrugged and spread his arms. Chloe read diffidence in the set of his shoulders but sensed it was camouflage. There was no mistaking the impatience behind his mask of calm.

It must gall him to be dependent on anyone.

'Until a replacement for David arrives?' Surely she could manage a few hours working with Declan.

He shook his head. 'There'll be no replacement. David knows my ways and so do you.' For one long moment it seemed he was looking at her, delving into those cravings she tried hard to hide. Inevitably, reaction stirred.

'You and I can work together until David returns. I don't need anyone else.'

Her heart dived.

In other words he didn't want anyone else to see him vulnerable, at a disadvantage because of his blindness. *She* didn't matter. She'd already seen him furious when he spilled food down his shirt or mislaid something.

She shivered, disturbed to realise she wanted him to want her for herself, not to shore up his pride.

More importantly she knew working with him daily would be a disaster—like walking a knife-edge. She'd never cope.

'What you mean is you're afraid to have anyone else here.'

Declan's head shot round, following the sound of her voice as she moved closer.

'What did you say?'

Was he hearing things now?

'You're scared of someone else seeing you vulnerable.'

She stopped before him. Her voice was low and close. Her light scent swirled around him.

Furious as much at his awareness of her as at her words, he lifted a hand to grab her, then stopped at the last moment. Remember what happened last time he'd touched her? How compelling the need to take more? To take *her*, with all the pent-up desperation of a blind man groping for the light? He'd never before been so needy. Or so bereft.

His arm dropped as if weighted with lead. Fire scorched his skin—desire and guilt. And fury.

'I don't employ you to pass judgment on my actions. I employ you to do what I say.'

'Even when it's a mistake?' Was that a wobble in her voice? As if she was nervous. She should be!

'I decide what's right for my business. No one questions my judgement.'

'You're saying you want yes-men? Staff who'll only tell you what you want to hear, rather than the truth?'

Declan tensed, thrusting his head forward aggressively. 'I assume you have a point? Perhaps you'd like to advise on the Middle Eastern project brief too, since you're such an expert? Or the staffing shortfall in Western Australia? Or the negotiations with government on—'

'There's no need to be sarcastic. You know I have no idea what you're talking about.'

Yet she stood her ground. That was more than his managers had done in Sydney last week. The realisation intrigued him. She intrigued him.

Declan folded his arms. 'Go on. I'm waiting.'

He heard her shuffle her feet. He'd been right: she was nervous.

'I think you'd be more…productive with one of your secretaries to help while David's away. You won't get through as much work with me helping. I don't know the ropes.'

'I'll teach you.'

'I've got other work to do.'

He tilted his head, trying to pinpoint exactly the expression in her voice. Reluctance, but something else too.

'What's really on your mind, Chloe? Why don't you want to work with me? I look ugly but I promise I don't bite.'

The words rang into silence and to his chagrin what filled Declan's mind was the realisation of how much he'd enjoy nuzzling the soft flesh of Chloe's throat and nipping it with his teeth. Ever since that day in his bathroom he'd been hard put not to think of her sexually.

'You only want me because you're used to me. I'm not a threat. If someone came up here from the Sydney office you'd feel vulnerable about them seeing you as you are.'

Oh, he wanted her all right. But not just because he was used to her. Though why he wanted her, when she continually stood up to him, never giving an inch, he didn't know. Perhaps he'd discovered a weakness for women who challenged him.

'You're becoming a recluse. That's dangerous, Declan.'

He opened his mouth to fire off an angry retort, then registered the wobble of distress as she said his name—as if she was worried. He frowned. He couldn't remember the last time anyone had been concerned for him except in a professional capacity. Doctors, nurses, investors…

That single, unexpected fact saved her from a blast of wrath.

'You're imagining things. I'm not a recluse.' Even as he said it Declan couldn't quite believe he was having this conversation. Perhaps the accident had knocked him off balance more than he'd suspected.

Needing to reassert his authority, he stalked behind his desk and sank into his ergonomic chair, pleased he hadn't needed to feel his way but knew exactly how many paces to every piece of furniture in the room. He swung round to face her. The familiar position gave the illusion of control in an unfamiliar world that threatened every shred of self-possession.

'You're hiding from the world.'

'Hiding? I suppose I was hiding last week when I had all those meetings in Sydney?' And since when did she have the right to express such views?

It took her a while to reply. But she didn't back down. 'That was just an extension of work. You bury yourself in work.'

'In case you hadn't noticed…' his lip curled '…it's devotion to work that's built my business empire.'

'But you use it to hide. You don't see anyone or go out anywhere unless it's business. It's not healthy.' She drew a sharp breath. 'It wouldn't be surprising if the accident had…affected you. Maybe a counsellor—'

Declan shot to his feet. 'Enough! I do *not* need a counsellor. Nor do I need your uninformed advice.'

'I realise you're upset…'

'Insulted is more like,' he murmured under his breath as he braced himself against the desk. The way he'd jumped from his chair had sent a jolt of pain screeching through his bad leg. His fingers curled into tight fists on the desktop. His physical limitations drove him mad.

'It's not insulting to suggest you might need someone to talk to.'

'Because I don't want to be mobbed?' He shook his head, sick of do-gooders telling him what he needed. 'If you'd gone through what I have you might prefer your own company too.'

'But you don't, do you? You're not happy.'

'Give me strength! Are you a psychiatrist now?'

She must have moved even closer. Her voice came from just in front of him. 'I only know that you've been through a lot and hiding yourself away won't help. It could lead to depression.' Her breath hitched.

About to lambast her, Declan stilled, his attention snagging on the word 'depression'. Instantly Adrian came to mind. He must have been depressed to have commited suicide. The thought sliced close to the bone, leaving Declan winded.

His bright, clever kid brother, so depressed he'd chosen to kill himself rather than go on. Declan blinked and drew in a ragged breath. How had he let that happen?

'You know about depression?' His voice was hoarse.

'I knew someone who was…troubled. If he'd had help, it could have made all the difference.'

Like Ade. If only Declan had come here sooner. He'd been eager to see his brother after so long apart. It had been five months since his last visit to London and over a year since Ade's last visit here. But with the easy assurance of past experience Declan had assumed their relationship hadn't changed. That, despite the physical absence, they were as close as ever.

How wrong he'd been.

Staying on in Asia to wrap up the latest, biggest contract had been a mistake. Letting Adrian persuade him everything was OK had been a mistake.

'Your friend, did he…?'

'I'd rather not discuss it.' Her clipped tone told Declan everything he needed to know. The last of his outrage disintegrated as he realised she'd been motivated by genuine concern and past loss.

Declan sank back into his seat, suppressing a groan of relief as the searing ache in his leg eased.

'I'll tell you what, Chloe, help me in the office six days a week and I'll increase your pay *plus* I'll even let you take me on an outing to the park with a rug over my knees so I don't get a chill.'

'You really are a sarcastic…'

Declan smiled to hear the spark of impatience in her tone. He discovered he didn't like it when she was sad.

'Deal, Chloe?'

'How could I turn down such an alluring offer?'

CHAPTER FIVE

'WHAT are you chuckling over?'

Chloe looked up to find Declan on the threshold of the kitchen. It was late afternoon, the hour she had off between working with Declan in the study and getting the dinner prepared. Slanting sunlight burnished his dark hair and highlighted his strong face. A smile hovered at the corner of his lips and her heart clutched.

Working with him had led to more than a truce between them. It had produced a camaraderie she'd never have believed possible, given Declan's determination always to be right. Yet behind the driven man, the man who still scared her with his occasional bleakness, she'd discovered a lurking sense of the absurd and a dry wit that kept her on her toes, plus a generosity of spirit. For all his lofty authority he was egalitarian and easy to work with, setting high standards but helping her achieve them. No wonder David adored his job and fretted over being absent so long.

'What is it, Chloe? Some racy gossip magazine?'

'Hardly. It's *Pride and Prejudice*.'

'And that's funny?' He sounded so sceptical she had to share.

'You haven't read it? How's this for an opening: "it is a truth universally acknowledged, that a single man in possession of a good fortune, must be in want of a wife"?'

He gave a humph and crossed his arms over his chest, the

epitome of eye-catching masculinity. 'You find that amusing? She's just telling it like it is. Or like the female half of the population pretends it is.'

Chloe tilted her head as she surveyed his expression. It struck her that she took advantage of his blindness time and again to watch him, fascinated not only by the earthy sexuality of his features but by the subtle changes of expression that merely hinted at his thoughts.

'You're so cynical.' She put the well-thumbed paperback down on the window seat.

He shrugged and propped one shoulder against the door jamb as if settling in for a chat.

Chloe knew an illicit thrill of pleasure at the way their relationship had developed. Instead of snapping her head off when she occasionally voiced concern for him, Declan took it in his stride, accepting her in a way he never had before they'd begun working together. She reminded herself it was the ease of a good working relationship, no more. Yet she couldn't help feeling there was something personal in the way he was so easy with her.

'If you were a single man with a fortune you'd understand.'

'You've had women set their caps at you?'

'If that's a quaint way of asking if they've tried to trick me into marriage, then yes. But never with caps. Transparent lingerie is more the norm,' he mused, rubbing his chin. 'Or lace. Or even—'

'I get the picture!' Chloe sat up, discomfited by the idea of so many women—doubtless sophisticated, accomplished women—throwing themselves at him.

A dart of pure jealousy shafted through her, stealing her breath. It was ridiculous when he was her boss, but she still hadn't been able to scotch her attraction to him.

'Attraction'! Such a mealy mouthed word for the searing swirl of awareness that was an ever-present undercurrent. Knowing him better, watching him fight every day, every hour, to find ways around his blindness—pushing himself to the limit with exercises to heal his leg, tackling life as best he could—Chloe felt so much more than desire. There was respect. Admiration. Sympathy. And more.

She felt…too much. Even without putting a name to it, surely what she felt for Declan was too much, too soon?

How had he sneaked past her defences? She'd been content for so long, living her quiet, contained life. He challenged her, invaded her space, made her think and *feel*.

She remembered the toll Mark's loss had taken and knew real fear.

By comparison this was no gently nurtured sentiment but a fierce alloy of emotions forged so deep in her soul she shied from dwelling on it.

'At least my condition means I've been spared that for a while.' He sighed. 'Sooner or later some enterprising female will decide I'm an ideal target for matrimony. Poor Declan with his scars and his blindness—he'd be grateful for a little female attention. Easy to dupe too.'

'Don't talk like that.' Chloe surged to her feet, her hands fisting at her sides.

'Sorry.' His tone was short. 'I don't usually wallow in self-pity.'

'It's not that.' Her voice was uneven as she strove to breathe normally. 'It's…' She shook her head, unable to put into words the protective emotion filling her. She hated it when he spoke of himself as less than he was, as an object of pity.

'You're too canny to be conned. You're a good judge of character.'

'You think? Not always. I've made mistakes.' He scowled and she guessed he was thinking of his brother. She'd seen and heard enough to know he blamed himself for not being here when Adrian had needed him. That knowledge made him all the more human. More likeable.

'You'll fall in love one day and that will be it.'

'Love?' His brows rose. 'I doubt it.'

'You don't believe in love?' The idea shocked her. Love

had been what turned her life around. Her foster parents' love, then Mark's. Without that she'd still be the angry, anti-social victim she'd believed herself as a teenager, hiding a sense of inadequacy behind bravado. Love was the one solid comfort when the world turned bleak.

'And you do?'

'I do.'

Was it his imagination that her words sounded like a vow?

Declan tried to summon the sceptical attitude that had seen him through years of success in the cut-throat world of international construction, countless grasping females and a false paternity suit. He sought the words to deny her certainty but, to his amazement, couldn't find them.

Instead he wondered what it would be like to have a woman like Chloe—forthright, honest and sexy as hell—believe she was in love with him.

Heat sizzled along his veins. His belly hollowed with something like excitement. Almost as if he *wanted* the picture she painted: the love of one woman.

A woman like Chloe?

He rubbed the back of his neck. What the hell was happening to him? He'd even taken to following her, needing her presence more and more to fill the void of emptiness.

He marched across the kitchen, flicked the switch on the kettle and reached for the tea caddy on the bench just below the window.

'How did you do that?'

Chloe's voice arrested him as he was in the middle of levering the top off the caddy.

'Do what?' If she was going to cross-question him about his views on love and marriage…

'Find the tea caddy so easily.'

Her words trickled into his consciousness and his heart gave an almighty thump.

How had he known it was there? The kettle needed no explanation. Chloe was meticulous in putting it back in exactly the same position so he could find it easily when he wanted it. But usually it was coffee he wanted, not tea.

There was a metallic clunk as the container slipped from his hands to the bench. His fingers spasmed as if trying too late to retrieve it.

Declan blinked but the unrelieved blankness gave no clue. Except that he could have sworn he remembered seeing light and darkness, sunlight and shadow, a moment before. As if the edge of the window where the caddy rested had been highlighted.

Impossible.

Yet his breath hissed in as he relived the illusion.

'Could you…*see* something?' Chloe's voice, soft and hopeful, came from right behind him. He felt her presence and inhaled her vanilla scent.

But before him was nothing but blackness.

Fury scorched him, incinerating the tiny bud of hope that had, for a moment, begun to unfurl. His fist thumped the counter. Bad enough to be blind, but to have the doctors keep hope alive, saying there was no reason he shouldn't regain his sight—it was too much!

Better to kill hope dead than face continual disappointment. He couldn't live like that. Nor could he hold out false hope to this woman who had come to mean so much.

'Of course not,' he snarled. 'I can't see a damned thing. You know that.'

Her silence was heavy with words left unsaid and Declan knew regret for lashing out.

It wasn't Chloe's fault. A better man would apologise, would explain. But, he realised as emotion grabbed his throat and stifled his larynx, he was scared what he might blurt out to her if once he started.

With Chloe he felt…different. He wanted more, though he managed to hide it most of the time.

'I have something for you.' Her voice was calm, blessed relief from his turbulent emotions.

'You do?' As ever, he turned towards her voice.

'Here.' She pressed something into his palm and closed his fingers around it.

Declan swallowed hard, unmoving. In all these weeks he hadn't touched her. Not since that day in his bathroom when the mere feel of her hand in his, the caress of her soft cheek, had almost blown his mind and his good intentions.

Now, without knowing it, she'd just unleashed the howling need he'd rammed into a dark corner of his soul, carefully guarded with every protection wit and hard work could provide.

A great shudder racked him and his hand shook in hers.

'Declan? Are you all right?'

'Fine,' he croaked. 'What is it?'

'You'll like it,' she assured him brightly. A shade too brightly. 'It's a sensor. You slip it over the rim of your mug. Here.' She guided his hand to a mug he heard her take from the cupboard. 'Put it on the lip, then when the water boils you make sure you've got the spout above the cup and pour. The sensor beeps when the water reaches it so you won't overflow the mug. Cool, eh?'

Declan felt her shift away. The warmth of her skin faded from his and he knew loss so profound it terrified him. He wanted to haul her back and hold her close. He wanted to keep her with him, the one bright spot in his murky world. She made life bearable.

'Declan?'

'Thanks, Chloe.' He forced his lips into a tight smile. 'It's perfect. No blind man should be without one.'

Chloe floated on her back in the heated pool. The sun had set in glory over the mountains and only the pool lights illuminated the scene. She should be in bed after another taxing day but she couldn't sleep.

Because of Declan.

He was always on her mind: his restless energy, his piercing intellect, his surprising humour once he lowered his guard enough to let her know the real man, his insight and understanding. Working with him daily, she was no longer surprised to discover he funded his staff to build clinics in India, a hospital in Haiti and wells in Africa, as well as taking on prestigious commercial projects. He didn't suffer fools but he was generous and had a conscience some of her previous employers had lacked.

Employers. She sucked in a quick breath. That taboo had crumbled before the force of her feelings.

She saw him as a man, not a boss.

Declan Carstairs had a dark intensity that made her shiver even as it tugged her closer.

He wasn't like Mark—gentle and decent in a quiet, unassuming way.

Declan was larger than life, demanding all her attention, stretching her, challenging her. Making her feel different. She liked and respected him and his pain, so carefully hidden, haunted her.

His unspoken grief forced her to confront her negative memories of his brother and wonder about the man Adrian had been at heart, before illness had changed him.

Declan's grief for his brother did him credit, proof of his deep capacity for love.

Love?

Her mind froze. She couldn't, *mustn't* think in those terms. Heart pounding, she tried to focus instead on the moment.

Chloe spread her fingers, letting water slide past. It was like swimming in liquid silk, the water caressing her hypersensitive body. A body Declan Carstairs had brought to life after six years of hibernation.

It frightened her that she couldn't thrust him from her mind. She couldn't silence the voice of desire that whispered

Declan's name in a litany of need. He'd smashed through the careful equilibrium she'd painstakingly built since losing Mark.

Too often she found herself longing to hold him, cradle him in her arms and ease his pain. Or let the flames of desire consume them.

It was as well David Sarkesian was due back soon. She'd miss the intimate sessions listening to Declan's voice, feeling it ripple across her senses like a call to heady pleasure. They worked in tandem, attuned to each other as if they'd done it for years.

Her feelings were too dangerous.

Soon she'd be safe. Not from Declan, but from her own longings.

The flagstones were warm from the long-vanished sun when Declan limped out of the house, stride lengthening as he approached the pool.

An instant later, arms overhead in a long, smooth dive he was airborne. That moment of heady anticipation was the closest he got to a thrill now extreme sports were denied him.

Water closed around him and, for a millisecond, he knew familiar regret at its safe embrace. How much simpler to throw himself over the edge and find not water but an end.

But Declan wasn't his brother. No matter how heavy the burden, he couldn't wish himself dead. Even now, half the man he was, weighed by guilt, there was too much to do. If not for himself, then to find justice for Adrian.

That was why sleep eluded him.

It had nothing to do with another day working with Chloe, her scent tickling his nose, her voice an invitation to pleasure.

What had David been thinking, hiring a woman whose voice, when she forgot to sound like Miss Prim, was sultry and beckoning?

For too long Declan had clamped down on unruly needs and wayward thoughts, on the seductive image of Chloe beside him, not just in the office but in his life. It was crazy but he'd found himself contemplating a relationship—not a brief sexual liaison, but a long-term partnership.

The sort of old-fashioned relationship he'd never had time for.

What kind of fool was he? Had blindness clouded his mind?

No woman in her right mind, much less a woman as bright, alluring and intelligent as Chloe, would tie herself to a scarred shadow of a man. Only a woman motivated by pity or greed could overlook what he'd become: a cripple, unable to do the smallest tasks without aid. A man who was hollow at the core, unworthy of love, unable to protect those most precious.

He didn't need pity.

He needed to work himself into exhaustion.

Declan's head broke the surface; he hauled his arm out of the water and brought it down in a stroke that collided with something floating in the pool.

Not something. Someone.

Automatically he righted himself. Slick flesh was beneath his hands; ripe contours of hip and waist; the heat of a breast against his chest. Long legs tangling with his.

His hold firmed at her waist, slipping into the neat indentation with a proprietorial ease that should have disturbed him. Instead it sent a jolt of instant pleasure to his groin. He kicked, keeping them both afloat, and again felt the slide of smooth legs between his.

Heat spiralled low like a rope pulling tight.

'Chloe?'

What other mermaid would invade his private domain?

She moved as he raised his hand, and he brushed one sweetly curved breast. The pebble-hardness of her nipple teased his palm.

Instinctively he cupped her breast, loving the fit of her in his hold, hearing her gasp through a veil of pounding sound as his pulse revved into gear. Did she push against his touch?

'Declan!' It was a soft plea. To his straining ears it sounded like a plea for more. Brutally he reminded himself it couldn't be. It had to be surprise, disgust.

Sanity seeped in and he dragged his hand away to grasp her arm instead. His palm felt branded by her breast, the outline of its perfect nub still teasing him.

Again her legs brushed his, only this time his erection got in the way. Heat slicked his skin.

Her indrawn breath was loud. She stopped moving. Was she frozen in horror?

Declan reminded himself he had every right to swim naked. It was late at night. This was *his* pool, his place of solitude and solace. *She* was the interloper. He'd come here to avoid thinking of her.

His lips twisted. Everywhere he turned she was there. His senses had taken on a preternatural keenness, even able to discern her humming from the other side of the house. She drove him insane. He didn't know which was worse: unrequited lust or the impossible dreams of long-term togetherness that corroded his commonsense.

'Are you OK?' he growled.

'Of course I'm OK.' Yet her voice was muffled, as if she had trouble getting her breath.

His own breathing had shallowed and his chest pounded.

'What are you doing here?' His voice, caught low in his throat, was gruff.

'Swimming. Well, floating. Relaxing.' Her voice was stilted, edgy. Who could blame her?

He tried to imagine her floating. Light hair and pale skin, she'd said. He imagined platinum hair rayed out, skin like moonlight, limbs spread as if waiting for him to come to her.

Inevitably frustration bubbled up. He wanted to see her for himself! He wanted...

'Declan.' Her voice whispered across raw nerves. 'You need to let me go.'

He tried yet his fingers held fast.

'You're not struggling to get away.' Amazingly she was pliant in his grip.

Because she feared what he might do? Did she recognise the beast within?

'Do I need to?' Her voice had a husky edge that sent shivers of pleasure to his groin.

'It would help.' His own voice thickened. 'But don't worry. I won't hurt you.'

'I never thought you would.'

A brittle laugh escaped him. Such trust.

He needed a workout to exhaust him just so he could put her from his mind. He was too aware of her sweet, yielding flesh. He was so hungry, so needy. Not for just any woman; that was the curse and the piquancy of it. For *this* woman. The one who'd driven him to the edge of sanity. Who'd incited impossible yearnings.

He'd never felt so out of control nor so unsure of himself.

'Declan?' A hand touched his face, cupped his jaw, her thumb resting on the hated scar. 'Are you all right?'

He didn't intend to tilt his face against her palm, but somehow he was leaning in.

'Perfect,' he lied. He teetered on a knife edge. 'Why aren't you getting out?'

Her hand slid from his face. He was so desperate, he almost believed the move was reluctant.

'You're still holding me.'

Of course; he had to release her. Grimly he dragged his hand from her arm till he held her only at the waist. He needed to unhook his arm but couldn't quite manage it.

He kicked slowly, keeping them afloat, and again his naked length brushed her. A shudder snaked down his spine and shot to his groin.

'Declan!'

'Sorry. It was unintentional.'

Was it? He yearned to press against her soft body, into her secret warmth. He longed to taste her.

'It's getting late,' she whispered. 'I should...'

It was a platitude he recognised. He sought relief in anger, knowing it was safer than anything else he felt.

'Run away?' he snarled. 'I don't blame you. Looking at my ugly face must be a trial. I...'

Her hand at his collarbone sucked the words away.

'Chloe?' She palmed his chest. It wasn't the touch of a woman who wanted to escape. Tentative, yes, but with a thoroughness that awakened every nerve ending.

'You're not ugly.' Again that throaty edge to her voice. 'I've wanted to touch you...'

'You have?' Astonishment made him reel, but not for long. Before she could come to her senses he kissed her neck and revelled in the pulse he found there pattering out of control. She tasted of salt water and sweet, vanilla-spiced Chloe.

'You should go inside.'

'I should want to leave.' Her voice trembled.

'Chloe?' Was he hearing things? Imagining what he wanted to hear?

But it was beyond him to push her away. With a groan, he captured her mouth.

He couldn't remember experiencing such a kiss before. Blindness made each sense more acute. She was sheer delight. He felt her smooth heat, each tiny tremble, smelled the fresh scent of her damp skin and devoured her sweetness—unique and addictive.

She pressed close, giving back kiss for kiss in a cycle that grew from tentative to lush, from slow to hungry.

Only the feel of water closing over their heads drew him back to sanity. Almost to sanity.

Urgently Declan propelled them through the water till they reached the shallow end of the pool. The water fell to thigh height and still he held her against him.

Each second he expected rejection, knew it was inevitable. Instead, he felt tiny ripples of arousal course through her. His pulse galloped. She kept one arm roped across his shoulders as the other slid down his abdomen.

'Don't.' His voice was a strangled burr. 'Not unless you want this over before it begins.'

Her hand slipped away and fear scudded through him.

'Do you want this, Chloe? Do you want me?' Once he'd never have asked such a question. Once he'd been confident, even blasé about sex. But now, disabled and scarred, doubt racked him.

He was so lost without his vision. He couldn't even read her face. Tension gnawed at his belly; uncertainty.

'I want you, Declan.' It was the voice of a siren, low and intoxicating. 'I want…'

The rest of her words ended in a gasp as he lowered her onto a wide step and placed his hand, broad and sure, over that sweet spot between her legs. He felt her response as he took her mouth hungrily.

Fire was in his blood, anticipation in every taut muscle. He'd only just sunk into her embrace, his fingers slipping beneath her bikini to find the nub of her pleasure, when she jolted in his arms, limbs stiffening.

He swallowed her gasp of astonishment, felt the heavy pulse of delight at her centre, and then she was arching up against his hand, coming apart against his touch with an innocent ferocity that staggered him.

'Declan!' Her voice was a stunned thread of sound that circled his senses, ensnaring and bewitching. She clutched him as if he was the one solid point in her world and his chest swelled with emotion.

He tasted her lips and her desperate enthusiasm drew him close to the edge. She was so hungry, so ready. That was an intoxication greater than any he'd known.

'It's been a long time for you,' he murmured. He'd never known a woman so desperate for him. For sex, he amended. Yet the idea that she responded to him alone had a subversive glamour he couldn't quite dismiss.

'Too long.' She pressed her lips to his, swirled her tongue between his lips. 'Years.'

Years? After just a few months of celibacy Declan was climbing the walls with frustration.

That explained why she was willing to ignore his scarred features. Right now he almost didn't care—he was so grateful for her eagerness and warm, responsive body.

Resting his weight on one elbow, he dragged the bikini bottom away. She reached for him but he brushed her hand aside. Time for that later.

It was the work of a moment to lift her higher on the steps so only her shins were submerged. Then he settled himself, low enough that her inner thighs were wet silk against his stubble. For a moment he wondered if his skin might be too rough, until she moaned and clutched his hair, drawing him to her.

'Chloe, you're driving me insane.' The words were muffled against her skin as his body responded with a surge of heady arousal. She tasted delicious, sweet and salt. Her legs, cool and smooth, closed round him and she raised herself, a gift to be savoured.

One kiss and she sighed. One slow flick of the tongue and her fingers tightened like talons in his hair. Declan didn't mind. He didn't want to be anywhere but here.

He nuzzled her tender skin and she moaned his name in that throaty plea he could become addicted to.

'You like that?'

'You know I do. I can't...'

Her words trailed off as he caressed her again, felt the tiny tremor of pleasure wash through her like a wave.

Declan smiled, savouring the taste of arousal, enjoying her reactions and the open, intensely exciting way she embraced pleasure.

Had sex ever been so simple, so satisfying? His body throbbed hard in anticipation.

One more slow, provocative kiss and the tremor became a quake that rocked her body, dragged the breath from her lungs in a shout of ecstasy. He tasted her pleasure, her thrumming pulse, and revelled in the feel of her finally relaxing in delight around him.

He lifted himself higher, pressed a kiss to one delicious breast. Another to her parted lips as she lay gasping for air. She was still, supine and spent.

On a tide of energy Declan got to his feet. He reached down to pull her up then stopped as sanity hit him with the cool night air.

Doubt stirred. Harsh reality. He sucked in a gasping breath as his brain engaged.

She'd been desperate for release. The merest touch had unravelled her. Would she still want him now, with the edge taken off her hunger? Or would his scars deter her? It was one thing to take what was offered, another to desire actively. He wanted her to come to him willingly, eyes open and sure, not out of pity or gratitude or indebtedness.

He couldn't bear the thought of her averting her eyes while he made love to her.

Declan stepped from the pool before he could have second thoughts. Water sluiced around him and for one unsteady moment he could have sworn he saw the fuzzy outline of the pool's rim lit by submerged lights.

Then the unrelenting blackness closed around him, a reminder that hope was fake.

Even so he refused to beg for scraps. Pride rose, his one defence.

'I'm going to my room.' His voice was thick. 'You know where to find me if you want me.'

CHAPTER SIX

SHE wasn't coming.

Ridiculous to be so disappointed.

He'd convinced himself Chloe wanted him as he did her. More, that they shared something even stronger—an understanding, a connection he couldn't put a name to.

He'd been a wishful fool.

Stupid not to have taken what was offered when he'd had the chance. He'd let pride interfere, convincing him Chloe must come to him so he could be sure she wanted *him*, not just an anonymous orgasm in the dark.

Now he cursed his ego. If he'd stayed, at least he'd have had release, pride or no pride.

His body ached with arousal. It would ache for days to come.

For weeks he'd considered finding a woman to ease the burn of need but hadn't followed through. It was Chloe he wanted. Chloe he needed. Not some sympathetic ex-girlfriend or stranger.

His jaw throbbed with tension and he cursed under his breath. This couldn't go on. One of them would have to go. Tomorrow he'd...

The sound of the door opening stopped all thought.

'Chloe?' Was that his voice—that husk of sound?

'It's me, Declan.'

His chest expanded mightily as he drew his first unfettered breath since leaving the pool. The weight between his shoulders lifted and the swirl of agitation in his belly morphed into a pulse of anticipation.

'You came.'

'How could I not?' Her voice curled around him, filling him with an unfamiliar sensation. Relief? Joy?

He shook his head, telling himself his imagination ran riot, blaming it on sexual frustration.

'Because you feel you owe me.' He gritted his teeth, so close to losing control he feared he wouldn't be able to hold back, even if she admitted she was here out of pity.

'No.' She paused and he could swear he heard her breath on the night air. 'Because I want you.'

Her words scooped the breath from his lungs, leaving him hollow and strangely vulnerable.

Was he really so desperate? It terrified him how much he needed that to be true. How much he needed from her.

'Doing it with a blind man turns you on, does it?' The words ripped out of his mouth before he could stop them.

Chloe stifled a gasp as his words grazed like shattered glass across tender skin.

Didn't he want her here?

Even now, seeing his rampant arousal as he stood naked in the light, she was tempted to turn tail. Hide again inside her shell of routine and professionalism and measured responses designed to keep emotions at a distance.

Yet she stood rooted to the spot.

She needed Declan like she needed to draw her next breath.

Lust, yes, but far more too.

It was too late to go back. It had been too late from the moment Declan had taken her in his arms.

She understood now that much of his anger was self-directed. Frustration at his limitations kept him on edge and ready to lash out.

Chloe told herself the rigidity in his big frame was from tension, not distaste. She'd felt his hands tremble with need before he'd abandoned her.

Yet it took all her strength to face him, letting her presence brazenly declare her need. She'd been gutted when he left, overwhelmed by doubts and fears as well as cravings she barely understood.

Declan Carstairs made her feel too much.

Her hands shook and the tray rattled.

'What's that?'

'A tray. Wine. Food.' As she spoke she walked to the other side of the king-sized bed and placed it on the hand-carved dresser. Holding the tray reminded her of her place in his household. Her paid role.

But tonight she wasn't his housekeeper. She firmed her lips, reminding herself they'd come together as equals.

'You're trying to turn this into some romantic encounter?' His mouth lifted in a sneering smile that cut her to the core. She stilled, heart thumping.

'You didn't eat dinner and I thought you might be hungry.' For the life of her Chloe wouldn't admit that preparing the trappings of a romantic tryst had calmed her rioting nerves.

Even after her abandoned behaviour in the pool, she had difficulty facing her desperate need for this man. She didn't do quick, meaningless sex.

Was she fooling herself believing there was more to this than sex?

'Are you this abrasive with everyone?' She planted her hands on her hips and stared at him across the bed. 'So eager for confrontation?' He looked magnificent, tall, powerfully muscled, outrageously virile. But he was an emotional minefield.

'Or is it that you don't want *me*, Declan, because I'm a mere employee?' Finally her own anger exploded. 'Is that it? You don't think I'm good enough for you?'

This man had shattered the barriers that had protected her feelings for six years. He'd broken through the impenetrable distance that had kept her safe and content. She hadn't wanted to care about him, much less want him. She resented the way he'd turned her into a woman she barely recognised.

'Of course I want you! What do you think this is?' He lowered one hand to cup his impressive erection and her mouth dried as a jolt of sexual arousal quaked through her.

She wanted to hold him there, feel the velvet-soft flesh over iron-hard erection. Her damp palms clenched and the pulse humming between her legs notched up to a heavy, needy beat.

'Then what's your problem?' Her voice was choked. 'Are you scared I'll expect more than you're willing to give? Do you think when the sun comes up tomorrow I'll forget my lowly place in your employ?'

Adrian Carstairs had tried to use her paid position as a lever to get her into his bed, at first cajoling and then threatening.

'I don't give a damn about your position.' Declan's voice was a lethal growl as he paced closer to the bed.

'Then why don't you like me?' Her chin tilted defiantly.

'Like?' It was a raw shout. 'Who says I don't like you?'

His hands fisted at his sides and, despite her anger and confusion, Chloe felt something inside melt at the erotically masculine picture he made. There was an elemental rawness, an unvarnished power that emanated from Declan even when dressed in a tailored suit. Now—naked, angry and aroused—he was breathtaking.

Dampness bloomed at the apex of Chloe's thighs and her pulse accelerated.

'If it's not me, then it must be you,' she shot back. 'What are you scared of, Declan?'

'I don't do scared.' Yet she saw emotion ripple across his features, catching at his scar and stiffening that side of his face.

Instantly her anger doused. There was something there… something troubling him…but he'd never admit it.

'Then prove it. Get on the bed.'

For an instant shock froze his features, then his lips curved up in a smile that looked more pain that pleasure. 'What? You want to minister to the cripple's needs? How magnanimous of you.'

Something thwacked her hard in the solar plexus. Her chest

tightened in a vicious cramp as she realised he truly saw himself as an object of pity. Tenderness welled with regret at how his accident had skewed his self-belief.

He was more virile, more attractive, more real and strong than any man she'd ever known.

Did he truly think she'd come here out of pity? She shook her head, her hair swirling around her shoulders.

Declan Carstairs had turned her world on its head with the sheer force of his personality, making her feel emotions she'd never wanted or hoped to experience again. She was fast falling in *love* and he thought she felt sorry for him!

'You're no more a cripple than I am. But if it makes you feel better let's pretend this has nothing to do with you.' Pain speared her. 'Let's just say I'm here to satisfy my own needs.' She hauled in a difficult breath, guessing if she revealed her feelings he'd turn away in an instant. 'Does that make it easier for you and your ego?'

'Chloe, I—'

'Don't, Declan. Please.' Suddenly she felt stretched too thin, her control fragile. Chloe wrapped her arms around herself, as if to hold in the tensions tearing her apart.

She couldn't take much more. She faced needs and emotions that stunned her, that had erupted out of nowhere in her safe, stable world. Plus she confronted Declan's hidden demons that she could only guess at.

'I'm sorry.'

Her gaze jerked back to his face, now solemn and calm.

'I *do* want you, Chloe. I've been going crazy these last weeks, trying to hold back.' His voice was hypnotically deep and enthralling, tugging her closer. His big hands clenched and unclenched at his sides as if seeking outlet for the raw tension within him.

'The question is, do you really want *me*?'

She shook her head that he even had to ask. 'I do.' The words sounded solemn in the silent room. 'Absolutely.'

His unseeing eyes focused on her as if seeking confirmation. Then he stepped forward, walking to the side of the bed. With one quick movement he climbed up and settled himself on his back, palms flat on the bedspread.

Heat fluttered in her stomach. From his torn leg and scarred cheek, to his thick dark hair and determined chin, he was more desirable than any man had a right to be.

Her heart squeezed at the vulnerability he strove to hide. At his proud, almost arrogant attitude that was no façade but part of the essential Declan. He was a man of depth and subtlety, of strength and secrets as well as charisma and sex appeal. He was the man who'd torn apart her defences and laid her heart bare.

It was on the tip of her tongue to ask if he was sure, her own doubts rearing up. But she bit back the words. Slowly she paced around the bed, feeling the swish of gossamer-fine fabric against her aroused body.

'Tell me what you're wearing.' His voice rippled across her skin.

Declan folded his hands behind his head. The movement accentuated the broad muscles of his shoulders and arms. Her breath caught at the sight of all that leashed power waiting for her.

'A robe.'

'Silk.'

'How can you tell?' She hesitated, suddenly uncertain. He stared directly at her, almost as if he saw her.

He shrugged and her mouth dried. She imagined those strong shoulders cradling her. 'It sounds like silk, like a whisper against your skin when you walk.'

She shook her head. She couldn't hear what he did, her senses hampered by the roar of blood in her ears.

'You look beautiful.'

Chloe smiled even as her breath snared. 'You don't know how I look.' She'd never been glamorous despite her unusual colouring. She doubted he'd give her a second glance if he could see.

'I know your face, remember?' His chest expanded mightily on a satisfied smile. 'You let me touch you. I remember your soft skin; your neat, straight nose and the bow of your lips. They're full, aren't they, Chloe—pouting and ready to be kissed?'

Sparks of heat flared in a twisting coil as his words curled around her. Her lips parted, tingling, as if waiting for the caress of his mouth.

'You'd look more beautiful without the wrap,' he murmured. 'Take it off.'

The sheer wanton thrill of his words stifled thought. He seduced her just with that rich growl that scraped like cut velvet across aroused flesh.

'*Now*, Chloe. I want you naked.'

Her fingers were unsteady as she fumbled with the knot at her waist. Finally it loosened. She shrugged and the robe slithered to the floor.

Declan's smile widened. 'Excellent. Now come to me.'

Chloe was already climbing onto the bed, her heart hammering high in her throat. 'Stop giving orders, Declan. You're not my boss now.'

She knelt over him, hands flat on the black and gold silk cover she'd smoothed across the vast bed only this morning. Bending, she pressed a kiss to his knee, feeling the tickle of coarse hair. Another kiss, a few centimetres higher, and his skin twitched and tightened.

Her third kiss brushed the scar that scored his thigh.

'Don't!' Strong hands reached for her but she resisted their pull. 'You don't have to. Not there.'

'My turn, Declan.' She didn't even care that he'd hear the breathless excitement in her strangled voice. She pressed another kiss, higher this time, to the heavy muscle of his thigh. It jumped beneath her lips and his fingers tunnelled into her hair, grasping and tangling.

'Like silk,' he murmured, and Chloe knew a flash of triumph that the sound was an uneven gasp. This desperate magic was shared. He was as unravelled by it as she.

She nuzzled his inner thigh and he froze. The hiss of his breath was loud in her ears.

Chloe smiled as she centred herself over him. 'Not so bossy now, are you?' Then her hand was on him, smoothing hot satin over iron-hard arousal. Her mouth followed, a gentle kiss at first, before she let her tongue lave the full, impressive length of him.

Fire ignited at her core and the hungry pulse between her legs clenched hard and tight.

She wanted...

'No.' Declan grabbed her shoulders and yanked her up high. 'You can't.'

Chloe revelled in the hard weight of his hands on her flesh, the heat of him beneath her, and the stark tension in his face. All for *her*.

'I can, Declan. I want to.' It was true. One taste and she craved more. She licked her lips, savouring the salt-and-spice taste of him.

But his grip firmed as he shook his head.

'No.' It was a hoarse whisper. 'I can't last if you do that.'

His face was taut, skin stretched across strong bones. He looked to be in pain. Tenderness welled within her and she cupped his jaw. The rasp of tiny bristles sensitised her skin.

Leaning forward, she whispered, 'Do you need to last?' The notion of Declan Carstairs yielding utterly to the magic of the moment filled her with heady excitement. 'I want you to lose control.'

She slid her hand down and curled her fingers around him.

He pulsed in her hold. Excitement blasted through her at his latent power and the fact that the pair of them together felt so *right*.

'Wait!' The order came through clenched teeth as he rolled on his side and reached for the bedside table. Reluctantly she released him. When he turned back he was sheathed and her heart gave a quick jump. She could scarcely believe she was giving herself to a man for the first time in six years. The only man since...

But there could be no second thoughts. Sharing herself with Declan was as inevitable as the sun rising in the morning.

She pressed her lips to his jaw, needing his scent in her nostrils, his taste on her tongue.

He tugged her down onto his body. His erection nudged her entrance, hot and thick, and a shiver of heat ripped through her. Chloe eased back as Declan rose beneath her and in slow motion the moment went on and on. Carefully, almost gently, he filled her aching void till she trembled on the brink of an awareness she'd never before known.

She quivered around him, her hands unsteady as she gripped his hard shoulders for balance.

'Chloe.' The word was a whisper. He sounded as stupefied as she felt. Nothing in her memory could match the word-stealing beauty of the moment.

Internal muscles clenched and abruptly the breathless moment shattered. Declan clamped his hands at her hips, surging high, and she gasped at the exquisite pleasure of his possession.

At his urging she sat back, knees spread around him. His hands went unerringly to her breasts, evoking ecstasy with the brush of hard fingers on crested nipples.

This floodtide of sensation, of desperate need and eager response was overwhelming. Declan urged her higher, faster, and she complied eagerly, fingers curling over his as he held her.

The pressure built with each thrust of his hips, each hungry slide of body on body. Chloe felt branded, possessed, yet cherished. Declan's powerful hands caressed her tenderly even as he pumped into her body with an urgent desperation that matched her own.

'I'm sorry,' he gasped. 'I can't...wait.' His pulsing length filled her and the fire exploded within, toppling her over the edge into ecstasy.

'Kiss me.' Her voice in the darkness roused him from the stupor of bliss that left him boneless. 'Please.'

She didn't sound like his crisply efficient housekeeper. She sounded...like he felt: drowsy, sated and stunned. As if the world had tilted on its axis and not returned to normal. For a moment he almost believed he saw shadow and light shimmer in his long-dead vision.

Then her hands cupped his shoulders and long, soft tresses spilled around his neck and shoulders. Instantly nerve endings that had all but been obliterated by that cataclysmic orgasm tingled into life. Declan's hands slid from her hips to her waist, closing there as if they belonged.

'I love your hair,' he whispered. 'You should wear it down all the time.' Then he could run his fingers through it at will, tangle his fist in it and draw her close whenever he desired.

He desired her continually. Working with her, not touching her, had been torture.

He heard the smile in her voice as she leaned near, her breath a tantalising puff of air on his face. 'It would get in the way.'

'I don't care.' Unable to resist, he caught long locks in one hand. 'I like it.'

'And what you want goes, is that it? I—'

'You talk too much,' he growled, tugging her to him. Unerringly her lips, petal-soft and delicious, met his.

A tremor shook him. Her mouth accommodated his, opening eagerly as he thrust his tongue in to delve between her sweet lips. It struck him abruptly that kissing Chloe was unlike anything he'd shared before.

Her taste was addictive. He anchored her head to him with one hand and plunged deep.

Their kiss was lush, slow and thorough. A mating of mouths that sent thoughts spiralling out of control and senses tumbling.

Women enjoyed kissing, so Declan had mastered the art early, learning to seduce and please in the lead up to the physical gratification that was his goal. Yet now this easy skill, a way of pleasing a woman and pandering to her desire for closeness, became something else.

A groan of hunger escaped him. Declan needed this kiss as much as she. He clutched her close, savouring the sheer pleasure of Chloe's lips on his, their breaths mingling. Joy rose, full and heavy in his chest.

In the dark, surrounded by her scent and taste, Declan experienced a closeness he'd never before known. As if his secret yearnings were made real.

Determination solidified in him. She *would* be his. Not just for one night.

CHAPTER SEVEN

CHLOE woke to grey skies and the sound of drumming rain. It was late, far too late to lie in bed.

Vaguely she remembered surfacing early, replete and warm in Declan's arms, only to find passion awakening as he feathered kisses over her face and throat.

Her pulse throbbed at the memory of their dawn love-making. Declan had been intent, his movements slow and devastatingly thorough, till she'd screamed her release, clutching him close. She'd fallen into blissful sleep moments after his climax made him slump, spent, in her arms.

She'd never slept as soundly as she had in Declan's bed.

But it must be mid-morning. She slid cautiously towards the side of the bed, trying not to wake him.

A hand on her upper arm stopped her.

'Where are you going?' Even drowsy, his voice held a deep, commanding timbre that tickled every sense.

'It's time I got up. It's late.'

'Don't go.' He hauled her back, wrapped his arm around her and turned her towards him.

She loved being cocooned against him, safe in his strong embrace. Her body relaxed like a cat cuddling into warmth. At the brush of wiry chest hair against sensitised breasts a jolt of response arrowed to her pelvis.

Chloe shook her head. How many times had they made love? Still her body melted whenever they touched. Surely that compulsion should have eased? This was all too new and unfamiliar. She needed time to find her balance.

Even as she thought it, he moved and the hot slide of his erection stroked her thigh.

'You're incorrigible!'

'Is that a complaint?' She loved the lazy chuckle in his voice, even though it turned her insides to mush. It was wonderful to hear him smile.

'No, but I need to get up. I can't stay here all day.' Though the idea was tempting.

'Why? What's so important?'

'The usual chores—cleaning, cooking, a trip to the shops. All the things a housekeeper does.'

'Nothing that can't wait.' He stroked a finger down her cheek and she almost purred aloud. She was so attuned to him, physically as well as emotionally. 'Except the shops. We'll go later; I've almost run out of condoms.'

Chloe choked on a gasp of laughter. The pulse between her legs quickened, shocking her anew.

For years she'd forgotten physical passion existed. Now she was at its mercy because of Declan.

She looked into his wickedly amused face, noting again how he seemed to meet her gaze though he couldn't see her. It was as if, even blind, he sensed so much about her.

Did he sense that, despite the stunning sex, for her this wasn't just about the physical? That what she felt for him grew perilously close to true caring?

'I really should get up.' She tried for crisp and decisive, but her voice came out wobbly.

'Why? Is your ogre of a boss going to give you the third degree over why you're late?'

One side of his mouth tilted up in a smile that tugged her chest tight. It was so rare, so precious, she wanted to savour it.

'My ogre of a boss probably has a stack of new emails for me to check. After I've cooked our breakfast.'

'Mmm, breakfast. Now you mention it, I *am* hungry.' He

lowered his head to her breast, sucking at the nipple till it stood erect, then nipping it with a gentle bite that sent every nerve ending into shivering overdrive.

'Declan.' Half-heartedly she pushed at his shoulders, distracted by the sensations he evoked. Finally he pulled back, heat simmering in the depths of his dark eyes.

'Maybe you're right about breakfast. What food is there on that tray you brought last night?'

'Fruit. You'll need something more substantial. I'll go and—'

'You're not going anywhere, Chloe. Not yet.' He tightened his hold. 'Are you always this dedicated to your job or are you looking for a reason to escape?' The humour left his voice and his brows drew down in a familiar frown. She wanted to reach up and smooth it away. It reminded her of his raw reaction last night when he'd thought himself the object of pity. What they shared was so fragile.

'Of course I don't want to escape.' Couldn't he tell by the way her body curled into his, her fingers threading through his thick, dark locks?

Slowly she released her hold and let her hand slide away. What she felt was so intense, so confusing. These weeks had been an emotional roller coaster that had thrown them closer with each sweeping turn. If she was sensible she'd find time away from him to sort out her feelings.

But she didn't want to be sensible. Didn't want to consider the barriers between them—his status and power or her role as his employee.

'It's just that I've got a job to do.'

'Take the day off. Boss's orders.' He stroked a finger across her lips to silence her protest. He lay back and pulled her close, settling her head on his shoulder and wrapping his other hand possessively around her waist.

He wanted her company as much as her body, she realised, remembering how he sought her out even when he didn't have work for her. Trembling excitement flared. Perhaps some of what she felt was shared.

'How did you come to be a housekeeper, anyway? Aren't you a bit young?'

'Old housekeepers must have been young once.'

He shrugged and the movement drew her closer. Chloe breathed deep, addicted to the spicy scent of his skin.

'Most of them come to the job after keeping house for their husbands and families.'

She'd shared a flat with Mark, but that wasn't what Declan meant, nor did she plan to reveal that part of her past yet. Her feelings for Declan were too raw.

'You know a lot about housekeepers? You've seduced plenty?' Chloe tried to keep the conversation light.

'Never. You're the first.' His voice rumbled up from beneath her ear and she snuggled closer. 'And I'm not sure I'd call it a seduction. More like a mutual explosion.'

He paused, as if waiting for her to say something but she kept her lips closed, afraid of what might slip out.

'Yes, I grew up with housekeepers, here and in the family home in Sydney. My grandparents had them too. Worthy women with aprons and no-nonsense attitudes.'

Declan's hand stroked her waist. 'You don't fit the mould, Chloe Daniels.'

She shrugged, trying to ignore the tremors raying out from his touch. 'Nevertheless, it's what I do.'

'Did you always want to keep house?'

Chloe shook her head. 'I never knew what I wanted. Except as a teenager when all I wanted was to rebel.'

'That's normal. I was only eighteen, wet behind the ears, when I broke out on my own rather than follow in any of the family businesses.'

'That sounds very…commendable.'

He shifted as if turning to watch her, though of course that was impossible. 'How did you rebel?'

Chloe smiled wistfully. Strange how good it felt to share

her past with the man who'd had her on edge for ages. She
wrapped her arm tighter round his chest and was rewarded
with a throaty murmur of approval.

'I was on the other side of the railway tracks from you, literally. By twelve I'd joined a graffiti gang and spent most of my
nights in back alleys and on deserted railway sidings wielding
spray cans.'

Declan shook his head. 'You never cease to intrigue me.
That's so far from the image you project.'

'Which is?'

His hand stroked her side and she shivered as waves of delicious pleasure spread from his touch.

'Competent, no nonsense, reliable.' His caress changed, slid
up towards her breasts. 'Delectable, sexy...'

'Enough!' Chloe grabbed his marauding hand. Tempted as
she was, every time she gave herself to him it felt as if she lost
a little more of her precious self-possession.

'You must have given your parents a few grey hairs.'

'I didn't live with my parents. I was fostered out.' Her lips
firmed on memories of being shunted between foster homes.
Of the desperate uncertainty, the hope, fear and distress of yet
another move when things didn't work out. She rarely spoke
of her childhood.

'That must have been tough.'

She shrugged, remembering the pressure to fit in, to be cute
and compliant, undemanding and above all helpful, no matter
how stressful the new placement. It had been a struggle for
a lanky kid with bright hair and freckles whose smart mouth
had hidden desperate self-doubt.

'I got by. After school I got a job as a chamber maid in a
hotel and from there sort of fell into housekeeping.'

No need to explain that was the only job she'd been able to
get with her poor school results. She and school hadn't got on,
not till right at the end when she'd been placed with her foster
parents Ted and Martha. Then she'd begun to blossom under
their loving kindness.

'How do you go from that to running a place like Carinya?'

Chloe paused. Her past and Declan's were so different. His, a success story from birth. Hers, almost the opposite, until Ted and Martha, and then Mark. Declan worked not because he needed the cash but because he loved the cut-and-thrust world of business. For her work was a necessity. She needed every cent of her generous wage to cover Ted's expensive private re-habilitation facility. Then one day, when she'd saved enough, she'd open a catering business.

'Hard work. I was determined to make a success of my-self. Lots of training—I did so many hospitality and catering courses I could whip up a *cordon bleu* meal for twenty if you needed it. Or a multi-tiered wedding cake.'

She halted, her pulse hammering as nausea rose at the idea of organising a wedding breakfast for Declan and some soci-ety darling. She hurried on. 'And there was luck too.'

'Tell me.'

She looked up at him, trying to gauge his interest. His dam-aged face, so familiar to her now, still had the power to make her chest squeeze tight.

'Why? It's not particularly interesting.' Chloe wasn't used to talking about herself. Was she afraid telling him would re-inforce the social chasm between them? Was she such a cow-ard?

'I'm interested, Chloe.'

He pressed a kiss to her lips and something inside melted. The tension that had risen thinking of her disastrous child-hood eased. Even her anxiety about this fragile new relation-ship ebbed in the face of the well-being she felt in Declan's embrace.

Was there anything more important now than sharing with him? Building on this closeness? She'd already laid herself open, letting him in. She needed the courage to go further. She shivered, acknowledging she wanted the chance to have him in her life, not just for a short fling.

'I was working at an upmarket hotel in Sydney when Damon Ives came to stay.'

'The actor?'

Chloe nodded, remembering the excitement among the staff when his visit had coincided with his first Oscar nomination. 'Yes. I was one of the staff rostered to look after his suite. He got to know me over the month he stayed and at the end he offered me a job.'

'Really?' The rhythmic stroke of Declan's hand stopped abruptly and she was sure she detected disapproval in his tone.

'Yes, really.' She stiffened. It wasn't the first time she'd encountered suspicion about her relationship with one of the country's most handsome and charismatic stars. 'And before you jump to conclusions, Declan Carstairs, let me say I impressed him with my willingness to help out when he needed extra assistance. That's all.' She didn't say more. Damon had a right to privacy.

She shuffled up onto her elbow so she could see Declan's face fully.

'Did I imply otherwise?' His brows rose.

'You wondered. I could hear it in your voice.'

His mouth quirked up at one side. 'A mind reader, are you, Chloe?'

'You made it pretty obvious.' Appalling how much that hurt. How easily Declan's words could wound her.

'Then I apologise.' He wrapped his warm hand around the back of her neck and pulled her down to him. 'Forgive me?' His lips brushed hers and her breath caught at the strength of her compulsion simply to sink into his arms.

Declan kissed the corner of her mouth, licked her bottom lip, and she shuddered. 'Please, Chloe?'

If he'd ordered she might have withstood him. As it was she surrendered with a sigh of pleasure.

But when his hands moved purposefully, one to her breast and the other to her bottom, she rolled away onto her side. Sex with Declan was wonderful, but what she really wanted was the comfort of being held close, sharing more than their bodies.

Was she crazy to believe this could lead somewhere?

'No?'

Her lips curved at the disappointment in his tone.

'Soon,' she promised. Despite her caution Chloe knew she couldn't resist him for long.

'Tell me about you,' she urged, wanting him to share with her as she had with him. She needed to know their intimacy was more than skin deep.

'Nothing to tell. My life's an open book.'

'Really?' She couldn't ignore a bubble of disappointment. 'Nothing at all you want to share?'

He shook his head. 'Unless you count the fact that I've been having x-rated daydreams about my housekeeper.'

Chloe stifled hurt at his blatant diversion. 'Is that so?' Her hand drifted to his face, stroking his cheek, the rough line of his scar. She reminded herself he was a man who kept his own counsel. Sharing wouldn't come easily to someone so self-contained. What had made him like that?

'Yes. She has this prim and proper voice that's a complete turn on. Just listening to her read out the notes of a meeting makes me hard with wanting.'

Suddenly he grabbed her hand and held it in his, palm flat against his scarred cheek.

'This really doesn't bother you?' The light-hearted tone disintegrated and for the first time there was an edge to Declan's voice that hinted at emotion.

'I told you it doesn't.' Her chest cramped as she read the confusion on his face. The desolation.

She'd wanted real. This was it. The accident had changed his life and his scars were the least of it.

'Do your injuries hurt very much?'

'No. Just a bit of stiffness and an occasional headache.'

Liar. Chloe had walked in on him more than once when he'd

been struggling, his face tight with pain as he pushed himself to the limit with his rehab exercises.

A wellspring of emotion bubbled up, filling her with the need to comfort him and herself.

He'd lost so much. And she... She feared she'd lost the safe, peaceful world she'd built for herself now this frustrating, intriguing man had burst into her life.

She laid her head on his shoulder, wrapping her arm over him and her thigh across his legs, as if to protect him from the demons that plagued him.

Yet who would keep her safe now the defences she'd painstakingly constructed after Mark's death had been scoured away?

'Chloe?'

Declan felt her blink against his chest. Was that moisture on his skin? Was she *crying*? The astonishing notion confounded him and stole his breath.

He couldn't remember anyone crying over him. He must be mistaken.

'Are you OK?' he asked, his voice rough.

'Never better.' She tightened her hold and he was hard put to concentrate on not responding physically.

'It must have been a terrible accident,' she murmured. 'For you *both* to have fallen from that cliff.'

Instantly Declan stiffened. Too often sympathy had been a ruse to elicit gory details of the tragedy that had taken Adrian's life.

Yet Chloe said no more, just held him close.

Perversely it was her silence, her refusal to ask, that loosened his tongue on a topic he never discussed. Or maybe it was the need finally to share—not just with anybody, but the woman he'd begun to care for.

He'd kept the truth of that day to himself. He'd held his friends at a distance since the accident. Even if he'd had family alive he wouldn't have burdened them with the knowledge of Adrian's despair. It was enough that Declan shouldered the guilt for not saving him.

'It *was* terrible,' he said finally, his voice scratchy, dredged up from a throat raw with pain. 'Like a nightmare.'

Surely it had happened in slow motion? Adrian's words, his cutting of the rope... So slow Declan should have realised sooner what he'd had in mind. Should have been able to prevent...

His hold on her tightened, her soft warmth balm against the hammer blows of guilt.

'It was a hard climb,' he recalled. 'Too hard.' He should have guessed that after years of soft living in London Adrian hadn't been up to it, despite his assurances.

'Hindsight's a wonderful thing.'

Declan tensed. 'That's no absolution.'

'Do you need it?' Her whisper lifted the hair on his arms.

There could be no absolution. Thinking of that day made his gut burn with familiar, hellish guilt. Every day, every hour trapped in this closed off darkness, haunted him.

'I'm... I was the elder, the more experienced one.'

'And your brother always did what you told him?'

Declan's mouth curled at the thought of Adrian taking advice. He'd always had to find out for himself. He'd been almost as stubborn as their father, or Declan.

'That doesn't excuse—' He shook his head. 'When I looked down and saw where Adrian had fallen...'

Chloe snuggled closer, her body a living blanket that surprisingly shaved away a fraction of the keen edge of pain. Remembering was anguish, but it was almost bearable.

'You didn't fall together?'

'No. My brother fell. This...' he gestured to his eyes and ruined face '...came when I climbed down trying to get to him.' They said Adrian hadn't survived the fall, yet Declan should have been with his brother at the end.

'You did your best. That's all anyone could ask.' The words feathered his throat as she rose up to kiss him. Her nipples brushed his chest and his arms closed hungrily around her, tugging her tight into him.

Chloe was the only real, sane thing in his world. She was safe harbour against the nightmares and the screams of conscience and he clung to her desperately.

He'd let his brother die and still hadn't brought the woman responsible to justice. Maybe, if he could do that, it would be some recompense for his failure.

With Chloe in his arms, a warm, sweet bundle of femininity, the raw gash of pain eased to a dull ache.

Declan took her mouth hard, demanding a response he was almost afraid she wouldn't give. But, as if sensing his desperation, she melted into him, yielding as his fingers bit into soft flesh and he tumbled her onto her back.

She didn't protest as he pressed her into the mattress, kneed her legs open and pushed into her honeyed warmth.

She didn't complain even when, with no foreplay or gentleness, he thrust hard and sure, again and again, slipping deep into her beckoning heat. Instead she wrapped herself around him, drawing him close. She rocked with him in a primal, desperate rhythm that beat in his blood so hard it obliterated guilt and memory and blasted away everything but them: Declan and Chloe.

He woke slowly, disinclined to lose the soul-deep wellbeing that came from a sated body, a warm woman and a comfortable bed. Not just any woman. Chloe. His Chloe.

Declan's hands twitched as if to hold her longer, seeking the peace, comfort and ecstasy she'd brought.

Slowly Declan made himself slide away, knowing if he stayed he'd wake her, demanding more. She needed sleep.

He shook his head. He'd never known anything like the cataclysmic sex they shared. The intensity of each touch, each breath, each shattering climax that ripped him asunder yet, conversely, seemed to rebuild him stronger each time.

He wrapped a hand around the back of his neck, grimacing.

He could tell himself blindness had its compensations: sharpening his other senses so physical delight took on a whole new meaning. But deep inside he knew the difference was Chloe.

She refused to let him sink completely into the well of guilt and pain. She dragged him towards the light, making him want more. Making him dare to hope.

He'd never felt dependent on a woman till now. Instead of it being a weakness, Declan knew his feelings for her made him stronger.

Beside him she slept on and his conscience stirred.

He'd been rough that last time, with no finesse. Yet she hadn't demurred, had simply clutched him close and ridden the wild surge of passion with him. Never, even in the throes of youthful exuberance, had he so lost control.

That worried him.

Better to get up now before he changed his mind about resisting temptation.

If he wasn't mistaken, the sun was out. He could feel it on his bare body as he swung his legs out of the bed. He could...

Declan froze, his sleep-slitted eyes opening in instinctive shock.

One deep breath. Another. He dragged them in, forcing air into lungs that threatened to collapse. His fingers clawed at the sheets till the blood throbbed in his veins.

Was this some trick? An illusion?

Or had the doctors been right?

He'd spent so long dismissing their hopes as a ruse to keep his spirits up; the chance they'd been right seemed impossible.

Yet there it was: a strip of light. He could see light. If he lifted his head it grew brighter, too bright for his long-dead eyes.

Hastily he lowered his gaze and there another shock awaited him: hardwood floor, rich with a century or more of polish. The hand-loomed rug in gold and black he'd purchased a decade ago on one of his first business trips to Asia. Bare legs, familiar, but for the wide scar that ridged one thigh.

He put one trembling hand to his leg, watching his fingers clench on skin, feeling his grip tighten as if in proof that what he saw was real.

Almost he was afraid to shut his eyes in case it was a dream. Like those mornings early after the accident when each awakening was a blow, a new reminder that he couldn't see, no matter how vivid his night-time dreams.

Air hissed from his lungs as he forced his eyes shut. His heart pounded against his ribs with fear and dreadful hope.

Carefully he opened them and the shock of sight froze him anew.

He could see! Hazily, not perfectly, but he could see. For days he'd imagined hints of light but had passed that off as wishful thinking.

His whole body shook in reaction. Thoughts flew through his brain too fast and incoherent to grasp. It was momentous, astonishing. He needed a witness, someone to share it with. He needed Chloe. She'd be ecstatic. He knew the hopes and concern she hadn't been able to hide, despite her brisk attitude.

Declan swivelled, shoving aside the sheet as he turned to her, his mouth already forming the words.

They disintegrated on his tongue, elation turning to bitter disbelief in an instant. He gasped, his breath constricting in reaction to an unseen blow that bludgeoned his chest, crushing his ribs.

It couldn't be. With a super human effort he dragged a breath into oxygen-starved lungs.

Frantically his gaze roved the woman asleep on his bed. She lay turned towards him, oval face tinted with the delicate flush of a well-loved woman. Fine, pale brows arched over closed eyes. Her long eyelashes were tinted darker than her brows, fanning ivory and rose skin. Her lips were as full and lush as he'd expected, reddened now, as was the delicate flesh near her lips and at her throat from his kisses and the abrasion of his stubbled jaw.

Something hard lurched in his belly as he saw how he'd marked her skin, branding her with his possession.

His hands clawed at the sheet as he catalogued her straight nose, neat jaw and cloud of wavy hair, rose-gold and glowing with life.

Declan slammed shut his eyes, forcing away the queasiness that stirred.

It couldn't be. It was impossible.

Yet even before he opened his eyes again he knew it was.

One final look and he catapulted off the bed, backing away to stand in the shadows, the thrill of restored vision eclipsed by the fact that he recognised this woman.

He'd seen her picture on Adrian's phone. Her sexy, slumberous smile had haunted his dreams for too long. Her identity had been a mystery he'd determined to solve from the moment Adrian had killed himself.

Chloe Daniels was his brother's girlfriend. The one Declan's investigator had failed to locate. Not surprising, as she wasn't a visitor to Carinya but lived here.

His brother's woman.

His breath stalled and his chest cramped as a leaden weight dropped through his belly. His flesh chilled.

She'd targeted Adrian then dumped him when she learned he'd lost his fortune. Declan had seen first hand how her betrayal and desertion had driven Adrian to suicide.

Nausea rose in his throat as he surveyed her naked allure, his numbed mind fighting instinctive denial.

This wasn't happening. It wasn't real.

Chloe was *his*. She was special. What he felt for her had even eclipsed the years of cynicism and distrust engendered by a false paternity suit and a scheming, avaricious ex-lover.

Chloe had taught him to trust again. She'd stood by him when he was vulnerable...

Most vulnerable.

Slowly his brain engaged. Nausea swirled anew and the world tilted as it all began to make sickening sense. Hadn't

Adrian said she'd left him to find herself a rich man? Wasn't Declan one of the wealthiest men in Australia?

He braced himself against the wall, his belly churning.

Chloe had tangled up his feelings. She'd pushed aside a lifetime's doubts engendered by watching his parents' less-than-close union. For the first time Declan had actually welcomed the idea of a long term relationship.

He remembered Chloe's patience despite his churlish demands for privacy. Her tenderness, well beyond the demands of her job. Her determination. The way she'd insinuated herself into his life, even his dreams.

Declan shook his head against the voice inside that screamed she was genuine, that she cared for him.

The evidence couldn't be shut out. She'd made herself indispensable to him while he was weak and grieving. When his defences were down.

What sort of coincidence was it that the woman who'd captured Adrian's heart then rejected him had become Declan's lover? He'd given up believing in coincidence when a smarmy lawyer had slapped him with a multi-million-dollar paternity claim for a child who wasn't his.

Abruptly he stumbled from the room, lungs labouring with each sawing breath. He needed space and time to confront this new nightmare. He couldn't think straight.

The only reality in Declan's world right now was the sound of his illusions crashing around him.

CHAPTER EIGHT

CHLOE woke to the roar of a helicopter. It blasted her consciousness with a heavy thud-thud-thud reminiscent of how her pulse had thundered when she and Declan made love. Instinctively she reached for him, but the bed was empty. Her heart dipped.

The vibration of the chopper's blades was so close it must be on the estate. She opened her eyes. The sun was so high she guessed it was afternoon.

On a surge of frantic energy she shot out of bed, only to discover her legs wobbled like jelly after a long night's loving. The realisation shocked her. She'd never experienced anything like the night she'd spent with Declan. Not even in the first flush of her relationship with Mark had passion been so all-consuming.

Chloe shoved the disquieting thought aside and stumbled to her feet, hauling her wrap on.

'Declan?' No answer from the *en suite* bathroom. He must have gone down to see who was arriving.

She cringed at the thought of being caught naked, emerging from her boss's bed. Last night they hadn't been employer and employee. But nor had they spoken of where their changed relationship might lead.

Chloe wished he was here to reassure her. So she could read the tenderness in his touch. A tenderness that had delighted her and eased her nerves.

Last night had been the culmination of weeks of tension

building like a storm head in a summer sky. Yet the depth of her feelings shocked her.

When Declan had revealed his injuries had come from trying to save his brother, her heart had cracked at such tragic waste and desperate loyalty. She'd wanted to hold him till all his wounds, physical and emotional, had healed.

Did she love him?

Her heart thudded so loud it blocked the roar of the chopper.

Chloe waited for panic to engulf her. Instead a sense of peace settled. Whatever this was, it was right.

Finally she remembered the need for clothes and moved. She was almost to the top of the stairs when movement out the window caught her eye.

The chopper was on the helipad beyond the tennis court. As she watched two men walked towards it, heads bent. One she didn't know. The other was unmistakeable—wide shoulders, wind-tousled black hair, imposing frame.

It was Declan in jeans and a dark shirt she'd laundered yesterday. His gait was clipped, uneven, as if his leg pained him more than usual.

Hot guilt stabbed her. Last night neither of them had made concessions for his injuries.

Then she realised Declan was getting aboard!

Her blood drained away. He was leaving? Chloe clutched at the window sill as she slumped in shock.

As morning-after etiquette, this was a killer. But then she had no experience of mornings after with any man but her husband. She shook her head, utterly bewildered, her stomach hollowing. *This couldn't be happening.*

Was she so easily dismissed? Had that tenderness, the closeness they'd slowly built, meant nothing? Was this how Declan behaved with all women once he'd had his fill?

Distress and mortification churned her insides.

At the last moment Declan paused and turned his head, almost as if he saw her. Chloe's heart leapt, then catapulted down as he climbed into the helicopter. A moment later it lifted off.

Chloe blinked, her hand pressed to her mouth. She couldn't believe it. Even if there was an emergency there'd been no need to leave without a word.

It had been Declan's choice.

His actions were a smack to the face, leaving her bereft, nursing shock and bewilderment.

Chloe stared numbly long after the helicopter had disappeared. She had the awful feeling that if she moved she'd shatter like discarded glass.

Some time later the phone rang. She jumped, pulled her robe tight and stumbled into Declan's room to take the call.

That meant confronting the wide, rumpled bed, the tray with the remains of their supper. The condom packet on the bedside table. The sight of it, empty and carelessly abandoned, jolted pain through her.

Eventually the shrill ringing forced her to move.

'Ms Daniels?'

Her knees gave way and she collapsed on the bed. Had she hoped it would be Declan?

'Yes?'

'Hi, this is Susie in Mr Carstairs' Sydney office.' She sounded young and bright, a millennium younger than Chloe felt.

'Yes?' Chloe's voice was odd—faded and hoarse.

'Mr Carstairs has instructed that Carinya be closed for the next few months. The gardener will act as caretaker. He wants you in Sydney tomorrow.'

Chloe shoved the hair back from her face with a trembling hand. 'Why Sydney?'

'Mr Carstairs will base himself there for the next few months.' Was that excitement Chloe heard in the other woman's voice? She could just imagine the stir Declan made among female members of his staff.

On a hiss of indrawn breath Chloe pressed a hand to her

chest. Was that what last night had been? Convenient sex with a willing, available employee? Yet, try as she might, she couldn't cast him as a sexual predator.

There had been much more to it than convenient sex. In the long, dark hours of loving, through the gentle caresses, the fierce hunger and the tentative sharing of words, she'd believed Declan experienced some of the magic she felt. Surely she couldn't have misunderstood?

'Ms Daniels? Are you there?'

'Sorry. I'm here.'

'Oh, good. Mr Carstairs wants you to take care of his apartment. You'll be based in Sydney till further notice.'

Two days later bewilderment had given way to fury. Two days without a sighting, even a phone call from Declan. All his instructions had come via his staff.

If well paid jobs weren't so hard to find, if she wasn't so desperate for the income to support Ted, Chloe might have handed in her notice.

Except she needed to see Declan again. Needed to know what had happened. Was he all right? Had something terrible happened?

He'd slammed into her quiet, contented life, torn it up by the roots and flung out of it again, leaving her seething yet bereft, hurting yet worried.

She needed to talk with him but that wouldn't happen any time soon.

An eager, excited crowd filled the huge, vaulted living space of his penthouse. The glittering throng was backlit by a stupendous view of Sydney Harbour Bridge and the white crests of the Opera House.

Glass doors to the landscaped roof-garden were open and guests spilled out to the lush, almost tropical haven. Tonight it was transformed into party central with a massive bar and candles floating in the long pool. The guests were glamorous and dressed to impress, wearing enough bling to sink a battleship.

She'd spotted celebrities enough to keep a gossip magazine in print for a year and there'd been paparazzi outside snapping shots as they had entered.

Thank goodness she'd changed. Instead of her usual skirt, blouse and sensible shoes, she wore a black dress and heels. Cheap jersey instead of silk. Simple rather than designer chic. Modest rather than sexy. But at least she didn't look totally out of place now she was forced into the role of reluctant hostess.

She smiled at the couple beside her who were extolling Declan Carstairs' business acumen and bit down on her own pithy assessment of his character. Two hours into his own party and he still hadn't showed.

Maybe his cavalier treatment of her wasn't unique.

Her jaw tightened and fire skirled in her blood. Yet still his behaviour didn't ring true with the man she'd come to know. That was the puzzle.

'Ms Daniels.' She found the manager of the catering team at her elbow, like herself dressed to blend with the guests. She read concern in his eyes.

Excusing herself, she turned towards him.

'We'll be out of champagne soon and the food's running low. There are at least fifty more guests than expected.'

Chloe nodded. She too had been surprised when guests had kept streaming in. And they wouldn't shift soon. Not when there was no host to call an end to what she knew from overheard conversation was a rare, must-attend event, a celebration in Declan Carstairs' private home.

Why had Declan decided to socialise on such a scale? It was unlike the man she'd known at Carinya. The reclusive man who'd treasured privacy.

The man she'd thought she knew.

The thought scoured a hollow ache inside.

'Your chef, he can have anything from the pantry, or bring in his own supplies, even if you have to wake people to get them. Mr Carstairs will cover the cost. As for the wine, there should be more delivered soon.'

At his questioning glance, she shrugged. 'The guests look like they're here for the duration. I ordered more a while ago.'

'Good thinking.' He smiled and she knew relief that she had an ally in this chattering mass of strangers. She'd kept herself busy these last days but she walked a knife edge, her nerves shot and her emotions a mess. Managing an A list party alone was the last thing she needed.

'Check what's delivered. If you think it's not enough, let me know.'

He nodded then looked over her shoulder. 'I think our host has arrived.'

Even as he spoke Chloe sensed it.

The hairs on the back of her neck rose and the bare skin of her shoulders tingled. Excitement rippled through the room. Heads turned. Women lifted hands to their hair and necklines.

Chloe swung around. There he was, devilishly charismatic in a dinner jacket and bow tie, dark hair cut ruthlessly short now. Heat suffused her and her heart hammered against her ribs.

He was all right, then. How often had she feared some terrible relapse? Relief made her knees wobble even as anger surged.

His formal clothes contrasted with the blatant masculine planes of his hard face and the disfiguring scar. Yet the latter accentuated rather than destroyed the character and compelling attraction of his features.

Chloe's breath disintegrated, her heartbeat accelerating to frantic. He looked debonair, powerful and innately dangerous, far beyond her league.

Yet the secret heat swirling low in her abdomen, the tight budding of her nipples, were proof her body knew his. It had been no dream.

'Declan!' A platinum blonde in a strapless dress of silver

sequins planted a kiss on his lips. She didn't seem in a hurry to break contact. Nor did he.

Chloe's fingers curled into claws.

'Vanessa.' Chloe just caught the deep burr of his voice over the chatter of the crowd. 'It's good of you to come.' His arm closed around the blonde's waist and she snuggled up to him.

On Declan's other arm a brunette with the face of a Latin siren and a curvaceous body in fitted scarlet pouted at him. As Chloe watched, Declan introduced the two women, both of whom remained cuddled close to him.

The crowd pressed forward. Declan smiled and shook hands, chatting easily. Chloe watched, fascinated, seeing him so at home in this high octane environment that reeked of wealth, ambition and success.

She was so absorbed it took a moment to process what she saw: Declan reaching out to shake hands. Declan greeting people by name as they approached.

Declan could see.

The realisation slammed into her with a force that punched the air from her lungs all over again.

It was fantastic, so wonderful she could scarcely believe it, but there was no mistaking the way he interacted with his guests.

She swayed and groped for support. Her hand clutched the sleeve of the catering manager.

In the same moment Declan raised his head, looking beyond a plump little man with his model-tall trophy wife, to stare straight across the vast space at Chloe.

As if he'd known she was watching.

As if he'd known exactly where she was.

Like those times before when he'd turned unerringly to her, sensing her presence though she hadn't said a word.

The reminder of that inexplicable link hit her anew. It weakened her knees and she staggered.

'Are you OK?'

Silently she nodded.

Across the room eyes dark as jet meshed with hers. A pulse of connection, an unseen wave radiating from Declan and devastating everything in its path, pinioned her.

His smile disappeared. His features tightened.

He didn't look like the man who'd cradled her in his arms. *He looked like a stranger.*

'I'm fine,' she whispered, releasing her grip on the catering manager and dragging her gaze away from Declan. Her skin prickled clammily and there was a buzzing in her ears. She swayed again but reminded herself she'd never fainted in her life. She wasn't about to start.

'You check those supplies. I'll come to the kitchen soon to see how things are.'

The caterer turned away and Chloe drew a shaky breath, trying to calm rioting nerves. She was torn between anger at Declan's behaviour and a thrill of joy at his restored sight. But when? How? Why hadn't he told her?

The crash of shattering glass jerked her head around. Over near Declan people stepped back, looking down.

In the ensuing hush she heard that low, familiar voice. 'It's all right, Sophia. The staff will deal with it. That's what they're here for.'

Across the room Declan looked straight at Chloe, his gaze unreadable. Again she was caught, transfixed by the force of emotions tangling around her.

Then Declan lifted one eyebrow. It rode high and challenging, a clear sign of impatience. It wasn't a request for help, that look, but an imperious command.

Cold drenched Chloe as she met his demanding gaze. His words circled in her brain. *The staff will deal with it. That's what they're here for.* Nothing more.

Something inside her shut down. On auto-pilot, she grabbed some napkins and made her way through the crowd.

So that was it? The sum total of Declan's feelings for her? Valiantly she fought off nausea. Could she really have been so mistaken in him? So naïve?

He'd had the hots for his housekeeper but it was over. He had his sight back and could choose from the loveliest women in Sydney. Chloe was merely an insignificant employee again.

Anguish tore a gaping hole where her heart had been.

All this time she'd known he was proud, even arrogant, but she'd never believed him to be a low life.

Lips firm, she forced her head up, ignoring the slashing pain as she reached him. He couldn't know her heart smashed against her ribs or that her self-possession hung by a thread.

'I'm so sorry,' murmured the brunette at Declan's side. 'I knocked my glass and—'

'No need to apologise, Sophia. If I don't care about a broken glass, why should my staff?'

His gaze met Chloe's and heat blasted through her, that familiar burst of electricity. She saw Declan's eyes widen, their expression waver. Then he turned abruptly, gathering Sophia's hands in his.

Shards of ice slid down Chloe's spine. Bewilderment and denial rocked her back on her heels. He'd felt it too—she'd read the shock of sizzling awareness in his eyes. But he'd turned from her as if it, she, meant nothing.

To have Declan treat her as if she didn't warrant acknowledgement almost felled her. Declan, the man who'd made her feel again.

Because of him she'd dared hope for something more than a life of routine and emotional seclusion. In her naiveté she'd once called that contentment, but Declan had made her see she'd been living a half life.

It had taken her family years of love and patient understanding to convince Chloe she was worth caring about. She'd fought hard to overcome self-doubt and build her sense of worth through hard work and education.

She was damned if she would let him dismiss her as nothing.

The only saving grace was that no one here knew her humiliation. To them she was simply an employee doing her job.

Declan had done nothing untoward. It was only he and she who knew how devastating his behaviour was.

Last time they'd been together she'd been in his arms.

Chloe dropped to her knees, her head spinning. Wine stained the hardwood floor and the edge of a fine cream rug. Her hands were quick as she gathered shards of glass. But her eyes prickled and she couldn't stop blinking.

She was all kinds of fool for caring.

Before her, less than a metre away, were his polished, hand-crafted shoes, the best money could buy. Above her his voice, deep and mesmerising, entertained his audience just as if she wasn't crouched at his feet.

Memory struck her of the day they'd met and she'd knelt before him, clearing another broken glass. She'd been annoyed by his arrogant attitude, not knowing it was blindness that made him so prickly.

He wasn't blind now.

He had his life back.

This was the real Declan.

Chloe gritted her teeth on a purging wave of fury that for a moment blanked out pain. When finally she stood, heat stained her cheeks.

'Oh, your dress! I'm *so* sorry.'

It was the brunette, gesturing to what Chloe now realised was her damp skirt. She'd knelt in the stain and not noticed. She supposed she should be thankful she hadn't cut herself into the bargain.

'It's OK,' she murmured, casting a reassuring look at the other woman. 'It'll come out.' In the meantime changing would give her a chance to escape Declan's presence.

By three a.m. everyone had gone. She was alone in the penthouse. Except she'd seen the light under the door of Declan's study and knew he'd retired there.

Was he alone?

Chloe thought of the brunette plastered to his side as he'd

said farewell to the other guests. She remembered the fine-grained leather sofa in the study, long enough even to accommodate Declan's tall frame. She pursed her lips. It was none of her business who he spent his time with.

It wasn't as if she wanted it to be her.

She wasn't masochistic. Once bitten...

Deftly she grabbed some glasses the caterers had missed and went to the kitchen. She didn't need to finish cleaning tonight, but it was pointless going to bed. She'd never sleep.

Chloe had her hands in warm water, cleaning crystal flutes, when her neck prickled. She paused, willing away the sensation of awareness and stirring excitement.

Instead of abating, the sensation grew. Her nipples drew tight as if responding to cold, but it wasn't cold she felt. It was heat, from the nape of her bent neck, over her bare arms and down.

She swivelled.

Declan lounged in the doorway, his shoulders almost filling the wide frame. The harsh kitchen light showed his scar, more livid than she remembered, slashing his firm cheek. His jacket was gone and the top buttons of his shirt were undone, revealing a hint of tanned flesh.

Chloe sagged against the sink, her hands sliding to the bench on either side for support. How could the sight of him still affect her? Faint hope stirred that he'd come to apologise. Yet what apology could he make?

'Yes, Mr Carstairs?' She was proud of her cool tone. She'd made a terrible mistake, but she told herself she'd get over it one day.

'We need to talk.' He straightened and entered the room. To Chloe's horror he kept coming till the space shrank around him. 'And what happened to "Declan"?'

'Clearly that's no longer appropriate.'

That damnable eyebrow climbed up, accentuating the saturnine cast of his face.

'Clearly?' he purred in that rich, rumbling tone that played havoc with her composure. It enraged her that she still responded to it.

Chloe straightened, her spine stiff as a steel girder. 'Oh come on, D—!' She heaved a deep breath and was disconcerted to see his gaze dip to the V of her wraparound dress. An instant later his jaw locked tight, his mouth grim.

She wanted to ask about his returned vision. Reach out to the man she remembered behind the stern visage.

Except now she realised that man had been a mirage. The real Declan was selfish and shallow. There was no other explanation for his behaviour.

'You've made your position abundantly clear,' she said. 'I didn't have to be Einstein to work it out. And you're right.' Pride supplied the words. 'We're employer and employee. Anything else was a mistake.'

Yet a bewildered, grieving part of her wanted to demand he explain, even hoped these last days had been a terrible misunderstanding.

He stopped so close she inhaled the spicy scent of his skin. A rolling tide of awareness washed through her, drawing her flesh tight.

'A mistake?' His brow puckered and for an instant he was all too familiar, the man who hid deep emotions and unspoken scars behind a brusque manner. She even thought she saw uncertainty flicker across his face.

Then Chloe caught the direction of her thoughts. When had Declan ever been uncertain? He didn't need an apologist. His actions spoke louder than words.

She shrugged. 'It shouldn't have happened and it won't be repeated.' Bravado hid wounds she refused to reveal.

'Why? Because you've set your sights on someone else?' The words bit like nails, hammered hard and fast. She sensed anger surge in him.

'What are you talking about?' She shook her head. 'Someone else?' The only man with whom she'd had anything like a private conversation was the caterer.

Her pulse raced. She couldn't cope with Declan so near. If he didn't go, she might fracture in front of him.

'What is it you need, Mr Carstairs?'

He stiffened, his face hardening. She told herself her tone was professionally cool, not insolent.

He stepped nearer, cramming her against the sink, but she refused to cower. Instead she met his dark look unflinchingly. *She* had done nothing wrong.

'You think this is all about what *I* need?' His eyes gleamed dangerously. Apprehension tingled in her veins but she stood straight. 'What about admitting what *you* need, Chloe?' His voice dropped to a ribbon of seduction that she despised at the same time she reacted to it. 'I've never known a woman as needy as you for what I can give her.'

Flame seared her cheeks and throat. She'd been abandoned, wanton with this man. She'd experienced passion such as she'd never known and she'd revelled in it.

She opened her mouth to say he'd been just as needy then clamped her lips. A slanging match wouldn't help.

'If there's nothing else, I'll get on with the washing up. It's late.' When he didn't move she added, 'I don't need or want anything from you.'

She reassured herself it was true. Or would be, if only he'd leave her alone.

Her hands had just sunk into the warm water when he gripped her shoulders and spun her round.

'That's a lie, Chloe. We both know it.' His voice was pure gravel as he loomed over her, his face taut. Suppressed emotion radiated from him in waves.

She opened her mouth to deny it when warm fingers settled over her right breast, sure, hard yet gentle as they cupped her. Shock stole the words from her mouth. His hand moved, caressing, squeezing, and her throat dried.

One touch and he evoked a longing she'd thought she'd evicted from her being. One tantalisingly erotic caress and her knees were jelly.

'No!' She clamped a wet hand around his wrist and tugged. Nothing happened. Nothing except she felt the pull and shift of muscle and tendon as he changed his hold, plucking at her budded nipple through the fabric of her dress. Heat coiled deep within.

'Don't lie. Not about *this*.' His voice thickened as he leaned in, undeterred by the hand she shoved against his chest. He bit the sensitive spot between her shoulder and neck and shudders of longing engulfed her. Even her anger and hurt couldn't prevent her response. Her head spun.

He kissed the spot then suckled it and her nerves shot to clamorous alert. 'You want me, you know you do.'

It wasn't him she fought but herself. How could that be?

This man had walked out on her, rejected her. She couldn't want him. She couldn't!

'No.' She shook her head, still pushing desperately against him. Or perhaps not so desperately. Why had her hand tightened against his shirt? Not to push back but to mould his warm muscle. 'I'm not available for a quick grope now your fancy friends have left. I'm not your bit on the side.'

'Ah, Chloe, you were never that. You were always...' He groaned and tightened his hold, feathering kisses at the corner of her mouth.

She had nowhere to turn or hide, caught between his unyielding frame and the sink. His strong thighs surrounded her. The ridge of his arousal pressed against her abdomen.

Had she stopped struggling?

Damp heat pooled between her legs as he slipped his hand beneath the V of her bodice and bra. The skin-on-skin contact was her undoing. She shuddered as he pinched her nipple then bent to suckle her other breast through the thin material.

'Declan.' It was supposed to be a protest, but her hoarse voice turned it into a plea.

This was wrong, wrong, wrong.

Yet it felt...

'Yes?' His mouth moved against hers again, his voice cajoling. He didn't kiss her fully, just skimmed her lips and moved on to nibble her ear. His other hand parted the discreet gap in her crossover skirt, and an instant later his fingers were against damp silk at the apex of her thighs. He pressed close and she almost moaned.

'You like that, don't you, Chloe?' His voice was a whisper of seduction in her ear.

She shook her head, struggling to drag herself from the whirlpool of sensation and think.

He pressed close, body to body, erection to her needy centre. A jolt of response rocked her whole being.

'Tell me, Chloe. Tell me what you want.'

She heard the words through a fog of sensual pleasure and rising need. Incoherent warnings flitted by but she couldn't grasp them. Instead all the emotions she tried so hard to ignore rose to the surface.

'What do you want, Chloe?' He breathed the words against her mouth and she arched into him.

'You,' she whispered on a sob. 'I want you.'

Bliss beckoned. He surged close, his arousal hard against her, his hands hot and possessive.

Then suddenly he was gone. His big hand slipped from beneath her bra, the other from under the edge of her panties. Cool air brushed her skin and dazedly she realised he'd undone the tie of her dress so it hung open, revealing her bare skin and sensible underwear.

She lifted a hand, whether to pull the gaping edges together or to reach for him she didn't know. Instead his voice stopped her.

'No!' The raw denial cut straight through the fog of sensual awareness. 'That will never happen again.'

Glittering eyes raked her. Then he spun on his heel and marched from the room.

CHAPTER NINE

AIR. He needed air.

His lungs couldn't suck in enough oxygen.

Declan strode away, shoved open a door and catapulted out onto the roof garden.

His lungs pumped frantically and now, finally, searing air filled his chest. For a minute there he'd wondered if he'd black out from lack of oxygen.

It was fury, he assured himself. Disgust at the woman who'd betrayed Adrian, broken his brother's heart and left him so distraught he'd committed suicide.

Together they were responsible for Adrian's death. She for driving him to it and Declan for not preventing it. Guilt swarmed like ants over his burning flesh.

What greater betrayal of Adrian than to take Chloe into his bed? To grab at the happiness denied his brother?

Nausea churned in his belly.

Chloe had tried to play Declan for a fool, deliberately targeting him as a rich, easy mark with his blindness and his grief. Hell! He'd been so gullible, wanting more from her than he'd wanted with any woman.

Even when his own eyes had confirmed her identity he hadn't wanted to believe the worst, had fought it with every fibre of his being. Till he'd been hit with even more proof of her culpability. Proof he couldn't ignore.

Yet still he desired her. He even—and it shamed him to admit it—felt jealous he'd shared her with Adrian.

Bile rose, nearly choking him. How low had he sunk?

In shock he'd left Carinya, unable to face the enormity of his disillusionment, or the woman who had torn him in two. She made him yearn to believe the impossible—that it was all some terrible mistake.

For the first time ever he'd run, he who tackled every challenge head on. For two days he'd been in meetings and medical appointments, confirming his restored vision should be permanent. But in reality he'd avoided her. Because he didn't want to face the moment she confirmed the truth with her own admissions. Was he such a coward?

He scrubbed a hand over his face.

Despite the new proof against her he was torn. Part of him clung to the memory of the honest, lovely woman he'd been on the verge of falling for.

Just now in the kitchen, desperation had driven him. He hadn't been able to keep his hands off her. He'd wanted to take her sweet mouth with his and lose himself in her sinfully addictive body. He'd craved it so badly his hands still shook with the force of control he'd had to exert.

He wanted the woman he'd known at Carinya. The woman he could respect and even…love.

Love? He'd almost fallen lock, stock and barrel for a fantasy.

She'd turned her sights on him when she'd discovered Adrian had lost his money with the failure of his London business. How convenient that Declan, wealthier than Adrian had ever been, had come to Carinya. She'd no qualms about going from one brother to another.

Was that why she'd delayed her return to the house? Had she feared Adrian had told Declan about her?

He stalked to the pool, reefing open his shirt. He needed more than air. He needed a workout to exhaust himself and dull the knowledge he'd been weak, touching her again.

That weakness sickened him. The mere sight of her tipped him over the edge and made a mockery of his guilt and her betrayal.

Declan tore his shirt off, his hands going to his trousers, ready to get naked and work off his frustrations in the pool. But the sight of the water brought him up short. Last time he'd swum, he'd surfaced and found Chloe.

He shuddered and dropped his hand. Suddenly the pool didn't hold the same allure. With each stroke the caress of silky water against his skin would remind him of her touch.

Even in basic black, without jewellery or designer flair, Chloe had stood out in the throng of pampered beauties. With her ivory skin and her rose-gold hair up in an elegant chignon, she'd caught his eye immediately.

Declan told himself she wasn't beautiful. It was just that he'd learned the silken texture of her skin and the lush softness of her body.

Tonight he'd almost lost it when he'd seen her cosying up to a stranger.

When she'd knelt at his feet, so briskly competent, obviously unmoved by seeing him again, he'd wanted to lose the women he'd gathered close as protection against her, against the urge to stalk across the room and grab her. He'd wanted to haul her to him and brand her as his even while he'd wanted to shake her for daring to touch another man.

He'd stood, transfixed by the tiny, unexpected sprinkle of freckles across her nose and cheeks that made her appear almost innocent.

Innocent! He stalked across the garden, impatient at his own weakness.

He'd gone to the kitchen because his conscience demanded he face her at last. But the sight of her in that dress, held together with a single tie, its soft fabric outlining every dip and curve, had got the better of him.

'What the hell was that about?'

Declan shoved his hands into his trouser pockets as her husky voice shivered across the bare skin of his torso.

Slowly he turned his back on the city view, pushing away a moment's reluctant admiration that she was no coward. She'd followed him almost immediately.

She stood a couple of metres away, her chin lifted. Her hair was up but softened by delicate wisps that framed her face. Her dress was knotted tight, too tight, given the way it stretched across her breasts.

Heat dived in his groin and he firmed his jaw. He was too savvy to be fooled by that trick again.

'I *said*—'

'I heard you the first time.' He shrugged and watched with satisfaction as her narrowed eyes widened and dropped to his bare chest.

Deliberately he crossed one foot over the other and spread his arms wide on the railing, projecting a nonchalance he didn't feel.

Her mouth sagged before she remembered to snap it shut. He'd never been one for an idle life, but in these last months the long hours of exercise in the pool had toned his muscles even more. Almost enough, it seemed to make up for the ravaged face that stared back from the mirror each day.

People winced when they saw him, averting their eyes. But that hadn't stopped women tonight latching on to him. They loved his money and power.

Had Chloe shut her eyes rather than look at him when she'd shared his bed? Distaste curdled his belly and soured his tongue.

He should have been prepared for the fact Chloe's care and attention was mercenary. Yet it hurt. He'd truly *believed*.

'Are you going to explain yourself?' Her voice was jerky, as if she had trouble keeping her breath under control.

'I thought my meaning was clear.' He spoke slowly, finding this harder than he'd expected. 'I wouldn't touch you even if you were sprawled naked in my bed.'

Yet, even as he said it, shuddering doubt undermined him. He watched her lush mouth firm and remembered the graze of her lips, hot against his skin. He remembered the way she'd knelt at his feet tonight and how it wasn't just the unexpected sight of delicate freckles that had held him rigid. It was the idea of her leaning in and…

'Why, because I dared to cross the line and stopped behaving as an employee?' He watched her wrap her arms around herself, as if cold despite the balmy night. Yet her chin stayed high, her eyes flashing. 'Don't tell me you have one rule for women and another for yourself? Once you've had a woman, you don't respect her. Is that it?'

He almost thought he discerned vulnerability in her face. Did he imagine that sexy mouth trembled? A rush of heat filled him and he leaned towards her. No, it was impossible. She was simply projecting emotion.

'Hardly.' He breathed deep. 'I like women. I just don't like you.'

Her jaw tightened as if he'd struck her. The pulse at the base of her throat trembled. He'd almost swear she paled.

He felt no satisfaction, only the desire to blurt out an apology. What sort of champion did that make him of his brother's cause?

'The feeling's mutual.' The words clipped out, sharp and precise from that lovely mouth. 'I've never met a more arrogant, rude man without even the most common courtesy.' She stopped and hefted in a breath that lifted her breasts towards him.

Declan kept his gaze fixed on her face.

'You're complaining about my *manners*?'

To his surprise Chloe stepped closer, her hands fisting on her hips. 'What *is* it with you, Declan? You think you can walk all over me? Nothing gives you the right to speak to me the way you have! Even if you've lost interest in me now you've got your sight back.'

'Oh, please, spare me the outraged innocence.' She must know by now he'd recognised her.

He watched one hand snap up towards him then stop abruptly, as if at the last minute she'd thought better of striking him.

Strangely, he'd almost have welcomed the slap. Punishment, not for his rudeness but for his weakness in still craving this woman.

He exhaled slowly. 'I know about you and Adrian.'

If he'd had any last, lingering doubts about Chloe's innocence, her instantaneous reaction banished them. Pale skin turned bone-white. Her eyes grew huge and her gasp was unmissable in the silence throbbing between them.

Disappointment swamped him. Had he really hoped she'd be able to explain away what she'd done?

Roiling emotion filled him. He had to force himself to stand still and face what he must. He owed Adrian, and himself.

'What do you know about Adrian?' Somehow she dredged the words from a throat shredded raw by the tears she'd fought back in the kitchen. Tears of fury and outrage, of self disgust and bitter, soul deep disappointment with the man who'd shown his true colours tonight. She'd hoped…

No! She couldn't go there. She couldn't face her naiveté in spinning hopes and dreams about him. She'd given so much of herself. Declan had merely enjoyed sex.

'I know everything.'

Stunned, Chloe looked up to find him standing closer, his feet wide and his arms crossed over his bare chest in a stance that signalled pure male domination.

A sensible woman would retreat but her feet were rooted to the ground. She felt punch drunk, hit by so many conflicting emotions it was hard to think.

How did he know about Adrian? Had Adrian confessed his behaviour? If so, why mention it only now?

'Adrian…spoke to you?' She frowned, finding it hard to believe he'd confided in anyone.

She'd urged Adrian to talk with someone, anyone, knowing he needed help. Help she'd been unqualified to give, especially given the role in which his increasingly delusional mind had cast her.

Adrian had been ill. He'd refused to listen and had become aggressive if she pushed. He'd seen every attempt to guide him towards help as betrayal.

'You don't deny knowing him?' Declan pounced.

'Of course not. He stayed at Carinya after he returned from the UK. While you were in China. You know that.'

'Yet you don't talk about him.' Slowly Chloe shook her head, still disorientated by the change of topic.

She'd decided before she returned to Carinya that there was no point dredging up the harrowing past. There was nothing to be gained by mentioning Adrian's fixation except distress for her and his brother.

Now Declan claimed to know about it. Chloe frowned. 'What do you want me to say? What *is* there to say?'

'How about saying sorry? That would be a start.'

She gazed up at his tight-lipped face, feeling she'd stepped into a parallel universe where nothing made sense. Why were they talking about Adrian and not what had happened between *them*?

'I've already said I was sorry to hear he'd died.' But from the look on Declan's face, he didn't believe her.

His nostrils flared, his jaw hardened and his hand shot out as if to grab her arm. Then it dropped to clench at his side. Silence engulfed them, broken only by the thud of her pulse in her ears.

'You're denying your role in what happened? You don't feel *any* guilt?' Declan drew a breath that shuddered through his massive chest.

Chloe watched, bemused. She put a hand to her brow, pushing back wisps of hair that feathered her face.

'What do you mean? I didn't do anything to him.'

'Oh, you're good. Very good.' Declan's words burst out like machine gun fire. 'You look the picture of innocence.'

'I had no role in his death. You know that. It was a climbing accident.'

He thrust his head forward, invading her space.

'It wasn't an accident.' A shudder rippled across his skin. 'He killed himself. Killed himself because of you.'

His accusing finger pointed directly at Chloe. Her heart spasmed and she gasped, pressing the heel of her hand to her chest.

'No. That's not true. It couldn't be.'

But Declan merely stared back, his face cast in harsh lines. Chloe waited for him to recant and say it was a lie, but he didn't.

Slowly, like dank, creeping fog, awful doubt filled her.

She recalled how Adrian's friendly interest had changed to stalking, the continual invasion of her personal space. Finally she'd been unable to stay at Carinya. With his brother overseas, there'd been no one to make Adrian see reason or force him to seek counselling. No one except her, and every time she'd tried he'd accused her of betrayal, of not loving him as he did her. She shivered.

Could he really have been so deluded by his fantasy world that he'd taken his life?

'Tell me it's not true,' she pleaded, her hands twisting. 'Please, Declan.'

For what seemed an age Declan stared back, his face eerily blank. When he spoke again his voice was devoid of inflection.

'We fell together but we were secured by a rope. Eventually I'd have found a way to get us back to safety.'

He paused, blinked, and then went on. 'He'd already shown me your photo. He'd described you in loving detail.' Declan's voice dripped acid. 'He raved about the wonderful woman in his life. How much you meant to him. How perfect your relationship was.'

Chloe reared back in instinctive denial, but Declan's hand shot out and grabbed her arm. His fingers burned like ice on her bare flesh, a living, unbreakable manacle.

'The day we climbed he was…different. Edgy, not so buoyant. And then, with the accident, it all came out. The truth he'd avoided telling me—how you'd betrayed him.'

Declan's hold firmed. 'How you'd used him then rejected him.' He grasped her other arm and leaned close, forcing her to bow backwards.

'How Adrian believed his life wasn't worth living without *you*.' Another tremor racked Declan's big frame and echoed through her.

'That's when he deliberately cut the rope and fell to the valley floor.'

A sharp cry pierced the air but Chloe barely recognised it as hers. Her mind was filled with the image Declan painted, of the troubled man she'd known falling down those endless cliffs.

Because of *her*, Declan had said.

It was nonsense.

It wasn't her fault.

Yet she felt herself shrivel and hollow with the terrible suspicion that perhaps, if she'd done more, it would never have happened.

She'd thought about putting in a harassment complaint with her employer but assumed, since the complaint was about her employer's brother, she'd simply lose her job.

She'd considered going to the police for a restraining order but had shied from such drastic action. After all, he hadn't actually hurt her.

She'd been a coward.

If she'd forced Adrian's increasingly unhinged mental state into the open maybe someone could have prevented his death.

Her blood froze.

The Adrian she'd met had been a loner, cut off from his London friends and in no hurry to re-establish himself socially in Australia. His brother had been busy overseas and Adrian was content to spend his time at Carinya.

Was she the only one who'd seen his descent into delusion? Who else had there been to witness it?

Guilt filled her. Had she done wrong in running that day he'd gone too far?

No. She might regret not reporting Adrian's actions, but she couldn't hold herself responsible for the fantasy relationship in his head. Once she'd left Carinya and heard the news of Ted's stroke, she'd put everything aside except the need to be with her beloved foster father.

It was regrettable, but it wasn't her fault.

It only felt like it.

Bruising hands still held her. Reluctantly she looked up into a face drawn sharp with grief and desolation. Did he hate her? Who could blame him when he thought she'd driven his brother to suicide?

'Let me go, Declan.' Her voice was heavy. 'You're hurting.'

Immediately his grip eased and she felt the brush of fingers on skin as his hands dropped. But he didn't step away, just loomed over her, his face a stiff mask.

She drew a deep breath. 'I need to explain—'

'You think I'd believe your explanations? You had weeks to tell me the truth yet you kept silent.' He turned his back and strode to the balustrade. He stood silhouetted by the city lights, arms spread wide and bare shoulders hunched. 'Your explanations won't bring him back.'

The stark despair in Declan's voice stopped Chloe even as she started forward. What she had to tell him about his brother would bring pain. Yet she couldn't let him believe she was to blame.

'Declan, it wasn't like you think.'

His bark of laughter ripped the night air apart.

'You believe I'm that gullible, Chloe? I know you for what you are.'

She took a step closer, torn between distress at his grief and the need to set the record straight.

Because even now she harboured some fragile belief that what she and Declan had shared was special?

'Your brother and I didn't have that sort of relationship.'

She watched the bunch and play of muscles in his back and shoulders as he flung his head back, as if taking in the smattering of stars half-obscured by city lights.

'You say he lied?' Disbelief and weariness edged his tone, reminding her he'd already gone through too much.

'He told you...his version of the truth.'

Was there an easy way to tell a grieving man his lost brother had been mentally unhinged?

'Your brother misinterpreted—'

'No. Don't you dare tell me he misunderstood what was between you. I saw the photo on his phone. There was no mistaking that.'

Chloe gasped, her blood freezing as she recalled waking to find Adrian in her room at dawn, taking photos of her in bed. That was the morning she'd decided she couldn't go on pretending to cope.

Her heart galloped as she recalled Adrian's nonchalance, his belief he'd had every right to be in her room.

'It wasn't what it looked like.'

'No?' Declan didn't turn but his voice told her he didn't believe a word. 'You're telling me your relationship was platonic? I suppose you two never even kissed?'

Chloe hesitated, her tongue glued to the roof of her mouth. She'd never kissed Adrian but he'd kissed her, cornering her in the pantry. She'd shrugged him off, trying to make light of it. Perhaps that had been her first mis-step. Maybe if she'd shown how horrified she was, instead of trying to maintain a semblance of dignity, it would have nipped Adrian's interest in the bud.

'I suppose you never shared confidences either, you and my brother?'

Chloe recalled Adrian lingering in the kitchen as she baked, telling her stories of his life in London and his plans to rebuild his career. Before she realised how unhealthy his interest had grown, she'd shared her dream of establishing a catering business.

'We talked, but—'

'You talked. You kissed. And now, I suppose you'll tell me that photo wasn't of you in bed.'

'It was!' she burst out. 'But not with my permission. Your brother had no right.'

'No right to expect loyalty from his lover?' Declan turned and skewered her with a stare so fierce it dried the protest in her throat.

If he believed that, why hadn't he sacked her? Why wait till now to mention it?

'It's funny,' he murmured. 'When I saw your picture I thought my brother a lucky man. I changed my mind when I learned how shallow and mercenary you were. But when I saw you in the flesh that first time, I understood the attraction.'

'The first time?' The words strangled in her throat. Surely the first time was tonight.

'At Carinya.'

'You knew...then?' She frowned, her brain whirling.

'I knew then.' His voice held a heavy, lifeless quality that twisted her heart. Till she read the contempt in his dark eyes that once had blazed with tenderness.

Pain scoured deep, radiating in all directions.

'You believed I'd betrayed your brother and yet you slept with me?' Her hand crept to her mouth in horror.

It couldn't be true. *It couldn't.*

Something flickered in his eyes, something Chloe couldn't read. Finally he shrugged, the movement jerky.

'There wasn't much sleeping involved.' He paused, as if gathering himself. 'Besides, I needed to be sure.'

Her gasp shattered the silence. Nausea rose.

No wonder he'd given off mixed signals that night, pushing

her away and taunting her even as he'd drawn her to him with his charisma and potent sex appeal. He'd known she wore silk and talked about how she looked.

How had she not *known*? She'd thought that night had meant something to him, as it had to her.

Chloe swayed and stumbled back. She squeezed her eyes shut for a moment, trying to stop the world spinning.

Out of the corner of her eye she caught a blur of movement, as if he reached out to steady her. But he didn't touch her. She must have imagined it.

'Sure about what?' Was that thread of sound her voice?

When she looked again his expression was unreadable.

'Sure you were the sort of woman who'd blithely betray my brother when a better opportunity came along. That's what I was to you, wasn't I, Chloe—a better opportunity? You had no qualms about sleeping with both the Carstairs brothers for what you could get out of it.'

She stood rooted to the spot, telling herself she wasn't hearing this. Her head spun dizzily.

'It was necessary.' Declan surveyed her as if he read and understood every tiny, tell tale reaction of her body. 'But not without some compensations.'

Her heart jerked hard against her ribcage as her hand smacked his cheek.

He didn't even flinch.

CHAPTER TEN

DECLAN strode down the corridor, ignoring the aromatic scent of coffee that teased his nostrils. He didn't want to face Chloe this morning.

Last night he'd confronted her with the truth and she'd had no answer for it. He hadn't felt vindicated or triumphant. He'd been gutted.

The hot imprint of her palm against his cheek had briefly raised his hopes that the real Chloe, the one he'd fallen for, was back. But the hope had been short-lived. She'd had no answer, no explanation. No excuse. He had to face the fact that the real Chloe was the one who'd seduced both his brother and himself in the hope of financial gain.

Yet the memory of her hurrying away last night, one hand pressed to her mouth, evoked guilt. As when he'd let her believe he'd slept with her as a test of her character and greed.

He'd lied.

Declan firmed his jaw. Pain had made him lash out, capitalising on her misunderstanding. He wasn't proud of what he'd done. He'd almost recanted in the face of her stricken look.

Till he'd remembered Adrian's anguish. Whatever Chloe felt was nothing to what she'd inflicted on his brother. Yet still he felt torn between what he owed Adrian and what he felt for Chloe.

Declan had worked it all out now. Adrian's mention in his note of her dumping him for a better prospect had been written just days before Declan arrived at Carinya. Why stick with the bankrupt when the other Carstairs brother was a billionaire?

He recalled how Damon Ives had offered her a job after they'd met in the hotel where she'd worked. It seemed all too likely she'd slept her way into the job.

She said she'd never had money. Had she been so poor, so desperate, she'd sell herself for a little luxury?

He dragged his fingers through his hair. Surely he wasn't finding excuses for her?

'Declan.' Chloe's voice, thrumming low across his senses, pulled him up.

She stood in the doorway: crisp white shirt, straight grey skirt and sensible shoes. Hair pulled back and hands clasped at her waist. A hint of white, flour perhaps, on one cheek, as if she'd been industrious in the kitchen. It added authenticity to her wholesome image.

If her face looked too pale, so those tiny freckles stood out on her cheeks and neat nose, he told himself it was the sign of a guilty conscience. That must also be the reason for the smudges beneath her eyes.

Yet Declan had to shove his hands in his pockets lest he be tempted to reach out and smooth the tiny frown pleating her brow.

'We need to talk.' Her jaw angled defiantly. The gleam in her eyes snared him and he found himself leaning closer.

Abruptly he straightened.

'Very well.' He turned and led the way to his study. She was right. They hadn't finished this.

'I've made cinnamon rolls and coffee in the kitchen.'

So she *had* been baking. Now she mentioned it, a sweet, yeasty fragrance mingled with the beckoning scent of coffee. Had she hoped to win him over with her cooking?

Lips compressing, he took his seat behind the vast desk. She entered slowly. Was she disappointed he didn't take up her invitation for a cosy kitchen chat?

He leaned back in his chair, steepling his fingers. 'You wanted to speak with me?'

Her pale eyebrows rose a fraction but she looked calm, her spine erect.

'I need to tell you the truth about your brother and me.'

Declan's heart lurched to a faster beat. He told himself it was anticipation he felt, yet the last thing he wanted was to hear about Chloe and Adrian together.

'You weren't in the mood to listen last night and I…' Her gaze darted towards the doors leading to the roof terrace. 'I found it difficult coping with so many revelations.'

He said nothing.

She turned and suddenly he found himself drowning in remarkable apple-green eyes. It was hard to believe anyone with eyes the colour of spring and innocence could be so culpable.

He'd been gullible. For the first time in his life, he'd truly opened himself to a woman—not as a short-term lover, but as something more. He'd wanted…everything with Chloe.

Silently he cursed himself for wishing even now the truth could be different.

'At first Adrian didn't have much to do with me. After all, I was the hired help.' Her mouth twisted as if in wry amusement.

Declan stiffened. He didn't want to know details of their journey into intimacy. But if that was part of his punishment for letting Adrian down, he'd force himself to listen.

'But he didn't seem to have anyone else to talk to.'

Familiar regret shot through Declan. If he'd known Adrian was troubled he'd have dropped everything to be there on his brother's return from the UK. But Ade had assured him he was fine and ready to enjoy some R and R.

'He had friends,' Declan said, assuring himself as much as her. 'Adrian grew up with a wide social circle.' It was unavoidable, given their parents' active social lives before their untimely deaths.

Chloe lifted her shoulders. 'All I know is that he kept to

himself. The people he spoke about were those he'd left in London, like his business partner, Diana. He talked of her all the time.'

'And you decided it was your duty to keep him company, because he was lonely?'

Chloe didn't react. Her face remained smooth of expression, unnaturally so.

'Tell me about him.' Declan was hungry for anything that would help explain Adrian's depression. Even now it didn't seem real. There'd been no hint of mental illness in their phone calls and emails, though he'd seemed more preoccupied than usual. Declan had put that down to natural concern over his bankruptcy.

Again her gaze shifted. 'He couldn't seem to relax. As the days passed he became restless, almost agitated.' She paused and Declan sensed her tension. Was it because she'd realised he wouldn't let her off the hook easily?

'He sought me out more and more.'

Declan swallowed a sharp retort. Had Adrian sought her out or had she pursued him?

She must have seen the disbelief on his face. Her eyes glittered and her jaw angled infinitesimally higher.

'It's true. He talked about his schemes for turning his business around and how good things were going to be when he pulled off some big business coup he was planning.'

Declan frowned. That didn't make sense. Adrian's business had gone bankrupt. Declan had had to assist his brother financially the last several months. There was no way Adrian's business could have been salvaged. Adrian had admitted to Declan he wasn't sure if he'd even go back to advertising or take up Declan's offer of a job.

As for him sharing his financial situation with Chloe—according to Adrian's note, that was when she'd dumped him.

'But it was more than that,' she continued. 'He *changed*. It seemed whenever I entered a room, he was there. He'd just… watch me go about my tasks.'

Did he imagine a tremor in her voice? 'What do you mean? He went out less so you saw more of him?'

Again Declan berated himself for not being there.

'That too.' She wrapped an arm around her waist. Emotion stirred at the sight of her apparent vulnerability but he thrust it aside. 'Mainly it seemed he anticipated my movements. Everywhere I went he'd be there, waiting.' Her words quickened. 'He even followed me when I went out. Then he'd question me about anyone I met or spoke to, as if he were jealous. It was…not normal.'

Declan sat up straight, his hands wrapping tight on the arms of his chair as precognition prickled his spine.

She couldn't be saying what he thought she was saying.

'You're telling me Adrian stalked you? That's preposterous!' The knot of inner tension combusted into indignation. How dared she say such a thing about Adrian?

Declan *knew* his kid brother. He'd virtually raised him since their parents had been immersed in business and social activities. Ade had been a great guy, without a malicious or devious bone in his body. He wasn't a stalker.

'You're maligning him because he's not here to defend himself.'

'I'm telling you the truth.'

Declan scoured his stunned mind for words. 'You ask me to believe he developed an *obsession* with you without any encouragement?'

Everything in him rejected the idea. Not Adrian. Not the brother he'd loved.

Despite his anger, Declan had been ready to consider there might have been extenuating circumstances prompting Chloe's action. That surely she wasn't the mercenary witch the evidence painted her. But with this allegation she'd gone too far.

'He did.' She met his disbelieving stare unblinkingly. 'I gave no encouragement except that I listened. But suddenly he was talking about us as if we were a couple, with a history between us. As if we were lovers.'

'And you weren't lovers?' Just thinking of it made his stomach curdle.

Chloe shook her head. 'We weren't. He wasn't my type.'

Declan heard a catch in her voice as if she found it hard to speak over welling emotion.

Then he remembered Adrian, just before he died, describing how she'd dumped him to go after someone with more money. He recalled how Chloe had decided he, Declan—disfigured, antisocial and brusque to the point of rudeness—*was* her type. How eagerly she'd given herself to him even when, after months of celibacy, he'd forgotten how to be gentle with a woman.

What could she have seen in him then but access to his wealth and an easy lifestyle? Just as years before an ex-lover had seen him as a shortcut to a pampered life.

He shied from remembering how much Chloe had meant to him in those dark days. It had all been a sham. The fact that even now he longed for the woman he'd known then made the anger and self-contempt in his belly burn hotter.

Torn between believing in the brother he'd known and loved for a lifetime and the woman he'd fallen for in a few short weeks, how could Declan even hesitate? He'd already failed Ade once. His shoulders slumped as a leaden weight settled in his belly.

His brother had never had trouble attracting women. Nor had he been a liar. Adrian wasn't a predator. He'd *never* have stalked a woman.

But then Declan hadn't realised Adrian was prepared to kill himself, had he? The damning voice in his head made him frown.

'He spoke of places we'd been together.' Chloe's creamy complexion flushed. 'He got angry when I didn't know what he was talking about and accused me of wanting to break off our relationship to take up with someone else.' She bit her lip.

'If my brother was bothering you, why didn't you report him?'

'I thought of it. I almost went to the police, but it was my

word against his. Besides, he had a right to be in your house.'
She looked away. 'But finally he frightened me. He was en-
croaching more and more and I thought—'

'Yes?'

'I worried about what he might do. There were days when
he seemed almost normal but more when I thought he might
act on his beliefs.'

'Force you, you mean?' Declan's blood congealed.

She spread her hands, her gaze skimming away. 'I don't
know. I just felt scared. That was why I left.'

'You went because of a family emergency. That was what
you told my personnel department.'

'It's true.' She paused. 'Well, I didn't leave because of that. I
left because of Adr... Your brother. But I'd no sooner got away
than I discovered my foster father had had a stroke. I used the
leave to be with him.'

'Quite a coincidence.' And very convenient.

Her gaze shot to his and energy jolted through him. He hated
that she could do that to him still.

'I suppose it is. But, believe me, I'd rather neither of those
things had happened.'

Declan clenched his hands. 'And your foster father?' If there
was a foster father. Once he'd have believed unhesitatingly.
Now he'd check.

'He's in a private rehabilitation facility.'

'I suppose he can vouch for what you say?'

'No.' Her posture wilted. 'I didn't want to worry him.'

'But when he was getting better, surely you'd share your
experiences with someone so close?' He paused, watching her
intently. 'Unless you have some other *intimate* friend for that.'

Something disturbingly like jealousy jabbed him.

'It was all over,' she said flatly. 'Your brother was dead and
I saw no point worrying Ted by raking over what was finished.'

Finished because Adrian had plunged to his death.

Because Declan had failed him.

Because Chloe had driven him to it.

She sounded plausible. That stoic posture and hint of a trembling lip spoke to the inner man who still, despite everything, yearned to cherish and protect the woman he'd believed in.

But Declan couldn't take her word for this. She forgot he *knew* his brother. She'd had all night to come up with a story, and that was all this was—a story to gloss over her role in his death.

'If you didn't go to the police, did you tell my people? My staff members have a right to safety at work.'

Her lips drew up in a pained smile. 'I was afraid I'd lose my job if I made a complaint about your brother. Good jobs aren't easy to find.'

'I see.' A convenient excuse. 'So you have no proof. It's your word against Adrian's reputation.' Disappointment filled him that she'd invent such a story. 'How does it feel, tarnishing a man's character when he can't defend himself?'

Scarlet slashed high across her cheekbones. 'It's not like that.'

She looked the image of innocent outrage.

Yet Declan had learned long ago that people weren't always what they seemed. Growing up with wealth, he'd discovered some would do anything for a fraction of what he had. A pity he'd forgotten that when he met Chloe.

'You ask me to believe by brother killed himself for love of a woman he barely knew? That he *imagined* the great love affair that had transformed his life?'

The colour leached from her cheeks. 'It's not so unbelievable. Some men become obsessed with women they barely know or have only seen in photos. They build up a fantasy that's more satisfying than reality.'

Declan shoved his chair back from the desk and shot to his feet, unable to sit while she slandered Adrian.

'You're an authority on the subject?'

'Of course not. But I read—'

'Stop!' His voice reverberated around the panelled walls. 'I gave you a chance to explain, Chloe.' He shook his head. 'But I refuse to hear more lies.'

He'd failed Adrian once. He wouldn't do it again. Giving credence to this story would be a betrayal. The brother he'd known would never have threatened a woman.

'They're not lies.'

Wearily Declan unlocked a drawer in his desk and dragged it open. His stomach clenched as he forced himself to reach in. A second later he slapped a slim black volume onto the desk.

'Then you can explain this.'

'What is it?' She eyed the book warily.

'Adrian's diary.' He watched her expression freeze. 'In it he details the time he spent with you. And there's a photo of the pair of you together at Echo Point.'

Declan shoved his hands into his pockets. He didn't like touching the book; it felt like trespassing. He'd read enough only to discover proof that Adrian and Chloe had been lovers—it was there in black and white—then he'd snapped it shut as nausea engulfed him.

When he'd left Chloe at Carinya his mind had been spinning, his emotions in a whirl. By the time he'd arrived in Sydney, he'd half talked himself into believing he'd been mistaken. Till Adrian's diary had killed all hope.

'Whatever he wrote wasn't true. As for the photo, he got a tourist to take it one day when he followed me out.'

Declan didn't answer. He turned on his heel and strode away, unable to stomach any more.

'Where did you get it? I don't remember seeing it.'

If she had, she'd have destroyed it. 'I found it the day after you left Carinya. I went back there.'

Foolishly he'd sought proof that he was wrong about her. Instead he'd found Ade's notebook locked in a bureau and with it heirloom jewellery their mother had bequeathed to Adrian. Had he withdrawn them from safekeeping to give to Chloe, to try to salvage their relationship?

Declan stared unseeing out the window. Everywhere he

turned there was proof Chloe was everything he despised. He should be glad he'd learned the truth about her.

Yet he felt no relief.

Chloe stared at his broad back in that exquisitely tailored suit and felt the chasm between them yawn impossibly wide.

'Whatever's in the book is a product of your brother's imagination.' She had a sinking feeling she knew what sort of imaginings Adrian had written.

Declan swung around and her words died in her mouth. Morning sun lit one side of his ravaged face, highlighting the scar that today seemed a symbol of all the harsh emotion within. It matched perfectly the air of danger that clung to him and the martial light in his eyes.

Chloe remembered how it had been between them, the growing rapport, the sharing and the excitement. The sense that whatever fragile filament spun them together was touched with magic, bringing emotions she'd never expected to feel again. Bringing hope and happiness.

It had been an illusion. Just like the shadow of anguish she thought she read now in his eyes. She blinked and it was gone.

In the stark Sydney sunshine, Chloe saw how ridiculous her hope had been.

She'd wanted to believe this was a mistake. That, despite what he'd said last night, Declan cared for her. That he lashed out now from shock and grief; confronting the truth about Adrian must be appallingly hard.

But she'd been wrong about Declan's feelings. He'd seduced her deliberately, unemotionally.

Pain lanced as if he'd used a knife on her.

What she'd imagined was mutual delight had been something tawdry.

Telling herself the man she'd fallen for was a mirage didn't help. Her stubborn heart couldn't take it in, as if, deep inside, she still believed what they'd shared was genuine.

'I'll never convince you, will I?' Abruptly anger was snuffed out by a sense of loss so great it reared up to engulf all else.

Loss for what might have been and for the grief Declan still carried. This was a lose-lose situation, with both of them doomed to suffer.

Chloe wanted to reach for him, plead with him, *make* him believe. But his loyalty to his brother ran deep. Their relationship had spanned a lifetime. How could she expect to compete with that? He'd never take her word over his brother's. She'd known the truth would be difficult for him to accept. Now she realised it was impossible.

Declan's grief outweighed everything else. And she understood. Hadn't she spent months blaming hospital staff for Mark's death when the truth was no one could have saved him by the time he'd got there?

Declan needed someone to blame. Himself and her.

'No. You can't convince me.' His tone was lifeless, like her hopes.

'In that case I'll go.' Her shoulders slumped. 'There's no point me staying.' Money would be tight; she didn't know how she'd meet Ted's costs, but she'd find a way.

'No.'

His voice jerked her head up. 'Sorry?'

'You'll stay right where you are.'

She took a step towards him then halted, reading his grim expression.

'You don't want me here, Declan, and I don't want to work for a man who believes me a liar. Why prolong the bitterness?' She spread her hands before her in unconscious appeal.

His lips twisted and for a heartbeat she thought she saw the man she'd fallen for—the one who hid his emotions behind a mask. Then he seemed to gather himself.

'And let you just walk away? You seduced Adrian when he was vulnerable after the loss of his business, made him fall for you then dumped him without a second thought.' He counted the accusations on his fingers.

'You knew he was depressed. I remember you talking so convincingly about your friend with depression. That was

Adrian, wasn't it? But you didn't raise a hand to help him.'
Another finger rose and her pulse thudded. For that, at least,
she felt guilt.

'Then you turned your sights on me.' His eyes flashed. 'I
was easy prey, wasn't I, Chloe? Blind. Alone. Sick with grief.
A little judicious sympathy and—'

'It wasn't like that!' Chloe's heart broke anew that he could
believe it of her.

'No?' One dark eyebrow shot up. 'You were so convincing,
you even made me…'

Chloe held her breath as she waited for him to finish. Made
him what? Care for her? Love her?

Foolish, hopeful woman.

'Was Adrian the first? Or did you start earlier with your
friend, Damon Ives?'

Her breath hissed from lungs pinched tight in disbelief.
Eventually she found her voice. No matter that pain made it
wobble.

'Why do you want me here, Declan? For revenge? Is that
it? To make me pay somehow?'

He didn't answer, simply watched her through narrowed
eyes. Meeting his shadowed gaze, she sensed the pain he kept
tightly shuttered. Her heart ached, but she couldn't help him.

She shook her head. 'This ends here.' Staying would be madness. 'I resign. I'll work out my notice and then I'll be gone.'
Pride stiffened her spine and kept her voice even.

She refused to run as if she was guilty. Declan mightn't understand the significance, he was so mired in grief and denial,
but it mattered to her. Pride was all she had left.

CHAPTER ELEVEN

'I'M SORRY, Chloe, but Mr Carstairs has changed his mind about tonight's dinner.'

At Susie's apologetic tone Chloe put down the whisk and bowl and shifted the phone that had been clamped between her ear and shoulder.

'You're joking.' Grimly she surveyed her preparations for an intimate dinner for two.

Declan entertained a different woman every night, reinforcing the huge chasm between Chloe and the accomplished, beautiful socialites he dated.

Steadfastly she'd concealed her hurt, telling herself it didn't matter. Yet working out her notice became harder each day. Nevertheless it was something she had to do, to show him he was wrong about her. As a kid she'd consistently lived down to expectations. It had taken years to convince herself of her own worth and she wouldn't relinquish that hard-fought achievement now.

She refused to run and have him see that as proof of her guilt. She'd leave with her head high.

'He's cancelled the dinner for two.' Susie paused. 'He wants something bigger. He said you'd have no trouble whipping up a *cordon bleu* meal for twenty. They'll arrive at seven-thirty'

Chloe looked at her watch and felt panic swell. It would be almost impossible to organise.

Then a wisp of memory surfaced that banished practical

concerns. Of her telling Declan that night in bed that she could whip up anything from a gourmet dinner for twenty to a wedding cake.

He'd remembered *that*?

What else had he remembered?

She shivered and tried to push away memories. But that night was still emblazoned on her brain. Not just the ecstasy, but the wonderment, the emotional awakening and the sense of connection.

Yet for him it had only been a distorted test of her character. Did the tests continue? Lately he'd left large sums of money lying around. Was he distracted or did he hope to catch her stealing?

Indignation burned. She'd been a rebel as a kid but never a thief.

'He also wants you to act as hostess.'

'Sorry?'

'Mr Carstairs wants you to attend the dinner and help with his guests. And one more thing. He asked that you wear your green dress.' There was curiosity now in the secretary's tone. 'The one with the tie, he said.'

Heat fired under Chloe's skin as she remembered the party. The way Declan had seduced her with his touch. How the soft jersey dress had come apart in his hands and how close she'd been to coming apart too.

Shame scorched her and she cringed. It wasn't enough to set her the impossible task of preparing this dinner. Or that he kept her on tenterhooks wondering if he really was bent on revenge. He wanted to gloat too. She'd have to sit across from Declan, watching him watch her and knowing he remembered how completely she'd been at his mercy.

It was the final straw. She'd had enough.

Chloe's jaw firmed. She'd wear the dress. She'd show him she was completely immune to him now. Then she'd leave. She refused to stay, pining for a man who didn't exist.

* * *

Declan couldn't tear his eyes from Chloe, vibrant and enticing at the far end of the table.

She assumed he wanted her here to exact revenge. Yet nothing he did now could bring Adrian back.

Another man might keep her close to prevent her seducing some other guy for his money.

Though, strangely, his investigator hadn't found evidence of previous wealthy lovers. Only a long-dead husband, a teacher. That news had floored Declan. His visceral reaction, far too like jealousy for comfort, disturbed him.

He'd found himself wondering anew about the feisty yet caring woman he thought he'd understood at Carinya. He'd wanted to take the investigator's report at face value, proof of his own gut instinct that Chloe was that woman.

Till he remembered Adrian.

Guilt scored deep. Did he want to absolve Chloe for himself because he yearned still for the delicious, unique woman he'd known? What of Adrian, his grief and despair? How could Declan let himself believe in the woman who'd betrayed his brother so fatefully? It meant accepting Adrian had been a dangerous stalker who'd made a woman fear for her life. The idea was anathema.

Declan gulped a mouthful of wine.

Never had he felt like this, as if caught fast in quicksand that deepened whichever way he turned.

It was as well Chloe didn't know he wanted her here not for revenge, but because he couldn't let her go.

It shouldn't be so. Yet he yearned for her with a desperation unlike anything he'd experienced. It tore him apart.

'Delicious rock lobster, Declan. Declan?'

He gathered his thoughts and found an encouraging smile for Sophia. She was exquisite in a fitted dress of beaded lilac and she hadn't stopped her engaging banter since the first course of what, he had to admit, was a superb meal.

Damn Chloe. Was there anything she wasn't up to? From dealing with impromptu parties, to fussy guests and requests at all hours, she'd proven herself a superb housekeeper. As if she really was what she seemed: hard-working, capable and with a skill for putting guests at ease. A skill he'd succumbed to in those dark days when loss and blindness had driven him to seek out her warmth.

Declan snapped his head up, cutting off that train of thought.

Chloe was far too sexy in that slinky green dress. His fingers tickled with the memory of how good she'd felt in it, and how much better she'd felt without it.

It had been a mistake to demand she wear it.

The slow burn in his blood flared hotter. He told himself the image she projected was a lie, yet doubts had crept into his certainty. Such as when he'd learned she did indeed have a foster father who'd recently suffered a massive stroke. Or when there'd been no tangible proof of rich lovers. The doubts turned each night into a restless trial as cold logic warred with the desire to trust.

His mouth tightened. He wasn't the only one drawn to Chloe. On either side of the table men leaned close, eager for her attention. But she played it cool, keeping a slight distance despite her friendly smile.

She was an expert at tantalising a man.

'I can manage on my own.' Chloe pasted on a perfunctory smile as she stopped at the kitchen door.

'Now, now.' Daniel wagged a finger as his gaze dropped to her breasts. 'Anyone would think you didn't like me.'

Chloe strove to unclench her teeth. Why, of all Declan's guests, did this lech have to follow her? 'I need to organise coffee—and,' she added with emphasis as his hand settled on her bare arm, 'I'll be quicker alone.'

He leaned in, his hot breath wine-laden. 'It would be a perfect time for us to get to know each other better, away from the crowd.'

'Let me go, Daniel. I didn't invite you to touch me.'

His blue eyes glittered as if her resistance fuelled his determination. 'But that's what you want, isn't it, Chloe? That aloof air is a ploy.'

She stiffened. She'd had enough of men who thought they could speak for her or judge her. Men who saw only what they wanted. Declan at least had grief as his excuse; this vermin had none.

'I asked you to let go. I won't ask again.'

The warning had no effect. 'Don't think I haven't noticed the way our host looks at you from the other end of the table.' He winked. 'It's obvious you're far more than a housekeeper. At a guess I'd say you're very...*versatile*.'

His gaze trawled and Chloe shuddered. He made her feel unclean as his hand brushed near her breast.

'I *said*—' she ground her heel onto his instep till he yelped and let go '—I need to see to the coffee. Alone.'

She was breathing heavily as she swung round, ignoring the whispered stream of swear words that burst from him.

Movement at the edge of her vision brought her up short.

Declan. Her heart gave a resounding thump.

He loomed in the doorway, bigger than ever. His face was a pale mask of fury and his scar stood out like a jagged warning. Beneath his tailored jacket, muscles bunched. His hands fisted as if he wanted to reach out and shake her.

Relief at being free of Daniel's grip dissolved as Chloe looked into those fierce eyes. She scented danger and the hairs on her nape rose.

Yet it wasn't fear she felt. It was anger.

'Chloe...'

Chloe refused to let him berate her for trying to seduce his guest. She was tired of being a scapegoat, condemned for what she'd never done.

Spinning on her heel, she shoved open the kitchen door.

When she emerged the guests had left the dining table and clustered in the sitting room. Instantly she located Declan at the far end of the room with an older man.

'He's quite something, isn't he?'

Chloe found a gorgeous brunette standing close, swaying a little on her needle-point heels. 'Sorry?'

'Declan.' The other woman, Sophia, waved her glass, sloshing wine perilously near her couture gown. 'I've known him for years and I've never met a better man. Or a sexier one, despite that horrible scar.'

She drained her glass. 'One thing about Declan, you can trust him. He's loyal and honest. Unlike some.' She looked daggers at a blond man in intimate conversation with another woman. 'And wasn't he wonderful with that snake Daniel?'

'Daniel?' Chloe looked again around the room. She'd expected another confrontation but hadn't seen him. 'Where is he?'

'You missed it?' Sophia waved her glass. 'I've never seen anything like it. Declan marched him off the premises by the scruff of his neck.'

'Declan did that?' Stunned, Chloe turned. Resplendent in formal clothes, Declan radiated charisma at odds with the wrathful man of just ten minutes ago. 'Are you sure?'

'Absolutely. Declan all but shoved him out the door. Goodness knows what he'd done.'

Something deep inside Chloe shuddered into life. Had he ejected Daniel for pawing her? The idea sucker-punched her. It was the strangest feeling to think he'd directed his scorching fury at her tormentor. That wasn't the action of an enemy. An enemy would have gloated.

Just then Declan's head snapped round, as so often in the past when he'd sensed her presence.

The air sizzled with a charge that electrified her. The gleam in his eyes held something other than the disapproval she expected. Something that confounded her. Something intense and almost possessive.

Flurries of heat danced across her flesh and her eyes widened.

She recalled his hoarse voice. *You were so convincing, you even made me...*

Every night those words circled in her brain. She'd heard his pain and despair and wondered if, against all logic, he *did* still feel something for her. It seemed impossible yet she couldn't dismiss it.

'Declan saw Daniel follow me and make a nuisance of himself.' The words escaped before she realised.

'See?' Sophia nodded. 'I told you he was one of the good ones.' She sighed. 'A shame I was never his type.'

With difficulty Chloe dragged her gaze from Declan's. She felt his stare like a touch. It drew her skin tight and filled her with an awareness that undermined her indignation and made a mockery of her anger.

It was still there, the connection between them that had ignited from the first. It was stronger than distrust.

She darted another look. His ebony eyes lingered on her, his brow puckered as if he, too, was at a loss. Could he be having second thoughts? She'd told herself time and the easing of his grief might eventually allow him to see the truth. Lately they'd lived in a cautious truce. Was it possible he'd begun to see past his pain?

Her heart crashed against her ribs as excitement rose.

'He's looking,' Sophia purred. 'Maybe it's time to see if I was wrong about not being his type.' She strolled across the room with a walk that drew all eyes.

Hurriedly Chloe turned to a cluster of guests. But, as the visitors gradually departed, the tension inside knotted tighter. Sophia remained plastered against Declan, his arm around her waist as she teetered on impossible heels.

Chloe busied herself, locating handbags and wraps, saying farewell to guests and tidying. But the knot inside drew tighter. *Jealousy?* How could she be jealous if she no longer cared for Declan?

She turned back into the sitting room, only to slam to a halt on the threshold.

One hand grabbed the door jamb as her knees weakened.

Declan and Sophia, kissing. Sophia's arms twined round

Declan's neck. Declan swinging her up into his arms and striding down the corridor to the bedroom, heedless of her jewelled sandals dropping to the floor.

Chloe pressed a hand to her gaping mouth. It didn't stop her gasp of raw pain.

Declan neared the end of the dim corridor where the master suite was. He didn't turn on a light but shouldered his way in, cradling Sophia.

In the stillness Chloe heard the snick of the bedroom door. Numbly she stared at the lilac stiletto heels that had tumbled on the floor. She sagged against the wall.

Declan and Sophia. Declan doing with Sophia all those wonderful things he'd shared with Chloe.

Her teeth began chattering and she hugged herself tight as reaction set in.

She'd tried to tell herself these past weeks it had just been sex between her and Declan. That it didn't mean anything, conveniently ignoring the fact she was anything but promiscuous and in all her life she'd been to bed with only two men. Two men who had moved her and touched her heart: Mark and then, against the odds, Declan. She'd assured herself it had been an appalling mistake but one she'd get over.

With a gasp of pain Chloe slid down the wall. She sat hunched, knees drawn in tight.

She couldn't pretend any more. She'd skirted the truth too long.

At Carinya she'd fallen in love with Declan Carstairs.

How could she get over that?

She tried to despise him. Yet, seeing him with his friends and colleagues, she knew he wasn't totally the ogre he'd acted with her. Many of the qualities she'd found so attractive in him were real. It hadn't all been a sham.

How much of his rage was driven by grief?

If only he could be that cold-hearted, vengeful bastard through and through. Then she could turn her back without a second glance.

Yet he was far more complex. She saw glimpses of *her* Declan again and again. That was what hurt most.

Now, whether wittingly or inadvertently, he'd found the perfect way to punish her for all those crimes she hadn't committed.

It took less than thirty minutes to pack.

Chloe was halfway to the foyer when a yell rent the air, curdling her blood. She froze, clutching her bag.

Silence thrummed loud with the beat of her racing pulse. Could she have imagined it? Impossible. Yet equally impossible it had come from the master suite.

Chloe made herself enter the vast sitting room where Sophia's shoes lay, proof that Declan wasn't alone.

There it was again: an agonised roar that prickled her skin. Dropping her bag, she swung towards the bedroom wing. It was dark, no light under any door. No sound. Surely if there was anything wrong…?

Then she heard it, a mumbling gasp, the deep resonance of Declan's voice. Talking to Sophia, of course.

Chloe's lips tightened as she moved away. She didn't want to overhear their pillow talk. But again she froze as a yell blasted the night and iced her veins. There was such pain in that cry.

It was Declan. Why didn't Sophia do something?

Knowing she'd regret it, but unable to turn her back, Chloe turned the handle and pushed open the door to the master suite.

Moonlight painted the room in silvery light. The king-sized bed was a mess of rumpled sheets, twisted and torn free. Instead of a couple there was only Declan, spread eagled across the mattress. His lips moved and his bare chest heaved. His head turned from side to side.

'Adrian!' This time she was close enough to understand his raw cry of anguish.

Quick as thought, she stepped into the room and closed the door.

'No, Adrian. Don't!' Declan's head thrashed on the pillow,

his shoulders heaving as if he fought to free himself from some terrible weight.

'Shh.' Chloe found herself beside the bed, looking down at a face distorted by anguish. 'It's all right.'

He didn't hear, just flung out an arm as if to thrust something away. Or to make a desperate grab. Her heart clutched.

'Nooo!' His cry was a barely audible keen of loss. 'Ade, no!'

Chloe put her hand on his shoulder, feeling the film of sweat on burning flesh. 'It's OK, Declan. It's a dream.'

Muscles rippled and flexed beneath her touch. He rolled towards her, capturing her hand tightly. But one look at Declan's face told her he hadn't woken.

The proud man she knew wouldn't want her to see him like this. Even in the gloom she could make out his spiky lashes clumped together, see the tears on his cheeks and feel the shudders racking his body.

'It's all right, Declan,' she whispered, bending close. 'It's over.'

But it wasn't. She'd known he grieved for his brother, but hadn't understood the full depth of his trauma.

Chloe thought of the small photo in Declan's study, a family portrait: Declan at around twenty with a devil-may-care smile; Adrian, years younger in school uniform, grinning up at his big brother. In the middle were their parents, dressed to the nines and smiling stiffly.

She'd been surprised by the photo. Then she'd done her maths and realised Charles and Maya Carstairs had probably died soon after that photo had been taken. Perhaps it was the last keepsake of their family. She'd picked it up, transfixed by what she saw. Declan, looking carefree as she'd never seen him. Adrian with hero worship in his eyes.

And now this—Declan, tormented by nightmares of his brother. To see him racked in agony tore at her heart.

He had so much anger inside. How much of that piercing fury was self-directed?

She'd known he blamed himself for not saving Adrian. But

she'd had no idea the guilt ran so deep. That shone a different light on his actions.

'Chloe?'

Startled, she looked down. His eyes were shut. His grip on her hand had eased as had his breathing.

'Sweet Chloe.' He rolled over, trapping her hand between his cheek and the pillow. 'Stay.'

It should have been easy to jerk her hand away.

Yet looking at that ravaged cheek, seeing the wet trail down his scar and the lines furrowing his brow, Chloe couldn't do it. Seeing Declan stripped of everything but the emotion he hid from the world, she felt the turmoil that drove him.

Even now he found no rest, no solace.

'Please.' The whispered syllable was so soft she almost missed it.

But she heard and, in a moment of honesty, knew she couldn't leave like this. Not yet. Wearily she settled on the carpet, her hand trapped against his warm skin.

She understood too well the weight of grief and how it could twist into self-blame. Was it grief that made Declan cling so obstinately to his guilt and his belief in hers?

Ever since that confrontation the night of the party, he'd looked different. As strong as ever, yet haunted. Often when he was by himself she'd find him staring into space. He'd looked adrift. Alone. As if there was nothing to anchor him.

Was she crazy to think he needed her now more than ever?

With a sigh she leaned her head against the bed.

She wouldn't be leaving today.

CHAPTER TWELVE

'DECLAN, you look like hell.'

'Thanks, David.' He felt like it too, after weeks sharing the penthouse with his cool, perfect housekeeper who kept him at arm's length in an uneasy truce. He missed Chloe's fire, her vivid personality, her body. Damn! No wonder he barely slept. 'Was there anything else or did you just drop by to comment on my appearance? And why haven't you gone home?'

'You need to see this.'

Declan scraped his hand across bleary eyes. He'd spent too long in the office trying to find peace in the familiar demands of business. It hadn't worked.

Nothing had worked.

There'd been no peace since he'd plunged into this nightmare where the woman he cared for had transformed into a calculating gold digger.

But *was* she? Circumstances said yes. The evidence said yes. Yet his instinct said no.

Instinct told him she was special, the woman he'd believed in before he'd learned of her connection with Adrian.

Yet how could he trust his instinct when it had given no warning Ade was on the brink of self-destruction?

He scrubbed a hand across his face again, his mind once more turning down endless tracks of self-doubt, disillusionment and longing.

'Declan.'

He looked up. David stood in front of the desk, holding out a package.

'This has just been sent through. It was posted the week before Adrian's death.' He paused as Declan's head jerked higher, every muscle tensing.

'Some fool in the legal office has been sitting on it all this time. When news came through about Adrian, they weren't sure what to do with it.' His PA snorted his disgust. 'Fortunately someone finally decided to check what it was they were holding and sent it on.'

He held out the small, padded envelope.

For a moment Declan stared. Sent the week Adrian had died?

A shiver slithered down his backbone. Another note from his brother? This time—and it filled him with aching guilt to admit it—he wasn't in a hurry to read it.

Yet it wasn't Adrian's writing on the registered envelope. It was Chloe's.

His hands closed around the parcel, his pulse racing.

What now?

He tipped the envelope and something soft fell into his hand. A piece of paper slid to the desk. He turned it over: *Please return to Mr Adrian Carstairs.*

That was all. No signature, but he knew Chloe's writing. Hadn't he pored over the notes she'd taken for him at Carinya time and again, as if seeking a clue to her character in her handwriting?

Declan looked at the soft pouch in his palm. It was weighty yet small. He tore it open and tipped out the contents. His breath stalled as he took in a familiar green glow. He stroked hard, perfect facets.

Slowly, reluctantly, realisation dawned.

'Declan! Are you all right? Will I get a doctor?'

Declan raised his hand. 'I'm fine.'

'You're not. You're white as a sheet. Is it your leg?'

Declan shook his head, eyes still fixed on the contents of

the package. 'I'm OK, David,' he lied. 'Why don't you pack up for the night? It's very late.'

His PA hesitated but finally Declan was alone. He turned the bracelet over. It was the most expensive piece in his mother's collection: huge emeralds of exquisite quality surrounded by myriad diamonds and flawless pearls. A stunning piece of jewellery worth a rajah's ransom.

Light dazzled off it and raw pain sliced through him.

If Chloe was a gold digger on the make, why would she return several million dollars' worth of jewellery?

Declan had a sickening feeling his instinct about her had been right. That he'd made a terrible mistake.

Chloe hurried across the marble and glass foyer of the apartment building, aiming to catch an early train to the mountains. It had been a long week since she'd seen Ted.

Exiting onto the pavement, she stumbled to a halt, eyes widening. A gleaming, low-slung car was pulled up at the kerb. Declan leant against it, arresting with his dark looks, casual leather jacket and long, nonchalantly crossed denim-clad legs. He was the picture of potent masculinity, his scar adding an undercurrent of intrigue and danger.

Chloe blinked and turned away, her pulse hammering. She had to stop responding to the sight of him. But it was easier said than done.

'Wait.' He straightened, staggering a fraction as he took his weight on his bad leg. Another step and he stood tall, as if that stumble had never happened.

Yet it stopped Chloe in her tracks. Declan had persuaded everyone that, apart from his facial scar, he was fully recovered. It was only in private, when he thought himself alone, that she sometimes noticed him limp at the end of a long day.

That reminded her of the other scars he carried, unseen, the grief that drove him and softened her contempt for his behaviour.

'What is it, Declan?'

'I'm going to Carinya. I can give you a lift to see your foster father.'

She swung round, meeting his shuttered gaze full on. He looked drawn, his features pared back to stark planes.

'How do you know that's where I'm headed?' Was he having her followed?

'It's your day off.' Her suspicion must have shown, for he shook his head. 'The concierge told me.'

'Why should we travel together?' True, they'd shared the penthouse for weeks, but as strangers. The strain of it drew her nerves almost to breaking point.

Running away would have been the easy option, if only she'd been able to bring herself to do it.

He stiffened. 'It's only for an hour or so. I'll have you there much faster than the train so you'll have more time for your visit.'

He was right. She was travelling against the daily commute and instead of an express she'd be stopping at almost every station.

'Besides, I want to talk with you.'

Chloe crossed her arms. 'So talk.'

He shook his head, stepping back as a woman walking a pair of dogs with jewelled collars slowed to pass. Behind her came two men in suits and a jogger.

'Not here. We need privacy.'

He was right. But to be cooped up in his luxury car all the way to the Blue Mountains? Breathing in his familiar spicy scent that, to her chagrin, still sent awareness tingling through her?

'Chloe.' He took a step forward then stopped, his face unreadable. But he couldn't mask the rough edge of emotion in his voice. It sounded like a plea.

Her breath quickened. What did he want? To tell her he was ready to see the truth about her and Adrian? Wishful thinking. How could she expect him to believe the woman he'd slept with one night over the brother he'd known a lifetime? She had no tangible proof. Besides, grief didn't pass so easily, nor, in her experience, the need to blame.

Unless Declan was stronger than she'd been when she'd lost Mark.

Yet hadn't he ejected one of his dinner guests because he'd pawed her? If Declan despised her he'd have accused her of seducing Daniel, or left her to fend for herself.

'Please, Chloe.' His ebony eyes met hers and heat shivered through her, igniting again that spark of connection. How could it still be so strong between them?

Everything she'd learned from his friends and colleagues indicated Declan was fair and honest. That he was clear sighted and generous. Was there a chance he might finally accept the truth?

She feared she was hopelessly optimistic.

Yet she yearned still for the man she'd fallen in love with. Love was too precious to set aside as if it had never existed.

She owed it to herself, and him, to try one last time.

Nevertheless, she had to force herself to get into his car. She trembled as she brushed past him and felt the heat of his body. Declan had hurt her, flayed her pride and her self-respect, betrayed her trust. Even knowing the pain that drove him, it was hard to put herself in his hands.

They drove silently through the city, except for the low, purring growl of the car. Declan seemed in no hurry to talk. Chloe stared at the city streets, anything rather than watch his clean, powerful profile or his capable hands on the wheel.

They were on the freeway heading west when finally he spoke.

'Thank you for taking care of Sophia.'

Surprised, Chloe turned to watch him. 'It was no bother.'

Sophia had emerged rumpled and sheepish from the guest suite on the morning after the dinner party, well after Declan's early start at the office. She'd been appalled at her behaviour the previous night, drinking too much and flirting outrageously to spite her ex-partner.

'She's not usually so…impulsive.' Declan shafted a direct stare at Chloe.

'I gathered that.' Just as she gathered Declan had been gentle but firm in rejecting her. He'd swept her to a guest suite to sleep off the effects of alcohol and misery.

Some men would have accepted what Sophia offered, even knowing she was drunk.

But Declan had behaved honourably.

Chloe remembered Sophia's praise for him over a late breakfast; it echoed what she'd heard from David and his associates. All thought him a paragon; a dynamo in business and an upstanding man.

Only with her did he show a dark side. To have seduced her, slept with her, opened up all those emotions and hopes it had taken years to suppress and then reject her…

'I'm grateful to you.' Tension edged his voice.

'It was nothing.' Organising fresh clothes, providing a sympathetic ear—none of it had been any trouble.

He shot her a gleaming look she wished she could read then concentrated on swinging the car up the first wide sweep of the incline to the mountains. It hugged the ground and Chloe realised with a frisson of shock that, despite all that horsepower under the bonnet, she'd never felt safer.

She drew a deep, fortifying breath. 'Was that all you wanted to discuss?'

'No, not all.' Even to his ears he sounded terse.

Could he blame lack of sleep? He'd only had one decent night's sleep lately—the night of the party when he'd dreamed Chloe had come to him. He'd woken to a sense of peace that had made a mockery of his distrust.

But the real reason for insomnia was his conscience.

Chloe looked so fragile. Lately she'd been pale but today she seemed as delicate as hand-blown glass. She'd walked from the apartment building and his gut had tightened as he saw the tension in her slim frame and the way her mouth turned down as if with grim thoughts.

His fault. He'd caused her distress.

The knowledge ate like acid. He remembered her poise and dignity even when he'd heaped the burden of his own guilt on her. He'd lashed out viciously. His skin crawled at the memory of all he'd said and done.

Because he'd needed a scapegoat for his pain, he'd made her suffer.

His hands grew clammy on the wheel, his heart thudding roughly against his ribs.

'Declan?' The low cadence of her voice stroked like velvet.

Abruptly he signalled, pulled over to the side of the road and switched off the engine. His hands shook. Had he subconsciously chosen to speak to her as he drove so he wouldn't have to look her in the eye?

Inwardly, he cringed. Chloe deserved better.

Declan turned to face her, his gaze roving with a freedom he hadn't allowed himself in weeks.

'I owe you an apology.'

She stared mutely, her eyes wide pools of shock.

'I've treated you appallingly.'

'You have.' Her brow pleated as if she didn't quite believe what she was hearing. Who could blame her?

'I acted out of shock.' And, he admitted now, out of sheer green-eyed jealousy. Some champion he'd been for Adrian. All this time he'd been jealous of his brother.

'I don't understand. What, exactly, are you apologising for?'

Chloe sat stiffly, obviously unwilling to take his words at face value. He reached out for her unresisting hand. It felt firm and capable, marked by work yet slender and feminine. His fingers closed tight around it.

'Everything.' He dragged a huge breath into his constricted lungs.

'I said I'd slept with you because I knew you'd betrayed Adrian. That my sight had come back and I wanted to test how easily you'd give yourself to a man with money who could make life easy.'

She tried to tug back her hand but he gripped it in both his, not flinching from her glare. He deserved her wrath.

'You were despicable.'

'I lied, Chloe.'

'What?'

Part of him wanted to find hope in the fact she looked so stunned. As if she couldn't believe him guilty of an untruth. After all he'd put her through...

'I lied. Out of fury and shock. I despise myself for it. I lashed out because I was angrier than I'd ever been in my life and I wanted to inflict some of the hurt I was feeling.'

'On me.' Fire blazed in her eyes. He almost welcomed it after her cool distance.

He nodded. 'On you. I'm sorry.' He drew another mighty breath and laid the truth before her. He'd never behaved so badly in his life and he'd regretted it ever since, especially when he saw the pain in her eyes.

'I went to bed with you because I was desperate for you. *That's all.* There was no plot, no test.' His hold tightened. 'I wanted you, Chloe, as I've never wanted any woman.' Her expression froze in disbelief.

'Just the sound of your voice or a hint of your fragrance as you passed turned me hard with need.' Declan's blood heated now, merely from touching her hands. For weeks he'd kept his distance, fearing what might happen if he got too close to the woman who stirred such strong reactions.

'I was trying to keep a lid on what I felt.'

Chloe scrutinised Declan's drawn face, reading regret and shame. His big frame tensed as if awaiting rejection. His hands on hers were firm but the tiniest of tremors passed through them.

Fear.

That was what she read in his face. Not just guilt and regret but, remarkably, fear.

Why? Fear she wouldn't forgive him?

Surely that couldn't be. Yet her heart tumbled hard as she grappled with this new Declan.

'I didn't regain my sight till after we'd slept together.' The admission sucked the breath from her lungs.

'The next day I recognised you from Adrian's photo. I was a coward.' He halted, grimacing. 'I didn't want to face you so I left.'

'Really?' She hardly dared believe. It had been bad enough to face Declan's accusations but worse by far had been the belief he'd deliberately seduced her in a tawdry test of character. Even now, the idea of being used like that sent a shiver of shame through her.

'You made me feel cheap.'

'I'm sorry, Chloe, more than I can say.' He leaned in, his voice urgent. 'I should never have let you believe it, even for a moment.'

'No,' she whispered, reliving the terrible searing pain of betrayal. 'You shouldn't.'

'There's no excuse for what I did. All I can say is that I regret it. That I'd do anything to make it up to you.'

Chloe stared. Declan was so intense, his words obviously heartfelt.

A tiny flicker of light flared in her battered heart.

'Why tell me now?' Steadfastly she concentrated on his words, not the feel of his strong hands enfolding hers or the fact she hadn't tugged hers away. She'd yearned for him to see the truth. Could her hopes be coming true?

'I couldn't lie any longer.'

His gaze seared hers. 'I've had doubts from the first. Every time I lashed myself into a fury about what you'd supposedly done I remembered how you'd been with me. Not seeking anything, just being yourself, caring and supportive, but always your own woman. I saw you interact with my friends. I saw your poise and strength in the face of my accusations, the way you rose above the worst of my behaviour.'

The naked emotion in his now unguarded eyes stunned her. He really meant it.

Could she forgive him? Her heart thudded faster.

'Then last night something happened that made me confront everything I thought I knew about you.'

His thumb stroked her palm, sending shivers of delicious sensation tingling through her.

She shouldn't let him touch her. He'd hurt her so badly. Yet she longed for his tenderness. Even now, trying hard to keep her distance, she relished his gentle caress almost as much as the salve of his words.

'Tell me.' Her nerves stretched taut in mingled expectation and fear of disappointment.

'The bracelet arrived. The one you returned.'

Chloe frowned. 'But I posted that to Adrian months ago. The day after I left Carinya. I'd told him I couldn't accept it,' she added quickly. 'But when I unpacked my things I found it stowed amongst my jewellery.'

She shuddered, remembering the shock of seeing it amongst her meagre collection of earrings. Adrian had obviously ignored her refusal and felt no qualms about rifling through her belongings to place it where he believed it belonged.

Declan shrugged. 'It never reached him. It got delivered to the firm's legal office and then news arrived of his death.' His voice hollowed but he continued. 'Some junior clerk sat on it, wondering what to do with it. I received it just last night.'

He leaned closer, his gleaming eyes intent.

'It's worth a fortune. If you'd been a gold digger trying to get wealthy from the Carstairs brothers you'd never have returned it.'

'I *told* you I wasn't interested in your money.' Her mouth firmed.

'I know.' He swallowed hard. 'I'm sorry, Chloe. Sorry for all the hurt I've caused. All along I've wished—' He broke off, shaking his head.

'So you believe me now?'

'I believe you.' His deep voice made it a pledge.

A shimmer of excitement rose within her. She'd never seen Declan look so earnest, yet she needed the words.

'Tell me.'

Declan looked into her clear green eyes and felt himself slide into temptation. How badly he needed her. He'd always needed her. Yet he forced himself to continue, not pull her to him as he'd dreamed of doing so long.

'I know you never schemed for money. I know you never deliberately enticed me or Adrian.'

Her natural warmth and generosity were enough to attract any man. Look at the way his guests had hung on her every word.

'I know you're honest and that I hurt you. Badly.'

His heart hammered as he watched emotions flit across her neat features. He stroked her hand possessively. He told himself he'd stop in a moment, that he'd just allow himself one final touch.

'I apologise, Chloe. Even knowing how your relationship with Adrian affected him, I was wrong to blame you. No one could have foreseen...'

'What did you say?' She stiffened.

'What happened wasn't your fault.' It might tear him apart to think of her with Ade but that was his problem, not hers. 'Obviously he was vulnerable with the loss of everything he'd worked for. He must have built up unreal expectations of his relationship with you—'

'His relationship with me?' Her voice held an odd, detached note.

He hurried to reassure her. 'I understand, Chloe. Adrian was good-looking and charming. You weren't to know he was... unstable.' Even now the word dried his mouth as if he'd swallowed ashes.

'I told you I wasn't your brother's lover.'

'It's OK, Chloe. I don't blame you.' If anyone was to blame it was Declan. He was Adrian's brother. He should have made it his business to check on him in person, not rely on long distance calls while he finished his business overseas. He should have done so much more.

'You still think Adrian and I had an affair?'

Declan frowned. 'I know you did. Adrian said so. He took photos of you in bed.' Bile rose at the memory.

Chloe yanked her hand free and shrank against the door. Her face turned milk-white.

'I *told* you, they were taken without permission. He came to my room and took photos while I slept. I felt *unclean* when I saw what he'd done.'

Declan shook his head. 'Don't. Please.' His gut twisted. Couldn't she just accept that he understood? Why continue to deny it?

'I've never lied to you, Declan.'

He gazed into her clear eyes and regret welled. His heart thumped a discordant beat and tension sank its talons into his flesh.

He didn't want this. He was trying to do the right thing.

When she spoke again her voice was leaden, like the cold weight in his belly. 'Why will you believe everything else, but not that? Why insist Adrian and I were lovers?'

Declan shut his eyes, his sinews stiffening and hands clenching into iron fists. He wished he could shut out the pain in her voice. Wished he could shut out the crushing weight of hurt inside.

'*Why*, Declan?' Her demand snapped his eyes open and he drank in the sight of her pain. Anguish filled him.

He was torn asunder between the two people who'd meant most to him.

He'd failed them both and he couldn't make it right.

Declan shied from her touch as she reached for him. Ice clamped his nape and chilled his veins.

'*Because it's that or believing the worst of Adrian.*' The words grated out. His heart catapulted against his ribs as he confronted the unthinkable.

'I either accept that he had an affair that went wrong, or...' he hefted a difficult breath into lungs that didn't seem to work any more '...believe the brother I knew and loved was a stalker who made you fear for your life.' Declan's voice cracked as pain splintered inside.

He dragged an unsteady hand through his hair. His chest felt like it would explode from the strain of holding in erupting emotions.

'You ask me to believe my kid brother turned into a *monster*?' He shook his head. 'I knew him, Chloe! That wasn't Adrian.' His fist thumped the console and pain streaked through him, but not enough to counteract the horror he faced.

'I know I frightened you with my accusations that you drove him to suicide. I overreacted, so of course you didn't want to admit the relationship.' The words scraped from his dry throat. 'But I can't believe the worst of him.'

Depression was one thing. Victimising an innocent something entirely different. That was *not* his brother.

Through a haze he eventually registered Chloe's stricken expression. Slowly she unclipped her seatbelt. Her gaze was dimmed, cloudy, as if some inner light had died.

His fault, his conscience screamed. No matter how hard he tried to make it right, his miasma infected her too.

'You're grieving, Declan. You feel you're to blame for his death. You're letting grief and bitterness blind you.'

Declan groped for a response but words were beyond him. He held himself together only by sheer will power.

She leaned nearer. Declan was hemmed in, trapped by her gaze and the words he didn't want to hear.

'I know what I'm talking about. I felt like that for a long time when my husband died—that it was my fault for not realising sooner he should be in hospital. That it was down to me he'd died. Or, if not me, the hospital staff.'

'This isn't the same.' He could barely get the words out. One unwary move and he'd crack in two.

'It is.' The subtle scent of vanilla filled his nostrils, teasing him with Chloe's nearness. 'Until you face your guilt and grief, they'll never let you go. They'll tie you up so your emotions grow stunted and you find yourself living a half life. That's what happened to me.'

She lifted her hand to him. Her fingers stopped mere centimetres from his cheek and he sucked in a laboured breath. If she touched him…

'You've got enough scars from that day.' Her gaze rested on the stiff line of scar tissue that was an ever-present reminder of his failure. 'Don't carry more than you need to.'

Moments ticked by, measured by the searing pain of each breath as her gaze searched his face and he fought for strength against the temptation of her words.

He didn't deserve absolution. She asked too much. If he'd been a better brother, Ade would still be alive.

Finally he shook his head. 'Finished?' The word reflected all the searing pain within.

Her hand dropped. 'No.' She regarded him steadily. 'I don't hate your brother for what he did, though he scared me. I feel sorry for him. He was ill.' She paused. 'But most of all I feel sorry for *you*, Declan, because you're too scared to let go and see what's before your eyes.'

Chloe's mouth twisted. 'I love you, Declan. That's what you're too blind to see.'

Declan's heart missed a beat as he stared into her taut features. Surely he was hearing things?

'I cut myself off from the world because of grief and because I was too scared to leave myself open to hurt again.' Her words were so soft he had to strain to hear. 'But you came along and *provoked* me into love. *Seduced* me into it. And I can't crawl back into my safe little world again.'

Chloe's voice wobbled and he wanted to reach out and ease the pain written across her face. Pain he'd put there.

His fingers stretched out but she leaned away, as far from him as possible.

'I told myself I stayed out of pride but it was because I

loved you, Declan. I couldn't leave knowing how much pain you were in, not when there was a chance I could make you see the truth.'

She hefted in a shuddering breath that tore at his soul. 'But my love isn't enough, not in the face of your distrust.' She spread her palms wide.

'I had no self-esteem as a kid, Declan. I was in foster care because my mum was a heroin addict who sold herself on the street for her next fix. I have no idea who my father was.'

Declan's heart cracked wide. 'Chloe—'

'No.' She raised an imperious hand. 'It took a long time and a lot of love for me to begin to believe in myself. To see that I was worth loving. And I *am*.' Her chin tilted in that familiar way that made his heart clench.

'I've loved you, Declan, but you're no good for me. I need a man who believes in me unquestioningly. A man who knows I don't lie. Not a man who thinks trusting me means disloyalty to his dead brother. I need a man who wants me, even when there's no proof I'm innocent except my word.'

The words slammed into him like projectiles, piercing him to the core. *Because they were true.*

He'd been so wrapped up in his pain he'd hurt Chloe, even when he tried to do the right thing. Even with proof that she was the woman he'd first believed her to be, he'd clung to what was safe. What was comfortable—for him.

What sort of caring was that?

He opened his mouth to speak but she was too quick.

'I'll find my own way from here.' Her tone stopped his instinctive grab for her. She snatched up her bag and pushed open the door. Her poise was brittle but determined.

'Don't come looking for me, Declan. *Ever*. It's over. I never want to see you again.'

CHAPTER THIRTEEN

CHLOE stared at the manager's name plate on the door and pushed back her shoulders.

It was a week since she'd left Declan and still the world reeled out of focus around her.

She'd been right to leave him. It would have been self-destructive to stay.

So why did everything feel wrong? Pain paralysed her when she thought of his anguish and grief; whenever she thought of never seeing him again. She might have done the right thing but it felt like part of herself had been wrenched away in the separation. Part of her that belonged with him.

But the world went on. Taking a fortifying breath, she knocked and was invited to enter.

'Ms Daniels.' The manager looked up with a smile. 'This is a pleasure. You've saved me a call. I was planning to contact you about your foster father's care.'

Chloe's heart plunged. 'That's why I'm here.'

At the other woman's invitation she slid into a chair facing the desk. The office, like everything else in the facility, was welcoming and well cared-for. It would be hard to move Ted from here but she had no choice. With no reliable income she couldn't afford it. Having emptied her savings to install Ted here, it was all she could do to keep a roof over her head in the tight rental market in the mountains. She'd discovered jobs were at a premium as well.

'I wanted to warn you, Ted will be moving,' she blurted out, her chest cramping with pain at what she had to do.

'Really?' The other woman's eyebrows stretched up. 'I don't understand.'

Chloe licked her lips, preparing to explain, but the manager continued before she could speak. 'I thought you were happy with the care here, especially after receiving this.' She picked up a paper from a neat pile.

'I'm sorry?' Chloe frowned. 'I don't understand.'

Wordlessly the manager passed over the paper. Letterhead danced before her eyes as she tried to focus. A familiar name appeared at the bottom of the page: David Sarkesian had signed it on Declan's behalf.

Heart pounding, Chloe stiffened in her seat, scanning the text. She gaped.

'Declan Carstairs is footing the bill for Ted's care?'

'And for any extra therapy or medical expenses.' There was a pause. 'You didn't know?'

Dumbfounded, Chloe re-read the missive. 'I had no idea.'

What did it mean? Why should Declan pay the expenses of a man he'd never met?

'Well.' The other woman's voice grew brisk. 'I hope perhaps that changes your plans. The occupational therapist has seen promising changes in your foster father and wants to expand his program. I have the details here.'

Declan stared out onto the vast lawn between Carinya's shrubberies and the pool.

In his mind's eye he watched a chubby boy race across the grass, his grin triumphant as he retrieved a ball and hurled it at the cricket stumps.

This was where he'd taught Adrian to play cricket, in those endless, dry summer holidays while their parents had been busy making more money and socialising in the city.

He could almost hear the plock of ball against bat, the crow of delight as Adrian mastered his drive. The same triumphant cry he'd given when he'd perfected his tennis serve on the gravel court around the side, after weeks of Declan's coaching. Or when, sinuous as an eel, he'd learned to somersault into the pool, creating a splash that would wet any unwary bystander.

Declan's mouth tilted up. Ade had always been utterly focused on each new achievement to the exclusion of all else. It was a trait that ran strong in the Carstairs men.

But in Adrian, had that strength also been a weakness? How easily had that tendency for tunnel vision morphed into obsession with a woman, with a fantasy? Had it been easier to lose himself in that than face the destruction of the life he'd devoted himself to for years?

Declan's smile faded as he recalled his recent conversation with Ade's ex-business partner in London. A woman who, he'd discovered, had rose-gold hair and ivory skin like Chloe. A woman who'd clammed up when asked about Adrian's personal life, but who had admitted she'd been disturbed by his mood swings and increasing despondency.

Declan shoved his hands in his pockets, fists tightening. Had Adrian fallen for *her*, the woman he'd worked closely with, and who was now so recently wed to a wealthy banker? Had Chloe merely been a reminder of the lover who'd dumped him? She could have been a convenient focal point for his thwarted feelings.

Declan would never know.

He wished things had been different. That he'd been able to intervene before Adrian had self-destructed. That regret would stay with him. But at least now he saw beyond it.

Turning, his belly tightened as he surveyed the spotless kitchen. Even empty it was full of Chloe's presence. He'd never seen her in this room, but like every other room in his home it was full of memories.

He only had to close his eyes to hear her husky laugh as she argued with him over how much chilli was too much in his favourite curry. To smell the sugar and yeast aroma of her baking and the even more delectable vanilla-and-sunshine scent that was pure Chloe. He felt warmth, not from the sun's rays, but from her presence.

He'd been *happy*. It was here he'd first faced his desire to be with her. Was that why he'd rejected so violently any hint his sight was returning? Because change might threaten their fragile relationship?

He'd hated the dark world of blindness but now... He surveyed the kitchen and emptiness welled.

Now with his sight and vigour returned, secure in his world once more, he knew a desolation that tormented him and turned his haven into a soulless place. He longed for just one day without sight, basking in Chloe's no-nonsense care, her tender concern, her love.

He'd had her love and he'd destroyed it.

His heart hammered and the bitter taste of self-disgust filled his mouth. He'd thrown away the most precious thing in the world, shoved aside the woman he should have cherished, not vilified.

Hearing about her past, he'd been stunned by her strength and resilience and shamed by the knowledge of how he'd treated her.

She was right to have left him.

She was better off without him.

He didn't deserve her.

Yet how could he go on without Chloe?

He spun on his heel and strode out the door.

CHAPTER FOURTEEN

CHLOE widened her stance on the tiled floor, trying to concentrate on the latest dinner orders. But her head was muzzy with exhaustion and her limbs felt heavy, aching with tiredness. Heat and the pungent odour of deep-fried food pressed down on her and in a sudden wave nausea hit again.

Staggering, she reached for the water she kept handy. There was a crash, glass splintering across the floor and she grabbed desperately for the worktop, trying to keep her balance rather than step into the shattered glass.

Her breath came in shallow pants as she fought back bile and tried to steady her spinning head.

'What's going on here?' An angry baritone thundered from the door to the café's dining room.

Great. Just great. Chloe squeezed her eyes shut, trying to summon strength to deal with her irate employer. He'd been in a foul mood all day, particularly since her replacement for the afternoon shift hadn't turned up, and he'd been taking out his ire on the overworked staff.

If she didn't need this job so badly, she'd have walked weeks ago.

She urgently needed to put away some savings plus she had to repay Declan for Ted's care. She hadn't been proud enough to reject his offer to foot that bill. But she was proud enough not to want to be beholden to him in the long term. She couldn't afford any ties to Declan.

'I *said*,' her boss bellowed, 'What's going on here?'

Slowly she turned, forcing herself to stand tall, though every muscle in her body ached. She slid one hand over her empty stomach, trying to force down the need to retch in the thick, fat-filled air of the kitchen.

'Just a broken glass.' She looked down at the shards littering the floor and realised she hadn't a hope of gathering them up. One unwary move and she'd either collapse or lose her battle with welling nausea.

'I really need to leave,' she found herself saying again. Only this time she'd make him understand. 'My shift finished five hours ago and I'm exhausted.' Not to mention she'd started the day well before that, cooking breakfasts in her other job in the kitchens of the mountains' most exclusive guesthouse. 'If I stay on, there are bound to be more accidents.'

'Stop making excuses.' He crossed beefy arms over his chest. 'There's no one else to cook. Just get on with it.'

Chloe stifled a protest. She knew half a dozen other staff who'd willingly work the extra hours. But she suspected he'd have to pay them more. She'd been so desperate to find a job locally she'd only just begun to question her very low wage. Had he read her desperation and taken advantage of it?

She untied her apron with fumbling fingers, then drew it over her head.

'I told you, I can't. I'm making too many mistakes. It's dangerous.' The sound of sizzling fat underscored her words and she turned to rescue an order of fish and chips.

'Walk out on me and you lose your job,' he snarled.

Chloe faltered, her flesh chilling at his threat. She needed this income so badly.

He paced towards her and automatically she stepped back into the corner. The look in his eye frightened her. She knew his temper...

'Lay a finger on her and you'll wish you'd never been born.' The lethally soft voice cut the thick air.

Chloe's head whipped round towards the door and shock

froze her. Declan? Was she dreaming about him when she was awake now, as well as in her sleep?

Her boss dropped his beefy arm and swung round.

'Who the hell are you?'

Declan stepped into the kitchen, letting the swing door close behind him. Instantly the room shrank. 'I'm the man who'll see you treat Ms Daniels right.'

Two more steps and he stood toe-to-toe with her boss. He looked down into that florid, choleric face while the other ranted.

'Enough.' One powerful hand sliced through the air and, remarkably, her boss's tirade stopped. Chloe swayed and groped for support.

Ebony eyes cut to her, seeming to take in everything from her stained black trousers and fitted T-shirt to the feelings she couldn't hide: disbelief, excitement and sheer exhaustion.

Declan's voice, glacial as she'd never heard it, penetrated her hazy brain: words like 'assault', 'threatening behaviour', 'exploitation', 'official reports'…

She told herself she could fight her own battles. She'd been doing that all her life, but right now merely staying upright was challenge enough.

'Don't move.' His voice pulled her up short when she would have shuffled to one side.

Looking down, she saw Declan's dark head, his long fingers gathering up wickedly sharp fragments of glass and depositing them in an old container.

The scene seemed unreal. If she dropped one hand she'd touch his thick, dark hair, feel the strength of his broad shoulder beneath her palm.

Chloe wanted to so badly. She blinked back hot tears as emotions bombarded her. Why couldn't he stay away as she'd demanded? It didn't matter that she'd regretted it ever since. That despite the need for self-preservation she didn't feel *whole* without Declan.

She'd saved her sanity and her self-respect but in leaving him she'd left part of herself behind.

'Don't cry, Chloe.' His voice was husky and his eyes fathomless as he looked up at her.

She blinked and stiffened her spine.

'I never cry.' It was true. She was strong. She'd had to be. It was just that she was so very tired.

'Where is he?' There was no one else in the room. Just her and the man crouched at her feet.

'Don't worry about him.' In one easy movement Declan rose and deposited the glass in the bin. Then, before she could guess his intent, swung her up into his arms.

She protested, of course. Chloe wouldn't put up with being manhandled without a fight.

But now he had her safe in his arms, he couldn't let her go. His hold tightened.

He remembered her cringing away from her bully of an employer and it had red-rimmed his vision. He'd wanted to beat the guy into a pulp. Only the realisation Chloe would then have to face police interviews kept him sane. Instead he'd threatened the lowlife with legal action for everything from aggressive behaviour to shonky employment practices, non-adherence to council bylaws and health regulations.

Declan held her close as they negotiated the door from the café to the pavement. She'd lost weight. She'd looked so small and defenceless back there, despite her defiant stance. Now he felt the press of her hip bone rather than the lush curve he remembered.

'Haven't you been eating?'

'What?' She broke off her protests and stared up at him.

Heat punched low in his belly as her green eyes met his. His breath stalled in his lungs as he fell into those crystal depths.

He'd longed to see her, to touch her. But not like this. Not with violet bruises under her eyes and her too-thin arms wrapped around herself as if to protect her even from him.

He opened the car with a click of the remote control. 'You haven't been eating. What were you thinking?'

Eyes rounded, she stared up at him as if he spoke another language. He took advantage of her silence to manoeuvre her into the car and strap her in.

'What are you doing? I never said I'd go with you.'

But her movements were slow and uncoordinated. He was in the car, its engine purring as he nosed it onto the street, before she could unclip the catch on the seatbelt.

Ten minutes later her protests had died to mulish silence as he pulled up under the *port-cochere* of an exclusive guest-house.

'What are we doing here?'

'I'm staying here.' He vaulted out of the car and opened her door before the staff could reach it, unsnapped her seatbelt and pulled her into his arms while she goggled at him.

'Put me down,' she hissed. 'I can't go in here like this. I *work* here.'

Declan suppressed a smile of satisfaction. He revelled in the feel of Chloe in his embrace, though he knew it was a fleeting delight. He'd take whatever crumbs he could get.

The thought of the emotional wasteland that was his life without her wiped the smile from his face. But he pulled her closer, as if daring any of the staring guests and staff to try separating them.

He even enjoyed the sensation of her turning her face into his shirt, the warmth of her breath against him, though he realised she was merely avoiding curious looks.

She felt so *right* in his arms.

He could have held her for hours, but too soon they were at his room. He shouldered his way in and let the door slam shut before striding across to a lounge suite in front of a balcony with an unparalleled view of the escarpment.

Reluctantly he put her down on the cushioned lounge, then stood, his blood sizzling in reaction, his breathing shallow not from exertion but emotion.

She was gorgeous, even in stained work clothes and with exhaustion stamped on her too-fine features.

Abruptly he turned and poured a glass of chilled water from a nearby carafe. She took it without comment but his belly clenched as she carefully avoided touching him.

'What do you want to eat?' His voice was gruff, not what he'd intended.

Fine eyebrows arched up. 'I'm not staying.'

She'd stay till he made sure she never went back to that café or any place like it. Till she promised...

His breath hissed out as he realised he had no right to demand anything from Chloe.

'I'll order some food.'

'I don't want food. I feel sick.'

Declan hesitated, noticing her pallor did have a sickly hue. She needed looking after.

'Humour me, Chloe. You look like you're about to pass out.' His gaze held hers till she looked away. 'I'll order a selection. Hopefully you'll find something to tempt your appetite.' He busied himself with the call to room service, trying to quell the need to haul her to him and never let her go. Her words still rang in his ears.

It's over. I never want to see you again.

He ended the call and turned towards her. She was where he'd left her, hunched at one end of the vast sofa staring out of the window. Her bare arms were too thin, the elegant line of her throat too fragile. The only rounded part of her was the tiny belly she rubbed with one hand.

A flash of memory smote him: Chloe in the café, backing away from her irate boss. There'd been fear in her eyes but instead of putting up a hand to ward him off her fingers had splayed protectively over her abdomen.

A stifled sound made Chloe whip her head round. Declan stood as if transfixed. His eyes gleamed as he raked her body. Self-consciously she slipped her hand from her tummy and reached again for the water.

Her teeth still chattered a little against the glass but she felt stronger. Much as she hated to admit it, being swept off her feet and into Declan's luxury car, carried through the exclusive resort as if she were breakable porcelain, had been like a pleasurable dream. A dream where mistakes and hurt didn't exist and where Declan came to her free of the past.

But dreams weren't reality.

'What are you doing here, Declan?'

He paced closer.

Too close, screamed the voice of sanity.

Yet her eyes ate him up. His tanned, bold features, the ebony hair, the liquid dark eyes, even the scar that raked his cheek—all were shatteringly familiar.

Part of her wanted to push him away so he didn't crowd her. The other part insisted he wasn't close enough. She locked her fingers around the glass lest they reach for him. Liquid slid down her parched throat. Still their eyes meshed, as if neither could believe the other was real.

'I came to see you.' His voice had an odd inflection. 'How long have you been feeling sick?'

Chloe shrugged. 'I've been working long hours in a stuffy kitchen, that's all.' She put the glass down and swung her legs to the floor. 'I really need to—'

'You're pregnant, aren't you?' His eyes glittered as they roved her and she froze.

How had he known? She barely showed. He *couldn't* know. She was only coming to terms with the news herself. She wasn't ready to discuss it with Declan.

'I'm just tired. Thank you for your help back there, but it's better if we don't see each other again.' She forced the words from her lips though she was no longer sure they were true. Just as she was no longer sure she'd been right telling him it was over between them.

Gingerly she stood.

'When is our baby due, Chloe?' The hoarse intensity of his voice sent a thrill zipping down her spine.

'*Our* baby?' In her wildest dreams she'd never imagined he'd call it that. Those simple words confounded her.

Like lightning his gaze lifted to hers, pinioning her.

'Our baby.' His tone held a quality she'd never heard before. It made something deep inside her clench. 'Don't worry; I can work out the dates myself.'

'What makes you think it's yours?' She lifted her chin and dared him to repeat it. He'd spent too long distrusting her.

'It's mine.' The look he bestowed her sent the blood hurtling through her veins and a flush seared her face. 'Yours and mine, Chloe.'

'You don't know that.' Bitterness filled her. 'Not so long ago you accused me of being a woman on the make. A woman who'd—'

His fingers across her lips stopped her words, their soft pressure a tantalising restraint. Chloe drew a shuddering breath and looked away, blinking as his hand dropped.

'Don't, Chloe.' His voice, low and hoarse, was strained.

'Why not?' She swung back to face him. 'You used condoms. There's nothing to prove this is your child. I could have gone to someone else's bed when I left you.'

Slowly he shook his head. 'I'm sorry for mistrusting you. If there was a way to take back what I said, I would.' He breathed deep and she watched his massive chest rise. 'You told me you loved me. You'd never sleep with someone else while you still felt like that. Not you.' His dark eyes bored into hers. 'You don't use sex for recreation, do you, Chloe? It's too important. It's about feelings, isn't it?'

It's about love, she wanted to say, but the words choked in her throat. How could Declan, the man who'd misjudged her so long, see right to the core of her?

This new Declan made her feel vulnerable, unsure of herself, as if he'd shifted the ground beneath her feet. He'd changed.

'It could be anyone's. Even—'

'It's not Adrian's.'

'How can you be sure?'

His lips curved in a sad smile. 'You told me, remember?'

Stunned, she groped for words. She searched his face and saw only certainty there. 'You didn't believe me.'

Declan shook his head again. 'I did.' He reached out his hand as if to touch her then let it fall. His mouth turned down, his skin pulling tight, sharpening his features as if under severe stress.

'I listened to everything you said and I knew it was true. I hid behind accusations so I wouldn't have to face the truth. I was a coward.' He shook his head. 'It was hell letting you walk away that day, but I knew I had no right to ask you to stay. I'd hurt you too badly. You were right—I was no good for you.'

And now? The words trembled on her tongue. But it was no use wishing for a fairy tale ending. This was real life.

She struggled to take in the change in him.

'I'm sorry for what I said that day. I know you were grieving.' The knowledge of his misery, so like her own past grief, allowed her to understand his obstinate loyalty to his brother, even when he'd hurt her.

'No. You were right, Chloe. You deserve a man who can be everything you need. Everything I wasn't. I can only apologise again for the appalling way I treated you.'

He speared his fingers through his hair. The infinite sadness in his expression made her heart clench.

'Adrian's actions were his own. You were never the cause of his pain. You were a victim.' He swallowed hard. 'I'm sorry.'

Declan's desolation confirmed what she'd known—that it was too late for them. A yawning void opened up between them and her heart plunged.

A knock on the door claimed his attention and Chloe turned and paced onto the balcony. The soft twilight wrapped round her. Out on the lawns a cluster of guests laughed and chatted. But here, alone with her thoughts, desolation crept in. She was glad Declan was finally able to face the past. Pleased he'd moved on from his grief. Yet still she wished…

A footfall behind her made her spin round. Declan's gaze

dropped to her abdomen then up to her eyes. His lips curved in a smile that stole her breath.

'What are you smiling about?'

'You're having my child.'

Her skin tingled at his words. He was so *sure*.

His certainty rocked her after his previous mistrust. He'd only changed his mind about her before when he'd learned she'd returned the bracelet. This time there was no proof short of a DNA test.

'There's no proof it's your child.' She blurted the words out, as if tempting him to distrust her.

His smile didn't dim. She blinked. He undermined her certainties.

'How did you find me?'

'Ted.'

'You rang my foster father?'

'No, I saw him. I wanted to meet him because he means so much to you.'

Chloe's heart fluttered. The intensity of Declan's scrutiny unnerved her. She felt poised on the brink of a precipice, not knowing what to expect next.

'You paid for Ted's accommodation. I want you to know I'll pay you back every cent.'

'I don't want your money.' He shoved his hands deep in his pockets and his shoulders hunched.

'I don't want to owe you anything. I want to be free.'

His lips curled, yet there was no amusement in his face, just the echo of suffering. 'If you feel a fraction of what I do, Chloe, you'll never be free.'

What did he mean?

'Did Ted persuade you to see me?' She knew Ted was worried about her long working hours, not knowing it was the loss of Declan that was the real problem.

'We didn't talk about you.' At her disbelieving stare, Declan shrugged. 'Not after I explained who I was. Then we just...

talked. About sport to start with and then his work on the railways.'

'You and Ted talked about trains?' Chloe sagged against the balustrade, struggling to take it in.

'Not just that. We touched on fishing, politics, working in China and the Middle East. He's an avid armchair traveller, your Ted.' Declan sounded approving, yet Chloe barely noticed. She was on tenterhooks, her tension growing with each revelation.

'Why are you here?'

Instantly Declan stiffened. 'I know you didn't want to see me, Chloe. That's why I kept away, but I needed—' He paused and looked down at the papers he drew from his jacket pocket. 'I had to give you this personally.'

Thick paper crackled as he handed it over. For an instant Chloe hesitated, then she forced herself to reach for it, feeling warmth where it had lain next to his body.

'What is it?' Slowly she unfolded it.

'The deeds to Carinya. I want you to have it.'

'What?'

She had to be hearing things. Yet the words on the top page suddenly began to make sense. Chloe stumbled a fraction then shot out a hand to support herself. When she looked up Declan was a mere pace away.

'You can't do that. Carinya is your family home. Wasn't it built by your great-great-grandfather?'

'I have no family now, Chloe.' At the grim twist of his lips, pain lanced her.

He turned and braced his hands on the balustrade. 'I want you to have it. I know you loved it and it will be a perfect place for Ted once he's ready.' Declan drew in a slow breath, his eyes fixed on the valley spread before them.

'I can't live there, Chloe.' His voice dropped to a deep resonance that tightened her skin. 'Every time I enter a room there, I smell your sweet fragrance. I hear you humming under your breath. I *want* you to be there.' He swung round to face her, his eyes glittering. 'It's not the same without you. I even moved out of my Sydney apartment. I was living in a hotel in the city before I came here.'

Chloe swallowed hard, seeing the emotion in Declan's eyes. He was letting her in, allowing her to read the feelings he usually kept shut away. It was heady and glorious and frightening.

'I can't accept—'

'You can, Chloe. I wronged you badly and made your life hell. It was easier to blame you than shoulder all the guilt for—'

'You're not to blame either.' Unthinkingly she put her hand on his sleeve and felt the muscle tense under her touch. She loosened her fingers to sever the connection but his other hand clamped hers in place.

Fire sparked in Declan's gaze and an answering heat flooded her.

'I'm still working on that one.' His smile was crooked and endearing and Chloe's heart flipped over.

'But this isn't about Adrian. After all you'd already been through, you deserved a champion. Not an accuser. I *hurt you*, Chloe.' His hand tightened and Chloe's pulse thudded faster as she read Declan's expression.

'I stayed away as long as I could. I visited your father because it was a connection to you. I reminded myself you never wanted to see me again.' He drew a deep breath. 'If you tell me to go now, I will and I'll never bother you again. But I had another reason for coming here.'

'Yes?' She could barely breathe over the tightness in her chest.

He hesitated so long she wondered if he didn't know how to continue. Yet that wasn't possible. Not forthright, decisive Declan.

'I've been desperate since you left. I knew I couldn't follow you, though I wanted to, more than anything. You had a right to make a new life without me. But I can't let go so easily, Chloe. I just can't do it!' Emotion clogged his voice.

'Did you know you left in such a hurry you didn't pack everything? There were CDs still in the player and books on the shelf. Since you left I've listened to your music and read the books too.' At her startled stare, he nodded. 'Pathetic, isn't it? I've become a fan of Jane Austen and Latin salsa and, Lord help me, Aussie hip hop.'

'Declan?' Chloe's voice wobbled.

'Ah, sweetheart.' He palmed her cheek, infinitely tender. 'I'm sorry. I really have made you cry when all I want is to look after you.' He dragged in a breath so shaky it made her wonder if, impossibly, Declan felt as nervous as she.

'I don't need looking after.' She watched his lips curve in a smile that warmed her from the inside.

'I love you, Chloe. I have for so long, but I was too caught up in blaming you.' Chloe's heart stuttered at the tenderness in his eyes, then tripped to a faster beat.

'I wish there was a way I could prove it to you. Prove I believe in you and always will, no matter what. Words aren't enough.' The gleam in his eyes dimmed and his mouth tightened.

'You did prove it,' she whispered, stunned by the realisation. The warmth within spread and intensified to a steady glow. 'You knew the baby was yours from the first, no matter what I said. *You believed in me.*'

His faith in her had been instantaneous. He'd *shown* her his change of heart.

With infinite care he brushed her hair behind her ear, letting his fingers linger in a delicate caress. Delight shivered through her. She stood unmoving, snared by what she saw in his eyes and what she felt.

'I love you, Chloe. For so many reasons. Because you stood up to me when I deserved it. You never let me railroad you into anything. You made me take a hard look at myself.' He pressed a kiss to the back of her hand and a ripple of heat sped through her.

'Because of the way your laugh always makes me smile,

even when the world seems black and unforgiving.' Another kiss, this time to her wrist, drew her skin taut.

'Because of your sexy body and your soft skin and the way you welcome a lover with all of you, body and soul.'

Chloe tried to pull back, but he held her firm and planted a kiss to the centre of her palm. 'Because you're honest and sincere. Because you had the generosity of heart to forgive my brother as I'm hoping you can forgive me.'

Her treacherous legs wobbled and he caught her close.

'I love you, Chloe. I have no right to expect you to love me, but I had to tell you. I've been a complete b—'

'Don't!' Her fingers sealed his lips as she found her voice again. It throbbed with all the emotion welling inside. 'I love you, Declan. Still. Always.'

The stunned look in his eyes made her smile.

'I love your intensity.' She held his gleaming gaze, reassuring him with everything in her. 'Your honesty and determination to do right. I love your loyalty.

'I love that you're a man of honour.' She suppressed a smile as she remembered jealousy over Sophia. 'And I love the way you make love to me.'

'I can't believe it.' He cradled her close, the look in his eyes something she'd carry with her the rest of her life. 'You make me feel invincible, even with *this*.' He lifted a dismissive hand to his scar.

'It's part of you, Declan. I even love that.' She smiled at his startled look. 'It gives you a swashbuckling air, like a marauding pirate.'

'Does it indeed?' He scooped her into his arms and held her close. 'You know what pirates do when they find beautiful wenches, don't you?' He strode from the balcony and across the room till he reached the huge bed.

Abruptly his grin faded and his grip tightened.

'I don't deserve you, Chloe. You'd have every right—'

Chloe stopped him in the most sensible way she knew. She tugged his head down and planted a breathless kiss on his mouth, opening for him, till with a groan he plunged in and took her with a thorough, ravishing kiss that made her head spin and her heart soar.

'The past is over, Declan,' she whispered. 'Let's concentrate on the future.'

'I'll spend our future showing you every day how much I love you.' The earnest light in his eyes and his tender smile were the most perfect things Chloe had ever seen.

EPILOGUE

CHLOE smiled as she turned the corner of the veranda and saw the impromptu football game on the lawn.

Ted's companion dog, a beagle crossed with no-one knew what, barked excitedly and pranced across the grass.

Amy, with all the fierce concentration of a two-year-old, tottered after the lightweight ball to where Ted guarded a goal of bright plastic buckets. He feinted to one side, pretending to use his walking stick to stop the ball. But anyone seeing the expression on his face knew he had no intention of spoiling his granddaughter's goal.

Amy kicked with such comical exaggeration that she fell over. But there were no tears, just a crow of delight when the ball slid past Ted.

'G'anpa, G'anpa! I did it.'

'I saw, sweetie.' Ted reached down and pulled her to her feet. Instantly she wrapped her arms around his legs.

Chloe's heart lurched as she watched her daughter and Ted together. She was so lucky to have them. So very lucky.

'They're good together, aren't they?' A deep, rich voice shivered across her skin as her husband stepped close, tugging her back against him.

'Hmm, hmm.' She smiled as he wrapped his arms around her and she sank into his familiar, warm embrace. 'They are.'

Declan's hands slipped down to her small baby-bump, caressing with a gentleness that always made her heart turn over.

'We're very lucky, my love.' He nuzzled her neck and sparks cascaded through her. Her nipples hardened and heat swirled deep within. 'I have to be the luckiest man alive.'

Chloe turned and wrapped her arms around his neck. She looked into his beloved face and read the love shining in his eyes. 'And I'm the luckiest woman.'

'You've got lipstick on,' he growled in mock anger.

'You expect me to go to the gala and not wear make-up? On the arm of the sexiest man there, who just happens to be the foundation chair?'

The foundation, named for Adrian, provided community support to people with mental illness. Its focus was on filling gaps left by other services, rather than on glitzy events. This annual fundraiser was the exception, attended by a who's who that always made the celebrity pages.

'You could have waited.' Declan leaned close, a tell tale gleam in his eyes. 'But no matter. You can put more on later.'

His breath was warm on her face and her eyes had just fluttered shut when a small form cannoned into their legs.

'Mummy, Daddy, I goaled. Did you see? Did you see?'

'We saw, darling.' Chloe smiled as she watched Declan pick up their daughter and hug her. Amy hugged him back, planting grubby hands on his tuxedo and dress shirt.

'We might be a little late leaving for the gala,' Chloe murmured. 'You'll need to take that off.'

The look he sent her was a sizzle of pure invitation. 'Promises, promises, Mrs Carstairs. I look forward to you helping me.'

* * * * *

SECRETS OF A
POWERFUL MAN

CHANTELLE SHAW

CHAPTER ONE

'THERE'S SOMEONE HERE to see you. A man...'

Darcey looked up from her desk, surprised that her usually unflappable secretary sounded flustered.

'He says his name is Salvatore Castellano,' Sue continued. 'He has been referred to you by James Forbes and wishes to arrange speech therapy for his daughter.'

'But James knows that the unit is closing.' Darcey was puzzled. James Forbes was head of the paediatric cochlear implant programme at the hospital and he had been vociferous in his condemnation of the financial cuts affecting the speech therapy unit.

Sue shrugged. 'I explained that, but Mr Castellano is insistent that he wants to see you.' She added in a conspiratorial voice, 'I think he's used to getting his own way, and he is demanding to speak to you. He's very *Mediterranean*—you know the type... Dark and intense. I know I shouldn't say this when I've been married to Brian for twenty-four years, but he's *hot*.'

He was *demanding* to see her? Darcey's brows rose, but she had to admit she was intrigued by this man who was responsible for turning Sue into a wilting heap of hormones. Fortunately she had no concerns that he might have the same effect on her. She was off hot men. From now on she would be perfectly happy with lukewarm and safe, perhaps even slightly boring, but definitely not a showman…like her ex-husband.

She glanced out of the window and noticed a sleek black saloon car parked next to her Mini. Her contract with the health authority had been terminated and she did not have to meet this Salvatore Castellano. But what the hell? There was only an empty house waiting for her, and a solitary dinner—if she could be bothered to cook.

'You'd better show him in.'

Sue stepped back into the corridor and Darcey returned to the task of clearing the drawers in her desk. The filing cabinets had been emptied and all that remained to do was take down the certificates on the wall which gave details of her qualifications: BSc (Hons), MSc in Speech and Language Therapy and an Advanced Clinical Skills Diploma for speech and language therapists to work with the deaf.

It was a pity that being an expert in her field had not been enough to save her job, she thought ruefully. The Inner London health authority's budget had been drastically cut and she had been made redundant. Losing her job had forced her to think about her future—and acknowledge the necessity of coming to terms with her past. Her decision to take a career break for a couple of months over the summer was primarily so that she could make plans for the private practice she intended to set up. But, more importantly, she was hoping to put her divorce behind her and get over her cheating rat of an ex-husband once and for all.

Her gaze fell on the nameplate on her desk. She had become Darcey Rivers when she had married Marcus and had kept his name after the divorce because she was reluctant to revert back to her maiden name and the notoriety that went with it. It had been painfully humiliating when she had realised that Marcus had married her because he had hoped that joining the famous theatrical Hart family would boost his acting career. Unfortunately she had been so in love with him, so bowled over by his wit and charm and undeniable good looks, that with uncharacteristic impulsiveness she had accepted his proposal four months after they'd met.

Darcey walked over to the window and picked up the potted plant on the sill. She had inherited the Maidenhair Fern two years ago, when she had taken up the post of senior specialist speech and language therapist. It had been half-dead and Sue had offered to throw it out— apparently this type of fern was notoriously difficult to grow successfully. But Darcey liked a challenge, and under her care the plant had thrived and was now a mass of bright green lacy leaves.

'Don't worry, I'll take you home with me,' she murmured. She had read that plants responded if you talked to them, and her words of encouragement seemed to have worked—although that was strictly between her and the fern. After all, she was a highly educated professional and *sensible* was her middle name; her family and friends would be astonished if they knew that she talked to plants.

The office door opened again, and she turned her head to see Sue usher a man into the room. Sunlight streamed through the window and danced across his rugged features. Darcey's first thought was that he was nothing like Marcus. But neither was he lukewarm, and he was definitely not safe. Now she understood what Sue had meant when she had said he was hot!

He looked as though he belonged to another century, when knights on horseback had fought bloody battles and rescued damsels in distress. Startled by the wild excesses of her imagination, Darcey forced herself to study him objectively, but the image of an ancient king still remained in her mind. Perhaps it was the dangerously sexy combination of black jeans and shirt and the well-worn leather jacket that emphasised the width of his shoulders. His height was equally impressive; the top of his head brushed the door frame and she estimated that he must be several inches over six feet tall.

Her heart gave a jolt as she raised her eyes to his face. He was not conventionally handsome like Marcus. Not a pretty boy. He was a man in the most masculine sense: hard-faced, square-jawed, with a strong nose and dark, penetrating eyes beneath heavy brows. His eyes gave away nothing of his thoughts and his mouth was set in an uncompromising line, as if he rarely smiled. His hair was thick and so dark it was almost black, falling to his shoulders. Darcey had a feeling that he cared little about his appearance and had no inclination to visit a barber.

As she stared at him she was aware of a coiling sensation in the pit of her stomach. The feeling was entirely sexual and utterly unexpected. She had felt dead inside since she had discovered that Marcus was sleeping with a glamour model with pneumatic breasts. The lightning bolt of desire that shot through her now was so intense it made her catch her breath. She sensed the power of the stranger's formidable physique and for the first time in her life acknowledged the fundamental difference between a man and a woman—male strength and feminine weakness.

She suddenly realised that she was holding her breath and released it on a shaky sigh. Somehow she managed to regain her composure and gave Salvatore Castellano a polite smile.

'Mr Castellano? How can I help you?'

He glanced at the nameplate on her desk and frowned. 'Are *you* Darcey Rivers?'

He spoke with a strong accent. Italian, Darcey guessed. There was an arrogance about him that set her on the defensive.

'Yes, I am,' she said coolly.

He looked unimpressed. 'I expected someone older.'

James Forbes had said that Darcey Rivers was an experienced and dedicated senior speech therapist. The description had put into Salvatore's mind an image of a grey-haired, professional-looking woman, possibly wearing a tweed suit and spectacles. Instead he was faced with a slip of a girl with a heart-shaped face and a sleek bob of conker-brown hair that gleamed like silk in the bright sunlight pouring through the window.

He skimmed his eyes over her petite figure, noting how her fitted suit, reminiscent of the style worn in the 1940s, emphasised her tiny waist and the gentle flare of her hips. Her legs were slender and he guessed she chose to wear three-inch stiletto heels to make her appear taller. Her face was pretty rather than beautiful; her mouth was too wide and her eyes too big for her small features, giving her an elfin quality. Beneath her jacket her blouse was buttoned up to her neck and he briefly wondered if she was as prim as her appearance suggested.

Darcey flushed beneath the stranger's intent appraisal. 'I'm sorry if I've disappointed you,' she said with heavy irony.

'I am not disappointed, Miss Rivers.'

His voice was deep-timbred, with a sensual huskiness that made the hairs on the back of Darcey's neck stand on end.

'I am merely surprised. You seem young to be so highly qualified.'

Darcey knew she looked a good five years less than her age. Perhaps when she reached fifty she would be glad to look younger, but at university and at job interviews she had struggled to be taken seriously. Of course her name had not helped. Once people realised she was a member of the famous Hart family they were surprised that she had not followed her parents onto the stage. At least Salvatore Castellano was unaware of her family connection. But she felt irritated that he had mentioned her youthful appearance.

'I'm twenty-eight,' she told him tightly. 'And Rivers is my married name.'

His expression was inscrutable, 'My apologies, *Mrs* Rivers.'

Why on earth had she said that? Darcey asked herself. Intimating that she was married had been a subconscious response to his comment that she looked young. 'Actually, I prefer Ms Rivers.'

His shuttered expression did not alter, but she had an unsettling feeling that his dark eyes could see inside her head. Sue had gone, and he closed the door with a decisive click and walked across the office.

'I'm glad we've got that settled,' he murmured drily. 'Now, perhaps we can sit down and I will explain the reason for my visit?'

His arrogance was infuriating. Twin spots of colour flared on Darcey's cheeks and she had half a mind to tell him to get lost, but she hesitated when she noticed that he walked with a pronounced limp.

'A fractured femur—the result of a car accident,' he said curtly. 'My leg is held together with a lot of fancy metalwork.'

She was embarrassed that he had caught her staring at him. He made her feel as if she was sixteen again, immature and unsure of herself, lacking the self-confidence that the other members of her family possessed.

'Don't act like a timid mouse, darling girl,' had been her father's regular refrain. 'Project yourself to the audience and believe in yourself—because if you don't how can you expect anyone else to?'

It was all very well for her father, Darcey had often thought. Joshua Hart had earned a reputation as one of the finest Shakespearian actors in a career that had spanned three decades. Charismatic, exciting and unpredictable, he could also be distant with his children when he was focused on an acting role. As well as being an actor he was a brilliant playwright, and three of his plays had been performed in the West End. The one thing Joshua Hart certainly did not lack was self-belief.

'Acting is in your blood,' he'd often told Darcey. 'How could it not be, with the combination of genes you have inherited from your mother and me?'

Her mother, Claudia, was a gifted actress, and Darcey's brother and her two sisters had all followed their parents into the theatre. She was especially close to her younger sister Mina, and was proud of how she had overcome her disability to become a respected actress.

Only Darcey had chosen a different career path, and Joshua had not hidden his disappointment. Sometimes Darcey felt her father had taken her decision not to uphold the Hart family tradition and train at RADA as a personal affront. He had never been the easiest man to get on with, and in recent years she had sensed a divide between them that she longed to breach.

'Ms Rivers?'

Salvatore Castellano's curt voice snapped her back to the present. Without waiting for an invitation he pulled out the chair by her desk and sat down, stretching his in-

jured leg stiffly out in front of him. Darcey decided that
she needed to take control of the situation.

'I'm afraid I can only spare you a few minutes, Mr
Castellano,' she said briskly. 'I have a busy afternoon.'

His brows rose. 'You mean you are holding appointments today? James Forbes led me to believe that the
speech therapy unit has closed down.'

Flushing, because in actual fact she had nothing
planned for the rest of the day, Darcey walked behind her
desk and sat down, placing the potted fern in front of her
like a barrier. 'So it has. I'm only here today to clear my
office. Once I've finished I have…personal things to do.'

What kind of things? Salvatore wondered. Was she
going home to her husband? Maybe to spend a lazy summer's afternoon making love? Glancing at her left hand,
he was intrigued to see she was not wearing a wedding
ring. He frowned. Ms Darcey Rivers's private life was
of no interest to him. All he was interested in was her
professional expertise.

'I have come to see you, Ms Rivers, because I wish
to employ a speech therapist who specialises in working
with deaf children, and specifically children who have
cochlear implants,' he said abruptly. 'My five-year-old
daughter had bilateral implants fitted two months ago.
Rosa is profoundly deaf. She communicates using sign
language but she has no audio-language skills.'

Darcey breathed in the subtle tang of his sandalwood
cologne and a quiver of awareness shot through her. She
wished now that she had not sat down at her desk, because rather than giving her a sense of authority all she
could think was that, close up, Salvatore Castellano was
devastatingly sexy.

For heaven's sake! She gave herself a mental shake and

concentrated on what he had told her. 'Did your daughter
have the implants fitted in England?'

'Yes. James Forbes is her audiologist.'

'Then James must have explained that although the
unit here is closing the speech therapy programme will
still continue at the hospital, but on a smaller scale and
with fewer therapists—which unfortunately will probably mean a longer waiting list before children can be
assessed,' she said ruefully.

'James treated Rosa as a private patient. She does not
qualify for the post-implant speech therapy programme
provided by your National Health Service.'

'I see,' Darcey said slowly. 'In that case, why did
James recommend me to you? Even if the speech therapy unit here wasn't closing, your daughter would not be
eligible for me to assess her because I am employed—
was employed,' she amended with a grimace, 'by the
local health authority.'

'James said that you intend to establish a private practice.'

'I hope to do so in the future, but my immediate plans
are to take a break from work and spend the summer in
the South of France. I'm sorry I can't help you, Mr Castellano, but I can give you the names of several speech
therapists who I'm sure would be willing to work with
your daughter.'

Nothing on Salvatore Castellano's chiselled features
indicated that he was disappointed by her response, but
there was a steely implacability in his voice.

'James says you are the best in the business.' He
speared Darcey with his penetrating stare. 'I want the
absolute best for my daughter, and I am prepared to pay
whatever fee you decide to charge for your expert knowledge.'

She frowned. 'It's not about money…'

'Experience has taught me that it is *always* about money, Ms Rivers.'

His sardonic reply riled her. Perhaps he thought that her decision to set up a private speech therapy practice had been made because she hoped to increase her earnings, as one of her ex-colleagues had suggested. But nothing could be further from the truth. What she wanted was more freedom to implement her own ideas and hopefully enhance hearing-impaired children's experiences of speech and language therapy. It was something Darcey cared passionately about, but she had a feeling that even if she tried to explain Salvatore Castellano would not understand.

She tried another approach. 'Obviously I can appreciate that you and Rosa's mother must be anxious for her to begin speech therapy as soon as possible. All the evidence shows that children with CI have the potential to achieve good communication and language skills if they receive therapy quickly after implantation.'

She hesitated, wondering where the child's mother was. It was strange that she was not with him. Alarm bells rang inside her head. She'd had past experience of parents who had not been in agreement over the type of help they wanted for their child.

'Can I assume that your daughter's mother agrees with your decision to employ a speech therapist?'

'My wife died when Rosa was a baby.'

Darcey shot him a startled glance, shocked by his revelation but even more so by the complete lack of emotion in his voice. 'I'm sorry,' she murmured. Her thoughts turned to his daughter. The little girl had been locked in a silent world for most of her life, and although she must be able to hear now that she had cochlear implants, sound must be a strange and perhaps frightening concept for her. Given that Rosa already had so much to cope with, the fact that she was growing up without her mother was desperately tragic—particularly as her father seemed as unemotional as a lump of granite.

Thoughts of her own mother flooded Darcey's mind. Six months ago Claudia had been diagnosed with a malignant melanoma. Luckily she had responded well to treatment, but Darcey remembered how devastated she had felt at the idea of losing her mum, and her heart ached for Salvatore Castellano's motherless little daughter.

She looked across the desk and found him watching her intently. From a distance his eyes had looked black, but now she saw that they were very dark brown, framed by thick black lashes. She wondered if his eyes became warmer when he smiled. Did he ever smile? Her gaze strayed to the stern line of his mouth. Would his lips soften if he kissed her? No doubt the dark stubble shading his jaw would graze her skin…

Snatching a sharp breath, she said quickly, 'I would like to help your daughter, Mr Castellano, but as I explained I will be out of the country for the next few months.'

'You are going to the French Riviera, I believe you said?'

'Yes. My family own a villa at Le Lavandou which I intend to use as a base. But I thought I might tour along the coast, maybe even drive into Italy.'

He gave her a speculative look. 'You speak as if you are going alone. Why isn't your husband going with you?'

It was on the tip of her tongue to tell him it was none of his damned business, but something in his expression made her drop her eyes from his piercing gaze.

'As a matter of fact I'm divorced,' she said stiffly.

'And there is no one else in your life? No boyfriend who is going to France with you?'

'I really don't see—'

'Because if that is the case,' he interrupted her, 'then there is no reason why you cannot spend the summer in Sicily and give my daughter the help she desperately needs. You mentioned you would like to visit Italy,' he reminded her. 'Sicily is the most beautiful part of Italy—although I admit I might be a little biased.'

The corners of his mouth lifted. It was not exactly a smile, but the hint that he wasn't completely made of ice, and even had a sense of humour, distracted Darcey's thought process.

'You're Sicilian?'

'To the depths of my soul.'

His accent was suddenly very strong. For the first time since he had walked into her office Darcey heard emotion in his voice, fierce pride in his heritage. 'I live in a castle that was built in the thirteenth century by one of my ancestors. Torre d'Aquila has been renovated and has all the facilities of a twenty-first-century home,' he said, mistaking her doubtful expression. 'You will be very comfortable. There is a private pool and the beach is nearby.'

She held up her hand. 'Mr Castellano, I'm sure your castle is lovely, but I haven't agreed to go to Sicily. For one thing I don't speak Italian, and I wouldn't be able to help Rosa learn her native language.'

'I have decided for several reasons that it will be better for her to learn English. My wife was half-English. Adriana died before Rosa was diagnosed as being profoundly deaf. I would like Rosa to learn her mother's language, and James Forbes thinks that now she can hear with the cochlear implants she might also be able to learn to speak Italian.'

Darcey nodded. 'I have met children with CI who are bilingual, but obviously it is important to concentrate on teaching Rosa one language to start with. I'm sure James has explained that, even though your daughter is now able to hear sound, developing language skills can be a slow process. She will need support and patience from her family as well as extensive speech therapy.'

'She is able to communicate using British sign language, which James tells me you are competent in.' Salvatore leaned across the desk and trapped Darcey's gaze. 'James spoke highly of your professionalism and skill, but more importantly, he said that you have a special empathy with deaf children.'

'My sister lost eighty percent of her hearing after she had meningitis when she was a child,' she explained. 'It was seeing how Mina struggled at first to cope with her deafness that made me decide that I wanted to work with hearing-impaired children.'

Salvatore heard the emotion in Darcey's voice and sensed she was softening. Determined to seize his advantage, he took his wallet from his jacket and pulled out a photograph of his daughter.

'Rosa is a shy child who, as a result of her disability, finds it hard to connect with people. I hope that the gift of language will help her self-confidence. I believe you can give her that gift, Darcey. James Forbes is confident that you are the best person to teach my daughter to speak.'

Oh, heavens! The way he said her name, in his gravelly, sexy accent, sent a little shiver down Darcey's spine. His dark eyes were mesmerising and his words tugged on her emotions. He was right, she thought. Language was a gift, but most people took the ability to hear and

speak for granted. Darcey remembered how Mina had
once confided that when she had lost her hearing she had
felt lonely and isolated.

She studied the photo of a startlingly pretty little girl
with a mass of dark curls framing a delicate face. Of
course nothing in the photo revealed Rosa's deafness.
Only when she looked closely did Darcey notice that
there was no sparkle in the child's eyes but a sense of
loneliness that was heart-wrenching.

It wouldn't hurt to see the child and make an assessment of her needs, Darcey mused. She could hand the
case over to one of her colleagues who had also been
made redundant and might be interested in working with
Rosa.

Unbeknown to Darcey, her indecision was reflected in
her eyes. She had beautiful eyes, Salvatore noticed. They
were an unusual light green colour—the exact shade of
the peridot pendant she was wearing suspended on a
chain around her throat. He was surprised by the flicker
of interest he felt. It was a long time since he had been
intrigued by a woman. The delicate fragrance of her
perfume—a sensual musk of jasmine and old-fashioned
roses—teased his senses, and his eyes were drawn to
the scattering of golden freckles on her nose and cheeks.

His mouth firmed as he reminded himself of the reason for his visit. His daughter needed the help of a speech
therapist and Ms Rivers came with the highest recom-
mendations. The fact that she was attractive was immaterial. There was no likelihood he would find her a
distraction. During his lonely childhood he had learned
to impose iron control over his feelings, and the loss of
parts of his memory four years ago had only furthered
his sense of emotional detachment.

'All I am asking at this stage is for you to visit my

house in London to meet Rosa,' he said. 'We can take things from there.'

Darcey chewed her bottom lip. 'It's not that I don't want to help your daughter, Mr Castellano—'

'Good,' he cut her off mid-sentence. 'I think the best thing would be for you to come and meet her now.' He got to his feet and towered over her, so that Darcey had to tilt her head to look at him. 'Can you postpone whatever plans you had for this afternoon?'

She wondered if he recognised the word *no*. He was like a steamroller, flattening any opposition to what he wanted, she thought ruefully. But she could not help but be impressed by his single-minded determination to help his daughter.

'I...I guess so.' Her cheeks grew pink as she recalled her white lie that she would be busy later. 'But I'm packed and ready to leave for France on Friday, so I don't really see the point.'

His dark eyes trapped her gaze. 'You would not say that if you were my daughter. Sadly, Rosa cannot say anything. She is unable to voice her thoughts, her hopes... her fears.'

He was deliberately playing on her emotions, Darcey recognised. But his ploy had worked.

She threw up her hands in surrender. 'All right, I'll come and meet your daughter. I'll assess the level of speech therapy she needs and then, if you wish, I will hand her case over to one of my colleagues. But I have to warn you, Mr Castellano, there is no chance I will go to Sicily with you.'

CHAPTER TWO

'I'LL TAKE MY car,' Darcey told Salvatore as they walked across the car park. Despite his injured leg his stride was twice the size of hers, and her stiletto heels tip-tapped on the tarmac as she tried to keep pace with him.

'There's no need for you to drive through the centre of London. I'll drop you back here later so that you can collect your car.'

She shook her head. 'I don't know you, Mr Castellano, and I'm not going to get into a stranger's car.'

Personal safety was an issue she took very seriously. Her parents also owned a touring theatre company and ran drama workshops in schools and youth clubs to promote ways for young people to stay safe. Before she had become involved in her own career Darcey had frequently performed with the company, Speak Out, which also promoted drama for the deaf community.

'I promise I have no plans to ravish you on the back seat,' Salvatore said drily.

He glanced at the petite woman at his side and idly wondered if the spark of fire in her green eyes would live up to its promise. Outwardly Darcey appeared cool and collected, but beneath her smart suit he sensed she was an explosive bundle of sexual energy.

He frowned, annoyed by his unexpected train of

thought. 'You are welcome to sit in the front with my chauffeur.'

Through the Bentley's smoked glass windows Darcey made out the figure of a driver sitting behind the wheel and she felt like an idiot.

'As for not knowing who I am,' Salvatore continued, 'do you drink wine?'

She gave him a puzzled look. 'Occasionally. My father is interested in fine wines and has built up a large collection.'

'Then he will almost certainly know that the wines from the Castellano Estate are the finest in Sicily.' Reaching inside his jacket, Salvatore withdrew a business card and handed it to her.

Darcey glanced at the logo on the card and recognition dawned.

'Castellano Wine! I've seen the label on wines in supermarkets and specialist wine shops. My father says the Castellano vineyards produce the best wine that has ever come from Sicily.' She looked uncertainly at Salvatore. 'So…do you work for the company?'

'I own it,' he said coolly. 'At least, I own the vineyards and the winery, and also a wine distribution business under the umbrella of the Castellano Group, which is a multi-faceted global organisation. My father retired from the company last year, leaving me and my twin brother as joint CEOs. Sergio is responsible for the property development division, and also has a personal interest in the Hotel Royale in Bayswater, which the company purchased and refurbished a couple of years ago.'

Salvatore opened the rear door of the Bentley.

'Now that you know as much about me as you need to know, will you accept my offer of a lift to my house in Mayfair?'

Darcey was still reeling from the realisation that he must be very wealthy—probably a multi-millionaire at the very least. Where else would he own a house but in the most expensive area of London? she thought wryly.

She shook her head. 'I'd still prefer to take my car.' It meant that she was in control and could leave his home when she chose.

Salvatore frowned. He was used to being obeyed without question, and he found Darcey's obstinacy irritating, but she was already getting into her car.

'I'll follow you,' she said, 'but you had better tell me your address and I'll put it into my sat nav.'

He gave her the postcode. 'It's on Park Lane, close to Marble Arch.' Salvatore snatched his eyes from the expanse of slender thigh exposed as Darcey's skirt rode up her legs as she climbed into her car and ruthlessly dismissed his faint stirring of sexual interest. 'It will be simpler for Rosa's sake if we drop formality and use our Christian names. Darcey is a charming name.'

Feeling hot and bothered by the predatory glint she had glimpsed in Salvatore's eyes, Darcey was glad of the distraction.

'It has both Irish and French origins. My father is half-Irish and half-French and he chose the name for me.'

'The meaning of Salvatore is saviour.'

To Darcey's surprise he gave a harsh laugh, and for a second she glimpsed a tortured expression in his eyes that was truly shocking.

His expression hardened and became unreadable once more. 'The irony isn't lost on me,' he muttered obliquely.

She wondered what he meant, but before she could ask he slid into the back of the Bentley and disappeared from view behind the darkened windows. He was a man of mystery and absolutely the last thing she needed when she was two days away from her holiday, Darcey thought as she started the Mini's engine and followed the Bentley out of the car park. For weeks she had been daydreaming about relaxing on a golden beach, eating melting Brie on crusty French bread, and drinking the local red wine. She was regretting her impulsive decision to meet Salvatore's daughter, but as she recalled the photo of Rosa she could not help feeling sympathetic towards the little girl with the sad eyes.

Traffic in the capital at the start of the rush hour was heavily congested, and Darcey had lost sight of the Bentley by the time she crawled along Oxford Street and turned onto Park Lane. Opposite was Marble Arch and the green oasis of Hyde Park, but she was too busy looking for the address Salvatore had given her to be able to admire the famous London landmarks. Suddenly she caught sight of the Bentley parked in front of a stunning neo-classical style mansion house. Hastily indicating to change lanes, she nipped into a parking space, thankful that her small car was so easy to manoeuvre.

Salvatore was standing on the front steps of the house and seemed to be in deep conversation with a striking blonde wearing a very short skirt and a low-cut top that revealed her enviable cleavage. Darcey sensed from their body language that they were arguing. The woman spun away from him, but he followed her down the steps and caught hold of her arm.

Feeling awkward at the idea of interrupting a lovers' tiff, Darcey remained in her car and watched the woman jerk free from Salvatore and climb into a waiting taxi, which immediately sped away. She was tempted to drive off too, but he was striding along the pavement towards her, his powerful masculinity in no way lessened by the slight unevenness of his gait due to his injured leg. With a sigh, she got out of the Mini and went to meet him.

'It might be best if I left,' she said, feeling her heart skitter when he halted in front of her. Her reaction to him was all the more unsettling because she could not control it. Since her divorce eighteen months ago she had not felt the slightest interest in men, and she was horrified by her body's response to Salvatore's potent virility.

He frowned, and she explained, 'I saw you arguing with your girlfriend and I thought you might want to go after her.'

'That wasn't my girlfriend,' he said curtly, and Darcey suddenly realised that his temper was on a tight leash. 'Sharon was my daughter's nanny. I hired her through an agency when I brought Rosa to England for surgery to fit the cochlear implants. The arrangement was that Sharon would accompany me back to Sicily and continue looking after Rosa. But she has just informed me that she has got back together with a boyfriend and is moving to Birmingham to be with him.'

'So who is looking after Rosa now?'

'Sharon said she had asked one of the maids to keep an eye on her.'

Darcey could imagine how confused and upset Rosa must feel at being abandoned by the nanny who was supposed to be taking care of her. 'Poor little girl,' she said softly.

There was no flicker of emotion in Salvatore's dark eyes. 'Unfortunately Luisa—the nanny who had looked after Rosa since she was a baby—left to get married shortly before we came to England. Finding someone able to use sign language at short notice was difficult, and Sharon was the only person on the agency's books. I admit that when I took her on I was unaware of her boyfriend problems.' He glanced at Darcey. 'Come and meet my daughter.'

He began to walk back towards the house, and after a moment's hesitation Darcey hurried after him. 'Was Rosa close to her previous nanny?'

He shrugged. 'I suppose so. My daughter has no memory of her mother and had only been cared for by Luisa. I imagine she missed her at first, but she's a resilient child.'

Darcey was chilled by his cool tone and his curiously detached air when he spoke about his little girl. She wondered if a five-year-old could really be as resilient as he seemed to think, but she made no comment as she followed him up the steps and into the house. With grey marble walls and floor, and elegant antique furniture, the entrance hall looked more like the foyer of a five-star hotel—with the same impersonal feel. It was obvious that expert interior designers had been given a limitless budget to spend, but although it was a beautiful house it was not a home, and seemed as cold and unwelcoming as its owner.

Darcey glanced at Salvatore's hard profile as they walked up the sweeping staircase. 'This is a stunning place,' she commented.

'Do you think so? There's rather too much marble decor for my taste, but I suppose it's impressive.' His tone was sardonic. 'My brother purchased the house to add to his property portfolio. When he married his English wife he considered using it as a London base, but he and Kristen have a very lively four-year-old son, and now another child on the way. They rarely visit England, so I bought the house from Sergio. Most of the time it is rented out to an Arab sheikh. I have only been staying here for the past couple of months, while Rosa had the cochlear implants fitted and adjusted.'

At the top of the stairs Salvatore led Darcey along the landing and opened a door. As she stepped into the room she noticed that a half-hearted attempt had been made to make the room child-friendly, with posters of fairies on the walls and a large dolls' house in the corner. A movement from over by the window caught her attention, and she watched a little girl slide down from the window seat and run across the room.

Rosa was tall for her age, and even prettier than the photo Darcey had seen of her. Her curly hair was tied in a ponytail, and her dark eyes, framed by long lashes, were hauntingly beautiful. A small earpiece attached to a wire that disappeared beneath her tee shirt and was attached to a battery pack was the only sign of her hearing impairment. Darcey knew that another wire running from the earpiece to a small circle taped to Rosa's head, was linked magnetically to the implant inside her skull, enabling her to hear.

Rosa's face had lit up at the sight of her father, but as she came towards Salvatore her steps slowed and she gave him an uncertain smile that made Darcey's heart ache. She expected Salvatore to sweep his daughter into his arms, but although he gave a brief smile he seemed strangely awkward and patted Rosa's head, as if he were a distant uncle who was unused to children.

Why don't you cuddle your daughter? Darcey wanted to ask him. He did not appear to notice the little flash of hurt in Rosa's eyes, but Darcey saw, and she felt a pang of sympathy for the child.

She recalled instances from her own childhood when she had felt rejected by her father. Joshua had never meant to be deliberately cruel, but he'd often been self-absorbed and careless of other people's feelings. As an adult Darcey understood his artistic temperament, but as a child she had been hurt and had believed that she had done something to upset her father.

She leaned down so that her face was level with Rosa's. 'Hello, Rosa. My name is Darcey,' she said gently, speaking the words at the same time as she signed them.

Hello, Rosa signed, but made no attempt to speak. She looked up at her father and asked in sign language, *Where is Sharon?*

Salvatore hesitated before he signed back: *She had to go and visit a friend.*

When is she coming back?

Another pause, and then he signed, *She isn't.*

Rosa's lip trembled. Darcey shot Salvatore a glance, willing him to lift his daughter into his arms and reassure her that, although the nanny had gone, he would never leave her.

But instead he signed, *Darcey has come to play with you.*

That's right—hand the problem over to someone else, she thought, flashing him a fulminating glare. She did not understand what was wrong with him. His determination to arrange speech therapy for Rosa suggested that he cared about the little girl, but he seemed incapable of expressing his emotions.

Perhaps he really was as hard as his granite-like features suggested and did not feel the normal range of emotions most people felt. Darcey could only guess what effect his detachment would have on his five-year-old daughter, who had to cope with deafness and was growing up without a mother. If any child needed her father's love it was Rosa, but Salvatore seemed to have a heart of stone.

'I will need to make a proper assessment to determine the level of speech therapy Rosa needs,' she told him. 'It should take an hour or so.' She frowned when he strode over to the door. 'I assumed you would want to be present during the assessment.'

'I'll leave you to get on with your job while I phone the agency and arrange a replacement for Sharon.' Salvatore saw no reason to explain that he was in a hurry to go to his study because he had just received a text message asking him to call his brother about an urgent matter.

'But—'

'Rosa will probably respond better if I'm not here,' he cut her off abruptly. He could tell from the glowering look Darcey gave him that she did not think him much of a father. Guilt clawed in his gut. She was right, he thought grimly. He was not the sort of father he wished he could be. The truth was he did not know how to act like a loving parent. When he had been growing up his father had been a remote figure. And as for his mother—well, the less said about her the better.

He had been five years old when Patti had left. He had never understood why she had forbidden him and his brother from calling her *mamma*. She had disappeared one day and taken Sergio with her. Salvatore had assumed she loved his twin and that was why she had taken him to America. It turned out that she had not loved Sergio either. Recently his brother had confided that Patti had been an alcoholic who had often beaten him when she'd had too much to drink.

Salvatore did not know if he felt better or worse now that his illusions about his mother had been shattered. For so many years he had put her on a pedestal and believed he was unworthy of being loved. That belief was still deeply ingrained on his psyche. Maybe it was why he found it so hard to show his emotions.

He wished things were different. He wished he could

be an openly loving *papa* to Rosa, like his brother, Sergio, was to his son, Nico. But always in the back of his mind was the guilt that it was his fault Rosa was growing up without her mother, the fear that one day she would learn the truth and perhaps would hate him.

He jerked his gaze from the accusatory expression in Darcey Rivers's bright green eyes. 'I will be in my study. Press nine on the phone if you need anything and a member of staff will attend to you.'

Salvatore barely glanced at Rosa as he exited the nursery, Darcey noticed. She could not understand his remoteness from his daughter. It seemed as though he preferred to hand over the little girl to a nanny, but now Sharon had left and Rosa had no one to take care of her.

She glanced at the child and her heart ached when she saw the wistful expression on her face. Smiling, she walked over to Rosa and crouched down beside her. *I like your dolls' house*, she signed. *Can I play too?*

Dark eyes studied her gravely for a few moments. Rosa had inherited her father's eyes, Darcey noticed. She tried to block out the image of Salvatore's ruggedly handsome face from her mind, annoyed by her inexplicable attraction to the cold and enigmatic man. She was here in her professional capacity, and she was determined to concentrate solely on the little girl who was smiling tentatively at her.

Over the next hour it quickly became clear that Rosa was a highly intelligent child, but although she was proficient in sign language she was unable or unwilling to attempt to speak. The little girl would need plenty of encouragement to develop self-confidence as well as to master language skills.

The nursery door opened and Darcey glanced over her

shoulder, expecting to see that Salvatore had returned.
But a butler stood in the doorway and informed her that
it was Rosa's dinner time.

'Mr Castellano is unavoidably detained and has asked
if you would accompany his daughter to the dining room.'

She could not refuse when Rosa slipped a small hand
into hers and gave her a trusting smile, and she was glad
she had stayed with the little girl when they walked into
the huge dining room. A single place was set at one end
of a long dining table.

Doesn't your father eat dinner with you? she signed
to Rosa.

The child shook he head. *Papa eats later. He is always busy in his office.*

Darcey felt another pang of sympathy for Salvatore's
little daughter, who was growing up in such isolated
splendour. Clearly she did not lack for material things,
but Darcey sensed that Rosa yearned for companion-
ship and love.

Will you stay and play with me? Rosa signed when
she had finished her meal.

Realising that there was no one else to take care of
her, Darcey decided she would have to stay with the little girl and wait for Salvatore. Back in the nursery, she
played a few more games with Rosa before helping her
to get ready for bed. Rosa removed the battery pack she
had worn during the day and the device behind her ear
that was the cochlear implant processor.

I don't like the dark, she signed when Darcey pulled
the curtains and was about to turn off the bedside lamp.
Will you leave the light on?

Recalling how Mina had hated the dark, because she
had felt cut off when she could neither see nor hear,
Darcey nodded. Rosa reminded her so much of her sis-

ter when they had been children. Perhaps that was why she felt an immediate bond with the little girl. But while Mina had grown up with the support of loving parents and family, Rosa had no one but her stern-faced father.

Darcey was appalled by Salvatore's seemingly uncaring attitude towards his daughter. He might be the sexiest man she had ever laid eyes on but beneath his devastating good looks he was as selfish as her ex-husband. It was about time someone told Salvatore Castellano a few home truths, she thought grimly.

Salvatore stared moodily out of his study window and noticed that the trees in Hyde Park opposite resembled black silhouettes in the gathering dusk. After he had spoken to his brother and learned that there had been a fire at the winery in Sicily he had been busy on the phone, dealing with the crisis, and had not realised how late it was. He felt guilty that he had left Rosa for so long, but the maid had reported that Darcey Rivers had stayed to help his daughter with her bedtime routine.

He grimaced. No doubt his absence had confirmed her belief that he was an uninterested father. The truth was far more complicated. He loved Rosa, but love was not something he'd had much experience of and he did not know how to get close to his child.

He closed his eyes, trying to control the searing pain in his head. The migraines that had plagued him since the accident four years ago had become more frequent in recent months, and were so debilitating that he was forced to resort to taking painkillers. It was no coincidence that this headache had started soon after he had spoken to Sergio and heard the shocking news his old friend Pietro was dead. The elderly vintner had suffered a fatal heart attack while trying to fight the blaze at the winery.

It was particularly poignant that Pietro had given his
life for the wine that he was so proud of, he thought.
Winemaking had been in Pietro Marelli's blood. A third
generation vintner, with no son to pass his knowledge on
to, he had instead shared his expertise with Salvatore.
But, more than that, Pietro had been a substitute father
who had welcomed a lonely boy into his home and his
heart. Every school holiday Salvatore had returned to the
Castellano estate and rushed to see Pietro first, knowing
that Tito, his father, would be working in his office and
would not welcome being disturbed.

It was strange that he could remember his childhood
but had no memory of the accident, Salvatore brooded.
He had a clear vision of himself as a ten-year-old boy,
walking through the vineyards with Pietro to inspect the
grapes, but no recollection of the events that had happened after he had got behind the wheel of his car and
driven Adriana away from that party. All he remembered
was waking to find he was in hospital and being told that
his wife had been killed when their car had spun out of
control on a mountain road and plunged over the edge.

The doctor had told Salvatore he had been lucky to
escape with his life, albeit with a seriously mangled right
leg and a head injury. It had caused no permanent brain
damage. His amnesia, so the specialist suspected, was
psychogenic. In layman's terms, his inability to remember the accident, or much of his marriage, was his brain's
defence mechanism in order to blot out the grim fact that
he was responsible for his wife's death.

Salvatore felt a familiar surge of frustration as he tried
to cast his mind back in time and hit a wall of blackness.
It seemed inconceivable that he could have married a
woman, who had given birth to his child, and yet he had
no recollection of their relationship. His mother-in-law

had put photographs of Adriana everywhere in the castle, but when he looked at the pictures of his wife he felt no connection to her.

The specialist had told him it was likely his memory would eventually return, but until it did Salvatore felt he was trapped in a dark place, with no past and no future, unable to forgive himself for robbing his daughter of her mother.

He kneaded his throbbing temples with his fingers and thought about the rest of his conversation with his brother. Sergio had reported better news about the estate workers who had been burned in the fire. Their injuries were serious, but thankfully not life-threatening.

Hearing a tap on the study door, Salvatore turned his head and watched Darcey enter the room. Her silky copper-brown hair framed her face, and she had taken off her jacket. He could see the shape of her small, firm breasts beneath her blouse. His analytical brain registered that she was very attractive, but he was surprised by the bolt of awareness that shot through him. Earlier, in her office, he had ignored the sexual chemistry between them, but tonight, to his annoyance, his eyes were drawn to the curve of her mouth and he fleetingly imagined covering her soft lips with his.

None of his thoughts were revealed on his hard features, however. 'Is Rosa asleep?'

'Do you care?' Green eyes flashed fire at him. 'Your daughter went to bed forty minutes ago and stayed awake for ages, waiting for you come and wish her goodnight.'

'I apologise.' Salvatore's eyes narrowed on Darcey's furious face. 'I had to deal with an important matter.'

'It's not *me* you should apologise to. Rosa was disappointed when you didn't show up.' Darcey's mouth tightened. As she had watched Rosa struggling to stay

awake she had recalled doing the same thing when she
had been a child, waiting for her father to come home
from the theatre. On the nights when Joshua had remembered to come up and kiss her goodnight she had fallen
asleep feeling happy, but sometimes he'd forgotten and
then she had cried herself to sleep.

Salvatore seemed to be unaware of how much his little girl needed him. Darcey glared at him, wishing she
could ignore his potent masculinity. He had discarded
his jacket and rolled up his shirtsleeves to reveal darkly
tanned forearms covered with a mass of black hair. His
brooding sensuality was dangerously attractive—but she
wasn't looking for danger or excitement, wasn't looking
for a man at all. And certainly not one who made her feel
so acutely aware of her femininity.

'What could possibly be more important than your
daughter?' she demanded. 'How could you have left her
for several hours with a complete stranger?'

'You work with children in your professional capacity. I knew you would take care of her. The butler told
me that Rosa seemed quite happy with you.'

His casual attitude inflamed Darcey's temper. 'So
your butler is an expert in child psychology, is he?' she
said sarcastically. 'You are *unbelievable*!'

She turned back to the door. It was none of her business that Salvatore was so distant from his daughter,
she reminded herself. Rosa was a sweet little girl, but
Darcey was *not* going to allow her soft heart to overrule
her common sense, which was telling her she needed to
walk out of this marble house and away from Salvatore
Castellano and his sad-eyed little daughter.

'I can't believe your uncaring attitude to Rosa,' she
said disgustedly. 'The poor little scrap doesn't have a

mother and, to be frank, from what I've seen she doesn't have much of a father.'

Her words hit Salvatore as if she had physically slapped him, but he revealed no emotion on his chiselled features. He was not used to being criticised and was irritated that he felt the need to explain himself to Darcey.

'I usually visit Rosa to wish her goodnight, but I've already said that unfortunately I was detained this evening.'

'You were too busy working to spare a few minutes for a lonely little girl?' Darcey said scathingly, recalling how Rosa said that her father was always busy in his office.

Salvatore's jaw tightened. 'Earlier this afternoon there was a fire in one of the warehouses at my winery in Sicily. Hundreds of barrels of prized wine have been destroyed, but much worse than that, three of the estate workers were injured in the blaze. I have been making arrangements for the men to be flown to a specialist burns unit on mainland Italy and organising for their families to be with them. I had not forgotten about Rosa, but I admit I was so involved with the crisis at home that I did not realise how late it was.'

He raked a hand through his hair and Darcey noticed the lines of strain around his eyes. He hid his emotions well, but he was clearly concerned about the workers injured in the fire.

'The agency that sent Sharon does not have another nanny on their books who is able to use sign language, and I haven't had time to try a different agency.' His dark eyes sought Darcey's. 'But thank you for taking care of Rosa this evening. The least I can do is offer you dinner here with me tonight.'

'No, thank you. I have to go.'

The idea of spending another five minutes alone with Salvatore filled Darcey with panic. His explanation about why he had not come up to the nursery to see Rosa was understandable, but she still sensed that there were issues with his relationship with his daughter that she did not understand. She did not want to get involved with this enigmatic man whose seductively husky voice was causing her heart to beat too fast.

Without another word she hurried out of the study. Her jacket and laptop were on the chair in the hall, where she had left them, but as she walked over to them, with the intention of continuing out through the front door, Salvatore's voice stopped her.

'Can your conscience allow you to abandon Rosa?'

'*Me* abandon her?' She spun round and glared at him. 'That's rich, coming from her father—who can't be bothered to spend time with her and expects the staff to care for her. *My* conscience has nothing to worry about.'

As she uttered the words Darcey discovered that her conscience was far from happy. The image of Rosa's trusting expression when she had tucked her into bed tugged on her heart. She remembered how the little girl had signed that she was afraid of the dark. Many young children shared the same fear, but for a deaf child that feeling of isolation must be worse.

'I have left notes of my assessment on Rosa which you can pass to another speech therapist when you find one who is prepared to go to Sicily.'

'My daughter has already bonded with you.'

She tried to ignore the pull his words had on her emotions. 'I suppose your butler told you that?' she said sarcastically.

'No, I saw for myself that Rosa likes you.'

Salvatore hesitated and to Darcey's surprise a hint of emotion flickered across his face.

'I came to see her while she was eating her dinner. The two of you were laughing together…'

She gave him a puzzled look. 'Why didn't you join us?'

'Rosa looked like she was having fun, and I did not want to interrupt.'

The truth was he had felt jealous as he had watched his daughter interacting with Darcey, Salvatore acknowledged to himself. Rosa did not laugh very often—not with him, anyway. The only time she seemed truly happy was when she was playing with her cousin, Nico.

He wished he could breach the distance that existed between them. A distance he felt was widening as she grew older. Even though Rosa could now hear with the cochlear implants, he did not know how to reach his little girl. Deep in his heart he admitted that he found her deafness difficult to accept. In his darkest thoughts he wondered if he was to blame for her loss of hearing.

Why was he allowing his mind to dwell on the blackness within him? Salvatore asked himself. He was sure that Darcey's expertise would enable her to help Rosa learn to talk and, more than that, he felt instinctively that she would be able to connect with his daughter in a way he could not. When he had stood outside the dining room and watched her with Rosa he had been struck by her genuine kindness to his daughter. Somehow he had to persuade her to come to Sicily.

'Rosa needs you.'

Darcey hesitated, her indecision apparent on her expressive face. Salvatore sensed that she was close to giving in. He glanced towards the butler, who had stepped into the hall.

'The chef has prepared dinner for you and your guest, sir.'

The timing was perfect. 'Thank you, Melton. Ms Rivers and I will make our way to the dining room,' Salvatore said smoothly.

CHAPTER THREE

'IT IS MY fault you were delayed tonight, and I feel bad at the thought of you driving home to cook a meal this late in the evening.' Salvatore forestalled the argument he could see Darcey was about to make. 'Also, my chef is French, and very temperamental. If he is upset he's likely to serve me frogs' legs for breakfast.'

Darcey chewed on her bottom lip, disconcerted by the revelation that Salvatore had a sense of humour. She was torn between wanting to leave, which was by far the most sensible option, and a wholly emotional response to his daughter, who aroused her sympathy.

While she dithered Salvatore opened the door to the dining room. 'Come and eat,' he invited.

His harsh tone had softened and the sensual warmth in his voice melted Darcey's resistance. Against her better judgement she followed him.

The moment she sat down at the table the butler appeared, to serve a first course of classic French *consommé*. The piquant aroma rising up from the bowl teased her tastebuds and her stomach gave a growl, reminding her that it was hours since she had eaten a sandwich for lunch.

The butler offered her wine, but knowing that she had to drive home she refused and opted for water. To her

surprise, Salvatore did the same. She glanced at chiselled
features that gave no clue to his thoughts and sensed that
his mind was far away. He was not the most talkative
host, she thought ruefully as she searched her mind for
something to say to break the silence.

'Why did you choose to become a vintner?'

He shrugged. 'As a child I was drawn to the vineyards. I was fascinated to see the grapes swell on the
vines and I wanted to understand the process by which
they were turned into wine. I was lucky enough to have
a good teacher.'

'Your father?'

'No.'

Salvatore saw that Darcey was surprised by his curt
reply, but her questions had ripped open his heart and
exposed the pain he had been trying avoid for the past
hours. He did not have time to mourn for Pietro now.
He would pay his respects to his old friend when he returned to Sicily. But for one of only a few times in his life
his emotions threatened to overwhelm him and grief lay
heavy in his heart. The painkillers he had taken had not
kicked in yet, and his head throbbed. He wished he could
be alone, but it was important that he secured Darcey Rivers's agreement to take the job as Rosa's speech therapist.

Truly, she had never met such a surly man as Salvatore, Darcey thought as she gave up trying to make conversation and finished her soup. She could see it was
going to be hard work to persuade him to interact with
his daughter.

It was a relief when the butler arrived to serve the
main course of herb-crusted salmon and new potatoes.
She picked up her knife and fork and realised that they
were made of solid silver, to match the ornate candelabra
standing in the centre of the table. Glancing around the

sumptuous dining room, she found her attention caught
by the painting on the wall that she had noticed when she
had brought Rosa down to dinner earlier.

'That can't be an original Monet?' she murmured. She
had recently read in a newspaper that one original Monet
painting had sold for several million pounds.

Salvatore flicked a brief glance at the painting. 'It is.'

Darcey looked at him curiously. 'Are you interested
in art?' An appreciation of art suggested that beneath his
granite exterior he might actually be human.

'I am interested in artwork for its investment value.'

She grimaced. 'That's not what I meant. Are you only
interested in things for their financial worth?'

'Money makes the world go round,' he said sardonically. 'And, speaking of money…' He slid a piece of
paper across the table towards her. 'This is the amount I
am prepared to pay if you will agree to come to Sicily.'

Her heart lurched as she stared at the figure scrawled
on the cheque.

'I hope you will find the amount adequate recompense
for forgoing your holiday. I thought the money would
be useful for when you establish your private practice.'

'It certainly would be,' she said faintly. If she accepted
the money she would not have to apply for a bank loan to
set up her business, Darcey mused. Heck, she wouldn't
have to work at all for a year. 'You must have a huge
amount of faith that I will be able to help Rosa.'

Salvatore shrugged. 'I trust James Forbes's judgement
that you are an excellent speech therapist, and of course
I checked your qualifications before I made the decision
to appoint you.'

Darcey stared at Salvatore's hard-boned face and felt
chilled by his complete lack of emotion. It was no good
telling herself that Rosa was not her problem. The lit-

tle girl needed her—just as her sister had needed her help and support when Mina had struggled to cope with her deafness. But Salvatore's arrogant assumption that she would be impressed by his wealth infuriated her. He was going to find out that, although he might be used to flashing his money around to get whatever he wanted, he could not buy *her*.

'You have no idea, do you?' she said as she tore up the cheque and pushed the pieces back across the table.

Salvatore's eyes narrowed. Why had he thought that Darcey might be different from the countless other women he had met who were seduced by his wealth? he asked himself derisively. Clearly she was out to get what she could, and having recognised an original Monet on the wall had decided to push for more.

'Is it not enough money?' he demanded curtly.

'It's an *obscene* amount of money.'

He frowned. 'I don't understand.'

'I know—and that's the saddest part. You think money can buy you anything you want. But money won't help your daughter learn to speak. Rosa needs time, patience and support—and not only from a speech therapist,' Darcey said, guessing what Salvatore was about to say. 'She needs those things from *you*.'

Darcey stared at Salvatore's shuttered expression and despaired of making him understand how vital his input would be with his daughter's therapy. With a resigned sigh she mentally waved goodbye to her holiday in France. Her conscience would not allow her to abandon Rosa.

'I have decided to go Sicily with you.' She saw a flash of surprise cross his hard features as he glanced at the torn up cheque. She continued crisply, 'My fee will be the same as the monthly salary I was paid by the health authority. I don't want any more than that. I am prepared to stay at your castle and give Rosa intensive speech therapy for three months, during which time I will help you to find another therapist who can provide her with long-term support. I have to be back in London at the end of September. That's non-negotiable,' she added, seeing the questioning look in Salvatore's eyes.

'Why do you have to be back then?'

'Personal reasons.'

Darcey briefly considered explaining why she had to return to London at the end of the summer, but she was reluctant to reveal that she was a member of the famous Hart family. She'd had previous experiences of people trying to befriend her because of her family connections—not least her ex-husband.

Memories crowded her mind: an image of Marcus in *their* bed with a naked woman. He hadn't even had the decency to look repentant, she remembered. But worse humiliation had followed in the ensuing row, when he had admitted that he had not married her because he loved her, but for the kudos of being Joshua Hart's son-in-law and the potential boost that would give his own acting career.

In the eighteen months since her divorce the pain of Marcus's betrayal had faded, but deep down Darcey felt ashamed that she had been such a gullible fool as to trust him. It was not a mistake she intended to make again.

There was no reason for her to give Salvatore details of her private life, she assured herself. She had agreed to go to Sicily in her professional capacity and the only thing he needed to know was that she was prepared to carry out her job to the best of her ability.

'Because of the fire at the winery I have decided to return to Sicily tomorrow,' he told her. 'Can you be ready to leave mid-morning? We'll travel on my private jet. Give me your address and I'll send the car for you.'

The man was a steamroller, Darcey thought ruefully. She shook her head. 'I have a few things to do. I won't be ready to leave with you. I'll book a commercial flight and come at the weekend.'

Salvatore was used to his staff following orders without question, and he felt a flare of irritation that Darcey seemed determined to argue about everything. 'It would suit me better if you come tomorrow.'

It occurred to him that if she had accepted the salary he had offered he would have had more control over her. He still could not quite get over the fact that she had ripped up the cheque, and he was aware that now the balance of power was in her favour. For the first time in his life money had not been the solution to a problem.

'But it will suit *me* better to fly out at the weekend,' Darcey said coolly, refusing to drop her gaze from his hard stare. 'I'm having lunch with my parents tomorrow.'

'Fine. I'll delay our flight time for a few hours and we will leave in the afternoon. You were going to go to France on Friday,' Salvatore reminded her. 'What difference will it make if you leave with me two days earlier? Rosa will be happier if you fly out with us—especially now that Sharon has gone.'

Darcey sighed. She suspected that Salvatore understood she had formed an emotional attachment to his deaf daughter and would not want to disappoint the little girl. 'I'll be ready to leave at three o'clock,' she said resignedly. She stood up from the table. 'But now you will have to excuse me so that I can go home and finish packing.'

'I'll escort you to your car.'

He walked across the room and held open the door. Darcey's stomach muscles clenched as their bodies brushed when she passed him. She breathed in the sensual musk of his cologne and wondered why he used it when the black stubble shading his jaw indicated that he had not shaved today. With his dark, brooding good looks he reminded her of a pirate, and she sensed that he was just as dangerous.

In the hall she slipped on her jacket, thankful that it concealed her treacherous body. Her breasts felt heavy, and she would be mortified if he noticed that her nipples had hardened and were straining against the thin material of her blouse. She followed him out of the house. The night air cooled her hot face, but her fierce awareness of him did not lessen as she walked beside him along the pavement to where her car was parked. She must have been mad to have agreed to go to Sicily with him, she thought despairingly. *It's not too late to pull out*, a voice in her head whispered. She hadn't signed a contract. She unlocked the Mini and slid into the driver's seat. Her fingers fumbled to insert the key in the ignition.

'Rosa will be excited when I tell her that you will be staying at the castle with us.' Salvatore held the car door open and leaned down so that his face was almost level with hers.

Oh, hell! Her gaze was drawn involuntarily to his stern mouth before lifting to his eyes. Something flickered in his dark expression and for a breathless few seconds she thought he was going to lower his head and kiss her. Time slowed and her heartbeat raced. His warm breath whispered across her mouth and she moistened her lips with the tip of her tongue in an unconscious invitation.

'Goodnight, Darcey.' Abruptly he stepped back and closed the car door.

Darcey tried to quash her disappointment. Of *course* she had not wanted him to kiss her, she assured herself as she turned the key in the ignition. She would go to Sicily for Rosa's sake, but she intended that her relationship with Salvatore would remain firmly within the boundaries of employer and employee.

'Hello, darling! What are you doing here?'

Joshua Hart greeted Darcey with a vague smile when she arrived at her parents' house in London's Notting Hill the following day. Her father held open the front door to allow her to step into the hallway.

'I thought you were on holiday.'

'I told you the last time I saw you that I going away at the beginning of July.' Darcey forbore to ask her father why he was wearing pyjamas and a dressing gown at midday. 'I've come to have lunch with you and Mum.'

'Oh, well—your mother never said. No one tells me anything,' Joshua grumbled. He pushed open his study door. 'You won't mind if I don't join you? I'm up to my eyes in *Othello*. The new production opens at the National Theatre next week and I'll never be ready,' he stated dramatically. He paused in the doorway and turned his piercing blue eyes on Darcey. 'Have you been studying the script I sent you? Remember, rehearsals for my play begin at the end of September.'

'I haven't forgotten,' Darcey said drily. She carried on down the hall and found her mother in the kitchen.

'I'm sorry about your father,' Claudia murmured ruefully. 'I reminded him three times that you were coming for lunch, but you know how forgetful he is when he's involved with work. He has locked himself away in his study for days while he studies this next role.'

Darcey understood that Joshua's artistic temperament and his perfectionism could make him selfish, but she could not help feeling hurt that he was too busy to have

lunch with her. The sense of rejection she had sometimes felt as a child returned to haunt her and gave her
added insight into how Rosa must feel when Salvatore
ignored her. The little girl was desperate for more attention from her father.

'I expect you're looking forward to your trip to
France?' Claudia said.

'Actually, there's been a change of plan. I'm going to
Sicily to give speech therapy to a deaf child who has recently had cochlear implants fitted.' Darcey handed her
mother the Maidenhair Fern that she had brought with
her. 'Will you take care of my plant while I'm away? It
needs a lot of TLC.'

Her mother sighed. 'Oh, darling, you need a break.
You've been working so hard lately, and you've had so
much to cope with, what with Marcus and the divorce.
And I know you have been concerned about my illness.
My consultant has given me the all-clear, by the way. So
you can stop worrying about me. I really think you should
reconsider taking this job. Isn't there someone else who
can work with this child?'

'Rosa is a sweet little girl who has been deaf since she
was a baby and is unable to talk,' Darcey explained. 'I'm
optimistic that speech and language therapy will make a
huge difference to her life.'

'I know you will do your best for her,' Claudia said
softly, aware that once Darcey had made up her mind she
would not be detracted. 'But I hope you'll have a bit of
relaxation time. What are Rosa's parents like?'

'Her mother died when she was a baby.' Darcey hesitated. 'Her father is…' she searched for a word to describe
Salvatore '…formidable.'

Her mother gave her a searching look. 'He sounds intriguing. Is he good-looking?'

'What does that have to do with anything?' She met Claudia's amused gaze and shrugged helplessly. 'I guess he is, in a dangerous sort of way.'

'Now you're worrying me, darling. The man is formidable, dangerous, and you're attracted to him,' Claudia added perceptively.

Darcey knew there was no point in denying it. Sometimes she thought her mother possessed psychic powers. 'Salvatore Castellano is handsome, admittedly, but he's also arrogant, egotistical—oh, and he likes to have his own way.'

Claudia laughed. 'Well, that's a trait you both share. It sounds as though sparks might fly in Sicily.'

Darcey shook her head. 'There's no need for you to worry. I don't intend anything to happen between us.'

'What a pity. A sizzling affair with a sexy Sicilian would do you the world of good!'

'*Mum!*'

'It's about time you put your marriage behind you,' Claudia said unrepentantly. 'You've never explained what really happened between you and Marcus, or the reason why you broke up—although I have my suspicions that he hurt you badly. But he's history now. You need to move on and allow romance back into your life.'

Darcey looked away from her mother. She had never spoken about what Marcus had done—how he had made a fool of her and tricked her into marriage by pretending to love her when in fact he had seen her as means of furthering his acting career because of her famous theatrical family. It was so humiliating that she had vowed never to reveal the truth to anyone.

As for her having an affair with Salvatore—the idea was laughable. 'Romance is definitely *not* on the cards with Salvatore Castellano,' she insisted.

Last night she had been unable to sleep for thinking about him, and had decided that she must have imagined that he'd seemed about to kiss her. He was not attracted to her, and the sooner she got over her ridiculous fascination with him the better.

'I'll be going to Sicily on a strictly professional basis,' she told her mother. 'I've agreed to stay for three months, so you can tell Dad I'll be back in London for rehearsals at the end of September, as I promised.'

'Your father is so pleased that you've agreed to perform in his new play.' Claudia gave her daughter an understanding smile. 'I know he put you under a lot of pressure to take the role, but he thinks you are perfect for it. Joshua has always believed that you could have had a wonderful career as an actress.'

Darcey sighed, feeling the familiar pang of guilt that she had disappointed her father by being the only member of the Hart family not to have become a professional actor. She loved the career she had chosen, and had no regrets that she had not gone to drama school like her brother and sisters, but there was still a need inside her to appease her father and earn his approval.

Joshua had written his latest play expecting that his wife would take the lead role, but Claudia had decided to take a break from acting while she recuperated after treatment for skin cancer.

'You are the only person apart from your mother who I can envisage playing the role of Edith,' Joshua had told Darcey when she had argued that either Mina or her older sister Victoria would be better for the part. 'You proved when you used to perform with Speak Out that you are a talented actress. If you won't play Edith then I'll abandon the project until such time—God willing—that Claudia is well enough to return to the stage.'

It had been blatant emotional blackmail by her father, Darcey thought wryly. But she had agreed to perform in the play. Partly because she hoped it would give her an opportunity to form a closer relationship with Joshua, but also out of curiosity, to find out if she *did* possess the same ability to act as the other members of her family. Shyer than her brother and sisters, all her life she had compared herself to her confident and extrovert relatives. Now she had the chance to prove to herself and to her father that she was a true Hart.

It was early evening when Salvatore's private jet landed at Catania Airport and they transferred to the car that was waiting to collect them. Rosa's child seat took up more than one passenger space, and Darcey was squashed up close to Salvatore. She could feel his hard thigh muscles through her lightweight skirt.

She turned her head and stared out of the window at the spectacular Sicilian countryside. The sun was low in the sky and cast a mellow light over the checkerboard of green and gold fields dotted with patches of vibrant red flowers. In the distance Mount Etna towered over the land, its upper slopes dusted with snow even in the summer. Darcey knew that Etna was the biggest active volcano in Europe. A stream of white vapour spouted from its summit, but to her relief the fiery giant was not spewing scorching lava today.

Unfortunately admiring the beauty of her surroundings did not lessen her fierce awareness of the man beside her. Her resolve to ignore her attraction to Salvatore had been blown sky-high when he had turned up at her tiny terraced house at precisely three o'clock. She had opened the door expecting to find his driver had come to collect her, but instead it had been Salvatore on the doorstep, dressed in a superbly tailored pale grey suit that made him look more like a business tycoon than the leather jacket had the previous day, but no less sexy.

She had felt strangely reluctant to invite him into her home, but she'd had no choice but to ask for his help in lifting her huge suitcase. Packing twelve pairs of shoes had probably been excessive, she conceded.

He had seemed like a giant in her small house, but it was not just his height and athletic build that made him impossible to ignore. He possessed a powerful magnetism that was accentuated by his brooding good looks. When they had walked through the airport she had noticed the attention he had received from other women—although to be fair he had seemed unconcerned by the excitement he generated.

She must have been mad to come to Sicily with him when he unsettled her so much.

Darcey unconsciously lifted her hand to the pendant around her neck and traced its familiar shape, as she often did when she was troubled.

'Your necklace is interesting. The stones are the exact shade of green as your eyes.'

Her eyes flew to Salvatore's face. 'It's a four-leaf clover, which in Irish folklore is a symbol of good luck. My father gave it to me on my wedding day.'

His brows lifted. 'But it didn't work? The pendant did not bring you good luck in your marriage as you are now divorced.'

'It would have taken more than a lucky charm for my marriage to Marcus to have worked.'

Salvatore heard the faint tremor in her voice and was curious, despite his resolve to keep his relationship with her on a strictly professional footing. He did not know what had come over him last night when he had been tempted to kiss her. And now he could not dismiss the image in his mind of the peridot pendant resting between her naked breasts.

Desire tugged in his groin, and for once he struggled to bring his body under control. He had ended his affair with his last mistress months ago—no doubt he was suffering from sexual frustration, he thought self-derisively. He had spent the flight to Sicily working through a backlog of paperwork, but his attempts to ignore Darcey had failed and he had read one financial report three times before it made sense.

Last night he had been unable to sleep. His thoughts had centred on his old friend Pietro, but for some reason Darcey had also crept into his mind. Today his temper was not improved by the fact that she had clearly enjoyed a restful night and looked perkily pretty in a pastel pink skirt and a white blouse sprigged with pink daisies. Her copper-brown bob of hair swung around her face, and every time she turned her head he inhaled the lemony scent of her shampoo.

For a moment he questioned whether it had been a good idea to bring her to Sicily. It was too late to change his mind now, he thought grimly. He was impressed by her kindness to Rosa and felt sure she was the best person to teach her to speak. His daughter was all that mattered, Salvatore reminded himself. For a number of reasons he was determined to ignore his inconvenient attraction to Darcey.

It was hot in the car and he opened the window, hoping that the fresh air rushing in would help to ease his headache. He closed his eyes and snatches of memory flashed into his mind.

He was travelling fast in a car and could feel the wind on his face. It was a sports car, and the sunroof was open.

The night-time sky surrounded him. The trees at the side of the road flashed past in a blur. He could see the needle on the speedometer rise higher and higher but he could not brake. He could see the bend in the road ahead but he couldn't turn the steering wheel…

Santa Madre! Salvatore's eyes flew open. He could feel beads of sweat on his brow and his hand shook as he raked his hand through his hair. *What the hell had that been about?* For the first time in four years he had remembered something about the accident, but his mind had played tricks on him. He *knew* he had been driving the car on the night of the accident, so why had he just had a memory of sitting in the passenger seat? It did not make sense. Perhaps the past would forever be hidden from him, he thought bitterly. It was his punishment for causing his wife's death.

He turned his head and found Darcey looking at him oddly. 'Are you all right? You had your eyes closed and you groaned as if you were in pain.'

'I'm fine,' he said curtly. 'I suffer from migraines occasionally,' he growled, when Darcey continued to stare at him.

He did not want her concern, or the sympathy that flared in her green eyes. The breeze from the open window carried the delicate floral scent of her perfume to him and he felt a sudden longing to press his lips to her slender white throat.

Muttering a savage oath beneath his breath, he jerked his eyes from her, and to his relief the car came to a halt in front of the ornate metal gates at the entrance to the Castellano Estate.

CHAPTER FOUR

TWO SECURITY GUARDS were on duty and immediately activated the gates so that they swung open. The car drove along a gravel driveway which then split into three roads. One led to a large white house that Salvatore told Darcey was where his father lived. His brother, Sergio, lived with his wife and son in a villa on another part of the estate.

Above the pine trees Darcey saw tall stone turrets, and a few minutes later she caught her breath when the car rounded a bend and an imposing castle came into view.

The brickwork was ancient and crumbling in places. Over centuries the stones had faded and were now a mellow sandy colour that deepened to gold in the late sunshine. The arched windows were flanked by thick wooden shutters and the huge front door looked as though it had been hewn from solid oak and had once repelled warring invaders.

'Wow!' she murmured as she climbed out of the car.

Salvatore smiled at her reaction. It was the first time Darcey had seen him smile properly and her heart lurched when his stern features softened. She did not know what had happened in the car, when he had seemed so tense, but as he looked up at the castle he visibly relaxed.

'Welcome to Torre de'Aquila. A castle was first built here in the thirteenth century, and gained its name because of the eagles that nested in the highest tower. Parts of the original building still remain, and eagles still nest in the tower. Look…'

He pointed to the sky and Darcey looked up and spotted a bird of prey with a distinctive hooked beak and huge wingspan circling the tower.

'It's a Bonelli's Eagle—sometimes called a white eagle because of the white feathers on its underside.'

'I've never seen an eagle in the wild before.'

Darcey felt awed as she watched the bird glide gracefully across the sky. The majestic eagle seemed utterly suited to the ancient castle. She glanced at the imposing man beside her. With hard features that could have been chiselled from stone, and his long dark hair, Salvatore looked as though he belonged to this rugged fortress. The first time she had seen him she had thought of him as a warrior knight: proud, noble and dangerous.

He was a serious threat to her peace of mind, Darcey acknowledged ruefully. It was safer to concentrate on Rosa, and she smiled at the little girl as Salvatore lifted her out of the car.

Can we go swimming, Papa? Rosa signed.

Salvatore shook his head. *Not now. Perhaps I'll have time to take you tomorrow.*

'It's important that you use language at the same time that you are signing to Rosa,' Darcey told him. 'Now that she can hear with the implants I think she will soon start to understand speech.'

She noticed the disappointment on the little girl's face and recalled how Rosa had told her that swimming was her favourite activity. 'Couldn't you take her for a swim?' She pleaded Rosa's case. 'It would do her good after she's spent the past few hours sitting in a plane or a car.'

Salvatore shook his head. He always visited Pietro as

soon as he returned to the Castellano Estate, but today, instead of going to Pietro's cottage, he would be going to the mortuary.

'There is something important I have to do,' he told Darcey brusquely.

'To do with work, I suppose?' Her voice was sharp and accusatory.

Salvatore's jaw clenched. He felt bad enough about disappointing Rosa, and Darcey's words added to his guilt. But he knew he would not be good company right now when all he could think about was the kindly man who had been a surrogate father to him.

'Your job is to give Rosa speech therapy, not to lecture me on my parenting methods,' he reminded her coldly.

Darcey stared at his arrogant face and wondered if she'd imagined that he had actually smiled a few minutes earlier. He looked away from her, towards the castle, and growled something in Italian as the front door swung open and a woman appeared.

'I wasn't expecting Lydia to be here,' he muttered.

For a moment Darcey wondered if the platinum blonde, heavily made-up woman was his mistress—or perhaps an ex-mistress, as Salvatore did not sound overly pleased to see her. She darted him a questioning glance.

'Lydia is my mother-in-law. She comes fairly often to see Rosa. Curiously, her visits usually coincide with her needing money,' he added in a bone-dry tone.

Rosa slipped her small hand into Darcey's as they walked up the stone steps leading to the castle's entrance, where her grandmother was waiting. The older woman gave Darcey a curious glance before turning her attention to her granddaughter.

'Hello, sweetie,' Lydia did not sign, but spoke to Rosa in a loud voice. She frowned when the little girl made

no response and looked at Salvatore. 'I thought you said
Rosa was going to have an operation that would make
her speak?'

'She has had a procedure in which cochlear implants
were fitted, allowing her to hear sounds,' he explained.
'It will take time for her to learn to talk. Ms Rivers is a
speech therapist who is going to help her.'

He made formal introductions. Lydia seemed friendly
enough, but Darcey was conscious of the older woman's
pale blue eyes flicking between her and Salvatore as they
all walked into the castle.

Stepping through the front door, Darcey stopped
dead and looked around in amazement. 'What a beautiful place!'

The entrance hall was a huge, airy space, filled with
light that streamed through the arched windows onto the
flagstone floor. Darcey had imagined the castle to be a
gloomy place, but the panelling on the walls was a warm
cherrywood, and the rooms she could see leading off the
hall were painted white and were bright and welcoming.
Colourful tapestries hung on many of the walls, and the
antique furniture had been highly polished—and a faint
scent of beeswax hung in the air.

Her eyes were drawn to the picture on the wall directly facing the front door. It was a photograph enlarged
to life-size of a strikingly attractive brunette who looked
as though she had been poured into her scarlet silk dress.
The picture was impossible to miss or ignore.

Following Darcey's gaze, Lydia said, 'That's my
daughter—Adriana. She was a top model and worked
with all the famous designers. Shortly before she died
she had been offered a role in a film. It was a tragedy
that she was taken so young, before she had a chance to
fulfil her potential—wasn't it, Salvatore?'

He made no response, and his hard features were unfathomable, but for a second Darcey glimpsed a haunted expression in his eyes that startled her. She sensed an undercurrent of tension between him and Lydia, and the atmosphere in the hall suddenly made her skin prickle, as if Adriana's ghost had walked past.

In a desperate attempt to break the edgy silence, she said to Salvatore, 'You have a beautiful home. I expect your wife loved living in a castle?'

'Why do we have to live in this crumbling pile of bricks? I want to move to a city. I'll die of boredom here...'

Salvatore frowned as the voice in his head faded away. It had been a voice from his past and he knew with certainty that he had heard his wife. 'No...' he said slowly. 'Adriana hated it here.'

Lydia gave a loud laugh that sounded curiously strained to Darcey. 'Of course she didn't hate the castle. The two of you were so happy here, Salvatore.'

'So you keep reminding me,' he said obliquely. He glanced at Darcey. 'One of the staff will show you to your room and bring your luggage up. This is Armond.' He indicated the portly man dressed in a butler's uniform who had just joined them. 'He will attend to you. Perhaps you would be kind enough to stay with Rosa? I have yet to arrange to hire another nanny, and right now there are other matters I must deal with. Excuse me.'

He strode out of the castle, but as he walked down the front steps Darcey noticed that he was limping, as if his injured leg was painful. She sighed. He was such an enigmatic man. She sensed that the air of mystery surrounding him was linked to his dead wife.

She gave a start when Lydia's voice broke into her thoughts. 'You must forgive my son-in-law if he appears abrupt,' the older woman murmured. 'He was so in love with my daughter and has never got over her death.' She gave Darcey a calculating look. 'Occasionally he has affairs with women, but they mean nothing to him. I'm afraid no other woman will ever take Adriana's place in Salvatore's heart.'

Darcey was reading Rosa a bedtime story when Salvatore walked into the room. The little girl had forgotten about swimming in her excitement at showing Darcey her bedroom, which was next door to the nursery, and when she saw her father her face lit up. To Darcey's surprise he came and sat on the edge of the bed. His hair was tangled and he smelled of smoke. Rosa gave him a puzzled look.

Why have you got black on your face, Papa? she asked in sign language.

He rubbed a hand over his cheek and looked rueful when he saw smears of soot on his fingers. *There has been a fire at the winery. I went to see the damage,* he signed. He dropped a kiss on Rosa's brow. *Goodnight, angel.*

Salvatore stood up, but as he went to turn off the lamp Darcey stopped him. 'Leave the light on. Rosa doesn't like the dark.'

'How do you know that?' he demanded as he followed her out of the room.

'She told me.' Darcey bit back a comment that if he'd paid his daughter more attention he would have known about her fear of the dark.

'I understand from Armond that you did not have dinner with Rosa?' he said.

'I wasn't hungry.' Noticing lines of strain around his

face, she said quietly, 'I'm sorry about the fire. Is there much damage?'

Salvatore pictured Pietro's lifeless body and grief roughened his voice. 'The winery can be rebuilt, but the men who were burned in the fire will take much longer to recover.'

'You look tired,' she said softly. 'Have you eaten tonight?'

Her gentle concern was something Salvatore had never experienced before, and he could not cope with it tonight when his emotions were raw.

'You sound like a wife,' he mocked. 'I can look after myself.'

Darcey flushed. 'That's good, because any woman foolish enough to marry you would need the patience of a saint.' She swung away from him, feeling guilty that she had snapped at him, because after all his wife was dead.

'Darcey...' He caught hold of her arm and turned her back to face him. 'I'm sorry. That was crass of me.' He exhaled heavily. 'Seeing the burned winery was... upsetting.'

It was the first time in his life that Salvatore had ever revealed his feelings to another person and his shock was mirrored in Darcey's eyes. What was it about this woman that got to him and made him act out of character? he asked himself. He hated the idea that he was in any way vulnerable, but Pietro's death, and the startling flashbacks to his past, were making him feel as though a layer of his flesh had been peeled away.

He glanced ruefully at his smoke-blackened clothes. 'Give me five minutes to shower and then we'll have dinner on the terrace. Lydia won't be eating with us tonight, and we can spend some time getting to know each other.'

Darcey found the prospect frankly terrifying—especially when his harsh features softened and he gave her a sexy smile that turned her insides to marshmallow.

'Is that really necessary?' she said coolly. 'I'm merely an employee, and I'm sure you don't take a personal interest in the other members of your staff.'

'As a matter of fact all the staff at the castle have worked here for years and I know them very well. You are going to be living at Torre d'Aquila for the next three months, Darcey,' he reminded her. 'I would like you to feel comfortable in my home and with me.'

Comfortable was not the way she would describe the way she felt when she stepped out of the French doors fifteen minutes later, Darcey thought derisively. Salvatore walked across the terrace towards her and she felt her stomach swoop as she took in his appearance. Wearing tailored black trousers and a loose-fitting white shirt unbuttoned at the throat, he had an air of brooding sensuality that set her pulse racing.

She had resisted the temptation to change her skirt and blouse for a more seductive outfit, and had simply brushed her hair and added a slick of pink gloss to her lips. It was not as if she wanted him to find her attractive, she reminded herself. But her heart thudded when he halted in front of her and his dark eyes rested on her face. She caught her breath when he lifted his hand and tucked her hair behind her ear.

'You are very lovely, Darcey,' he murmured, half to himself. His gaze lingered on her mouth and the atmosphere on the terrace altered subtly, became heavy with unspoken sexual awareness.

'We can go inside if you are cold?' He broke the spell and stepped away from her.

Darcey wondered if he'd guessed that it was not the

air temperature that had made her shiver. 'I'm fine—just tired from travelling today,' she lied.

He held out a chair at the table. 'Then let's eat.'

Armond served a simple supper of seafood risotto accompanied by a crisp white wine from the Castellano estate. Darcey felt herself relax as she sipped her wine, although perversely her awareness of Salvatore intensified.

'Tell me about Darcey Rivers,' he invited, his eyes meeting hers across the table.

'What do you want to know?' She ran through a mental list of subjects that were off-limits. Her famous family she preferred not to talk about, and her marriage and her ex-husband's behaviour would never be open for discussion.

'Why did you choose speech therapy as a career?'

Work was a safe topic. 'I think I told you that my sister is deaf? Growing up with Mina gave me an understanding of how important communication is. Mina had learned to speak before she lost her hearing, but for Rosa speech is a new concept. It will take time and patience for her to learn language skills.' She hesitated. 'I can give Rosa speech therapy sessions every day, but they won't magically enable her to speak. Therapy has to be continual, and it has to become part of your life as much as Rosa's. I will need to work with you as much as with her, and teach you how you can help her. It is important that you make time for your daughter. I don't mean ten minutes at bedtime when you say goodnight to her. I'm talking about a serious commitment to spend several hours every day giving her your undivided attention. That means coming out of your office and switching off your mobile phone so that you can play games and read stories to her. Surely that's not too much to ask?' she said huskily when he made no response.

He looked away from her, but not before she had glimpsed a flicker of pain in his eyes.

'Rosa always preferred to do those sorts of things with her nanny, Luisa,' Salvatore said roughly. 'And although she had not formed the same close bond with Sharon she seemed happier in her company than mine.'

It was on the tip of Darcey's tongue to tell him that if he wasn't so remote with his daughter she would probably feel more confident with him.

'I'm sure Rosa would love to play with you.' She hesitated, aware of a need to be diplomatic. 'I think she might respond better if you could relax a bit more when you are with her. She's your daughter, after all. Perhaps it would help if you could think back to when you were a child and the games you used to play with your parents?'

'My mother walked out when I was five, and when I was seven my father sent me to boarding school in England. I don't remember spending time with either of my parents, and they certainly did not play games with me.'

Shaken by the harshness of his tone, Darcey did not know what to say. It was not surprising that Salvatore found it hard to connect with his daughter when it sounded as though his own childhood had been so loveless, she mused. He must have been traumatised from being abandoned by his mother when he had been so young. She thought of her close-knit family and felt a stirring of sympathy for the stern-faced man seated opposite her.

'Why did your father send you away to school?'

'He said he thought it would be better for me to grow up with companions of my own age.' Salvatore shrugged. 'But I believe the reality was that he wasn't interested in me. He was devastated when my mother left and focused entirely on work and furthering the success of the Castellano Group.'

'And now history is repeating itself,' Darcey said quietly. 'Rosa has no mother, and her father spends too much time working rather than giving her the attention she needs.'

Darcey's criticism was not unfounded, Salvatore acknowledged grimly. He did not know how to be a father to his daughter. The truth buried deep in his heart was that he was afraid to get too close to her. What if he actually couldn't be a good father? What if he failed Rosa as his parents had failed him? Since she was a baby he had found it easier to hand her over to the care of a professional nanny.

'I do not require your opinion on how I choose to bring up my daughter,' he said curtly. 'All I'm interested in is your expertise as a speech therapist.'

Who was he kidding? Salvatore thought derisively. He could not ignore his attraction to Darcey when every time he looked at her he felt a primitive urge to pull her into his arms and claim her lips with his. With her shiny bob of hair and her buttoned-to-the-neck blouse she looked as wholesome as Mary Poppins, but her lush mouth held a promise of sensuality that he knew he must resist.

Dio, he had no right to want to make love to her when he could not even remember the woman he had been married to. His mother-in-law constantly told him that he had loved Adriana, and because of his amnesia he had no alternative but to believe Lydia. But when he looked at photographs of his wife he felt nothing.

He looked up as the butler hurried across the terrace.

'*Signor*, one of the maids heard Miss Rosa crying. When she checked she found the child distraught.'

Salvatore immediately got up from the table. 'Thank

you, Armond. I'll go up to her.' He looked at Darcey. 'It might be better if you come too. Rosa sometimes has nightmares and she might prefer you to comfort her.'

The soul-wrenching sounds of a child's sobs were audible as Darcey hurried after Salvatore up the staircase, and when she followed him into the nursery the sight of Rosa's tear-stained face made her heart ache. With the cochlear implant device switched off Rosa could not hear, and she was obviously too upset to communicate in sign language. The terrified expression on her face indicated that she had not fully woken from a nightmare.

Salvatore hurried over to the bed, but instead of lifting the little girl into his arms he hesitantly patted her hair and glanced at Darcey. 'She feels hot. Do you think she's ill?'

Rosa's cries had quietened to soft whimpers that tore on his heart. He wanted to hold her in his arms and comfort her, but the fearful expression in her eyes stopped him. What had she dreamed of that had upset her so badly? Rosa's nightmares were becoming more frequent, and Salvatore wondered if the trauma of losing her mother when she had been a baby was somehow the cause. Gripped by guilt, he stepped back from the bed so that Darcey could comfort Rosa.

Darcey felt the little girl's brow. 'She's not feverish. It's likely that she got too warm under the covers—that could have triggered a nightmare.'

She sat on the bed and signed to Rosa—*It's all right. You're safe. You just had a bad dream. Would you like me to stay with you for a while?*

Rosa nodded and flung her arms around Darcey's neck, clinging to her as if she never wanted to let go. Darcey stroked her hair and gradually the child grew calmer.

Salvatore watched them, envious of Darcey's easy rapport with Rosa, and once again he was struck by her inherent kindness. His phone rang. He swore beneath his breath and made to cut the call—until he saw that Sergio was on the line.

'It's my brother,' he told Darcey. 'He said he would update me on the condition of the men injured in the fire. Would you mind staying with Rosa for a while?'

She nodded. 'I'll sit with her until she falls back to sleep. At least my room is only next door if she stirs in the night.'

Promise you'll stay with me in case the monsters come back, Rosa signed.

Darcey gave her a reassuring smile. *I promise,* she signed back.

She was touched by the little girl's obvious loneliness and her eagerness for them to be friends. She watched Rosa's eyelashes drift down but decided to stay for another half-hour to make sure the child was deeply asleep. It was warm in the bedroom, and she undid the top few buttons of her blouse before lying back on the bedspread. Rosa immediately snuggled closer and Darcey's mothering instincts kicked in. She put her arm around the sleeping child.

When Salvatore walked back into the nursery half an hour later he was greeted by the soft sigh of breathing from the woman and child fast asleep on the bed. Rosa was tucked up between the sheets and Darcey was curled on the bedspread beside her.

As he crossed the room Darcey rolled onto her back and he saw that her blouse was partly open, revealing a tantalising glimpse of the upper swell of her breasts above a sexy semi-sheer bra. His body responded instantly and his erection strained beneath his trousers. Once again he asked himself why he had brought her to Sicily and he seriously considered sending her back to England. She was a complication he could do without, he thought grimly.

He moved closer to the bed and saw that even in her sleep Rosa was clutching hold of Darcey's hand. He could not put his daughter through the trauma of separating her from someone else she had bonded with. It had been hard enough for her when first Luisa had left, and then Sharon. Rosa needed a mother figure to take the place of the mother he had deprived her of. He was not expecting Darcey to take on that role, of course, but Rosa needed help from an expert speech therapist.

It was warm in the bedroom, and Rosa's face was flushed from where she was lying close to Darcey. Concerned that if the little girl became too hot she might have another nightmare, Salvatore touched Darcey's shoulder, intending to wake her. He hesitated, remembering that she had said she was tired from travelling. Her bedroom adjoined to the nursery, and it seemed more sensible to carry her through to her room.

Neither of the sleepers stirred when he lifted Darcey into his arms. Her neat bob of burnished-copper hair framed her face and her long eyelashes made golden crescents on her creamy cheeks. She weighed next to nothing. It should be the easiest thing to carry her into the other room, deposit her on the bed and leave. But the delicate fragrance of her perfume assailed his senses.

Jaw tense, he strode through the connecting door. As he leaned down and placed her on the bed she murmured a soft protest and looped her arm around his neck, pulling his head down so that his face was centimetres from hers.

Madonna, this was not what he had intended to happen. His conscience insisted that he must wake her up, but his body was remembering how he had wanted to kiss her on the terrace. He had been transfixed by her soft pink mouth and desire had swept like wildfire through his veins.

He must fight his fierce attraction to Darcey, Salvatore told himself. His instincts warned him that she was not like the sophisticated women he'd had affairs with in the past. She was curiously innocent, and he wondered if she'd had any lovers since her marriage had ended.

His eyes were drawn to the creamy mounds of her breasts and the darker skin of her nipples, which he could see through her semi-transparent bra. This was madness! Every muscle in his body clenched as he resisted slanting his mouth over her moist lips that had parted slightly, as if she wanted him to kiss her. Could she really be unaware of what she was doing?

Carefully he tried to ease away from her, but she curled her arm tighter around his neck and gave a little mew of protest. 'Please…' she whispered, and Salvatore's self-control shattered.

CHAPTER FIVE

DARCEY'S DREAM WAS becoming increasingly erotic. It had begun with the shadowy figure of a man—a strong, powerful man—who held her in his muscular arms. She felt safe with the man, even though she did not know him. His face was hidden from her but he seemed familiar, and his musky, masculine scent was intoxicating, arousing an ache inside her that she had not felt for a long time.

His broad chest felt warm and solid beneath her fingertips—surprisingly solid, considering that he was only a dream. She was aware of his hands on her body and she felt his breath whisper across her lips. Why didn't he kiss her? She wanted him to—just as she wanted him to move his hands over her, up to her breasts and down to the junction between her thighs. She moved restlessly and lifted her hips in a silent plea for him to touch her there...

'Please...' she whispered. She wished she could see his face, but it did not matter, because now his mouth was on hers, as light as gossamer, teasing her lips apart.

No man had ever kissed her so beautifully.

The thought pushed through the fog clouding Darcey's brain and she became aware that she was lying on a bed. She gave a puzzled frown. She had only ever been to bed with one man, so the dream man must be...

'Marcus?'

'Who the hell is Marcus?' a harsh voice demanded.

Darcey's eyes flew open and shock ripped through her as she stared at Salvatore's darkly handsome face. *He* had been the man in her dream?

'What are you doing?' Heat flooded her cheeks when she glanced down and saw that her blouse was gaping open. She remembered that she had felt hot and unfastened a few of the buttons when she had lain on the bed with Rosa. Now she was in her own room, lying on her bed, and Salvatore was leaning over her, his chiselled face all angles and planes in the moonlight.

He must have carried her in here, but why? Her eyes widened as she remembered the feel of firm lips on hers. She hadn't been dreaming. Salvatore had kissed her, and if her memory served her right she had kissed him back.

'How dare you take advantage of me.'

He frowned. 'I did not take advantage of you.'

Despite his denial, Salvatore's conscience prickled uncomfortably. He knew he should have woken her, or left her sleeping and walked out of her room, but when she had said *please* in that sexy, whispery voice he had decided that she must be awake.

'You were aware of what you were doing—and that it was me you were with,' he growled.

'I was asleep and dreaming.'

'If so, then you were dreaming of me. You begged me to kiss you.'

Thank God she hadn't voiced the other things she had wanted him to do to her, Darcey thought, feeling sick with embarrassment as she remembered how she had longed for him to slide his hand between her legs, where he would have discovered the moist heat of her arousal. She had been asleep, she tried to assure herself. But innate honesty forced her to acknowledge that she had recognised the man in her dream.

She had been thinking about Salvatore while she had waited for Rosa to fall asleep and must have dozed off with his image still in her subconscious. It was also true that she had asked him to kiss her. She shuddered with mortification at the memory. But he must have realised that she had not been fully aware of her actions, she thought angrily.

'There's no getting away from the fact that you behaved dishonourably.'

Salvatore's hot Sicilian pride flared. Attacking his honour was going too far.

'You can try to kid yourself all you like, but this isn't going to go away for either of us.' He leaned over her, placing his hands flat on the bed on either side of her head so that he could stare into her wide green eyes. 'Your eyes give away your secrets, *cara*. They tell me you are interested in me.'

'I certainly am not,' she denied, too quickly.

The corners of his mouth curled in a sardonic half-smile. 'Liar. You felt it just as I did—the second I walked into your office.'

Darcey was trapped by his mesmerising gaze. 'Felt what?' she whispered.

'Sexual attraction, chemistry—call it what you like. The point is that within the first twenty seconds of us meeting we were both imagining making love on your desk.'

She gasped. 'I did no such thing.' She was outraged by his boldness, and mortified that he had seen what she had so desperately tried to hide. The truth was she had never felt such fierce physical awareness of a man. Not even Marcus, with his model-perfect looks, had evoked the fierce surge of lust that Salvatore Castellano incited in her.

'Tell me you don't want me to kiss you and I'll walk out of the door before you can blink,' he taunted.

Obviously she was going to tell the arrogant so and so to get lost, Darcey thought furiously. It was just that the words seemed to be stuck in her throat. Her gaze was trapped by the predatory glint in Salvatore's eyes. She caught her lower lip between her teeth and his eyes narrowed.

The sexual tension simmering between them was unbearable. Something had to give. Her heart lurched when he lowered his head towards her.

'You want this as much as I do,' Salvatore growled.

She had got under his skin since the moment he had walked into her office and she had blown his preconceptions of the mature speech therapist he had expected to meet sky-high. Ordinarily he would have dismissed his reaction to her as an inconvenience. But the news of Pietro's death had ripped his insides out. He had been genuinely fond of his old friend. The elderly vintner had been more of a father to him than Tito, and he knew that Pietro had loved him like a son.

It hurt him to think of Pietro. He wanted to block out thoughts of death with a reaffirmation of life and lose himself in the sensual promise of Darcey's soft mouth and slender body. And she would not deny him. Her pupils were dilated and her breasts rose and fell jerkily, drawing his attention to the hard points of her nipples that he could see clearly beneath her sheer bra.

Darcey lifted her hand to push Salvatore away. At least that was what she intended to do. But when she touched his shoulder and felt his powerful bunched muscles her common sense disappeared and feminine instinct took over, so that she spread her fingers wide and felt the warmth of his body through his shirt. She could not tell him she did not want him to kiss her because it would be a lie. And clearly he had taken her silence as acquiescence because his head had descended and he made a harsh sound in his throat as he covered her mouth with his.

He was not gentle like before, when she had been half-asleep. This time his mouth moved over hers with total certainty, demanding her response and forcing her lips apart so that he could push his tongue between them. His fierce passion was shockingly primitive. Darcey felt overwhelmed by his potent masculinity. He evoked a level of need in her that she had not known she was capable of feeling—and, terrifyingly, she could not control it or subdue it.

She caught her breath as Salvatore slipped his hand inside her blouse and cupped her breast. The heat of his skin scorched through the sheer lace bra which offered no protection when he flicked his thumb-pad across the taut peak of her nipple. She could not restrain a soft cry as desire arrowed through her. Molten heat pooled between her legs and she squeezed her trembling thighs together in an attempt to ease the tense throb of her arousal.

Nothing had prepared her for the intensity of sexual hunger that swept through her. She had only had one lover. Marcus had teased her about the fact that she had been a virgin until she met him, but she had wanted to wait for her soulmate. She had thought she had found him. Making love with her husband had been enjoyable, although not earth-shattering, she admitted. Certainly with Marcus she had never felt this wild, wanton urgency to have sex that Salvatore was making her feel.

Everything faded and she was conscious only of Salvatore's mouth on hers as he deepened the kiss and it

became incredibly erotic. Darcey responded to him helplessly, utterly captivated by this stern-faced man, this
dark stranger who, inexplicably, she felt she had been
waiting for all her life. She ran her hands over his chest
and felt the thunderous beat of his heart before she moved
lower and traced the hard ridges of his abdominal muscles. Driven by instinct, she pulled his shirt from the
waistband of his trousers and slid her fingers beneath the
material to skim over his naked torso, loving the sensation of his satin skin overlaid with rough hair.

Salvatore made a guttural sound when he felt Darcey's
fingers drift over his abdomen. Her touch was as soft as
a butterfly's wings on his sensitised flesh, and just imagining her stroking his manhood with her delicate fingers
was making him hard. He was desperate to guide his
throbbing shaft between her soft thighs and lose himself in her sensual heat. Why not enjoy a few moments
of carnal pleasure before he had to face the pain of his
old friend's death?

He brought his mouth down on hers once more, crushing her lips that parted obligingly so that he could explore her inner sweetness with his tongue. He could not
remember ever feeling this out of control. His hunger for
her consumed him, made him forget everything as he focused on the feel of her silky skin when he eased her bra
cups aside and caressed her naked breasts. The sight of
her dusky pink nipples jutting provocatively forward was
an irresistible temptation, but as he lowered his mouth to
one taut peak a muffled sound pierced Salvatore's consciousness. It was little more than a soft murmur from
the adjoining room, but it catapulted him back to reality.

Rosa!

He snatched his hands from Darcey's body. *Dio!* What
the hell was he doing? What if his daughter had walked

in? He sat up and raked an unsteady hand through his hair, breathing hard as he fought to bring his body under control.

It was fundamentally wrong for him to make love to Darcey when he could not remember his wife, whom presumably he had loved, he thought with savage self-contempt. He could never move forward with his life until he regained his memory and discovered what had happed in the accident that had resulted in his wife's death.

He glanced at Darcey and his jaw clenched when he saw that her lips were reddened and slightly swollen from his hungry passion. His gut ached with unfulfilled desire and he sprang up from the bed before he betrayed himself and pulled her beneath him.

'This should not have happened.'

He caught the stunned expression in her eyes and felt a flash of guilt when her bottom lip quivered and she bit down hard on the soft flesh. Her hand shook as she pulled her bra into place, and Salvatore tore his eyes from the sight of her pebble-hard nipples visible through the sheer fabric.

'I should not have kissed you,' he said harshly. 'I'm sorry.'

Darcey watched Salvatore stride over to the door, her disbelief that he had stopped kissing her rapidly turning to humiliation. She did not know why he had suddenly torn his mouth from hers, but the look of self-disgust she had seen in his eyes had doused her desire as swiftly as if she had plunged into an ice bath. He had kissed her senseless and aroused her until she was trembling with need, but now he was walking away from her and he was *sorry*! Thoughts swirled around her mind. Why had he stopped? Had he suddenly discovered that he did he not find her attractive or exciting?

She remembered how Marcus had complained that he wished she was more adventurous. She had naively believed he was satisfied with their love life, but according to her ex-husband she had been boring in bed. No doubt his mistress with the over-inflated chest had been a sexual gymnast, Darcey thought bitterly. Maybe that was what all men wanted, and maybe Salvatore had been disappointed with her.

He paused in the doorway and swung round. She saw his gaze flick to her gaping blouse. Blushing hotly, she yanked the edges together to hide her aroused body from his narrowed gaze.

'I hope you will agree that we cannot allow what just happened to affect our arrangement for you to stay here and give my daughter speech therapy. For her sake the best thing we can do is forget the incident,' he said brusquely, as if the 'incident' was something he could easily dismiss from his mind. 'I give you my assurance that it will not happen again.'

Salvatore strode through the connecting door to Rosa's bedroom, leaving Darcey gritting her teeth. Damned right it wouldn't happen again, she thought grimly. She would not risk making a fool of herself for a second time, or give him the chance to reject her as he had just done. He might be able to dismiss what had happened, but there was no chance she would forget, and for that reason her only option was to leave the castle and return to London.

Through the half-open door she watched him pause by the bed and bend down to pick up a teddy bear from the floor. He placed the bear on the pillow beside Rosa and then, to Darcey's surprise, leaned over and gently kissed the little girl's brow before he tucked the covers around her and walked out of the bedroom.

As soon as he had gone Darcey jumped up from the

bed, with the intention of packing the suitcase she had only unpacked a few hours earlier. But the memory of the tender expression she had witnessed on Salvatore's face when he had kissed his sleeping daughter lingered in her mind. Darcey felt certain that he loved Rosa, but for some reason he could not connect with his child or show her how much she meant to him. Perhaps it was a result of his own childhood. It sounded as though he had not had a close relationship with either of his parents.

She walked into the other room and looked at Rosa's innocent little face. If the little girl could speak, would that somehow help her to develop a closer relationship with her father? Darcey bit her lip, torn between never wanting to see Salvatore again and her conscience, which would not allow her to walk away from his motherless daughter. If she could encourage Salvatore to become involved in Rosa's speech therapy perhaps he would bond with his child and show her the love that she so clearly wanted.

Darcey sighed. She had always had a soft heart. As a child she had frequently rescued stray dogs and injured wildlife—memorably a hedgehog which, to her mother's horror, had been covered in fleas. Her brother had used to tease her that she could not save the world. But in this instance she had the expertise to help a deaf little girl.

She bit her lip as she recalled the grim expression on Salvatore's face when he had abruptly snatched his mouth from hers. Her common sense told her to leave before she became any deeper involved, but her heart was telling her something else.

A heat haze shimmered over the white tiles surrounding the pool and Darcey insisted on applying sunscreen to Rosa when she came out of the water. The memory of her mother's melanoma emphasised the importance of taking care in the sun.

Rosa had taken off her external listening device while she had been swimming, but once she had attached it again Darcey spoke and signed simultaneously to her. 'You're a very good swimmer. You're like a little fish.'

Rosa giggled. It was lovely to hear her laughing, Darcey thought, feeling a surge of affection for the little girl. She only wished that Salvatore was here to spend time with his daughter. The butler, Armond, had informed her at breakfast that Salvatore had gone out and would be away from the castle all day. Darcey had felt relieved that she did not have face him after what had happened the previous night, but Rosa had clearly been disappointed by her father's absence, and to cheer her up Darcey had offered to take her swimming.

Armond spoke good English and had explained that the pool was a new addition to the castle grounds that Salvatore had commissioned a year ago. Darcey had been startled to discover that the pool was heart-shaped. Recalling Lydia's statement that Salvatore had not come to terms with his wife's death, she wondered if he had chosen the shape of the pool as a declaration of his love for Adriana.

'Have you finished swimming?' she asked Rosa.

The little girl shook her head and pointed towards the far end of the pool area, where a young boy was hurtling towards them, followed by a tall man whose features bore a striking resemblance to Salvatore's and a heavily pregnant woman with long hair the colour of ripe corn.

'Nico, be careful!' the woman called as the little boy ran to the edge of the pool. She gave Darcey a rueful look. 'My son is such a daredevil. I just hope his new brother or sister won't be quite such a handful. I'm Kristen, by the way, and this is my husband, Sergio.'

She smiled at the handsome man at her side, her face radiantly beautiful. Darcey caught her breath as she observed the look of love that passed between the two of them. Sergio Castellano patently adored his wife, and Darcey felt a pang of wistful longing to be loved so utterly and unconditionally.

Sergio held out his hand. 'You must be Darcey. My brother told me you have come to Sicily to give Rosa speech therapy.' He gave an easy smile. 'If you can persuade her out of the pool! My niece is a real water baby.'

Darcey watched Rosa dive into the water. 'She's an amazingly good swimmer for such a young child.'

'Salvatore taught her. Swimming is good physiotherapy for his leg, and he took Rosa into the water with him from when she was a baby. He had this pool built for her—' He broke off. '*Nico*, don't go to the deep end until I'm with you.' Sergio laughed and pulled off his tee shirt. 'I'd better go in the pool and keep an eye on these two.'

Darcey stared at the heart-shaped pool. 'So Salvatore *does* love Rosa,' she murmured beneath her breath.

'Yes, he does. But, like you, I wasn't sure how he felt about his daughter when I first met him,' Kristen said quietly. 'The Castellano men find it hard to show their emotions.' A fleeting sadness crossed her lovely face. 'For a long time I didn't know that Sergio loved me, but thankfully we were able to work through the problems in our relationship. Both the brothers had difficult childhoods and were badly affected when their mother and father split up.'

'I suppose being sent away to boarding school when they were young didn't help,' Darcey commented.

'Sergio didn't go to school with Salvatore.' Kristen

hesitated. 'The brothers were separated when they were five years old.' She did not give any more details and lowered herself into a chair with a heartfelt sigh. 'Two weeks until the baby is due! I feel like an elephant, but Sergio insists that pregnancy suits me.'

'You look lovely,' Darcey assured her truthfully.

'Thank you.' Kristen gave her a friendly smile. 'I know it will be worth it in the end. Sergio is so excited about the baby, and it will be nice for Nico.' She sighed. 'It's a shame that Salvatore hasn't met anyone else. I think Rosa would love to have a mother, and perhaps a little brother or sister. But since Adriana's death Salvatore shuts himself away in his castle. He rarely leaves the estate, and all he focuses on is the vineyards and making wine. He has gone to the village chapel today to arrange the funeral of the head vintner. It's such a tragedy that Pietro died while he was attempting to save some of the wine. The old man was a good friend of Salvatore's.'

'I knew that some of the workers were injured in the fire, but I didn't realise someone had actually died.' Darcey felt guilty as she recalled how she had accused Salvatore of putting work before Rosa. How terrible that he had lost a friend in the fire.

'Salvatore is coming now.' Kristen shielded her eyes from the sun with her hand as she looked across the fields at a horse and rider galloping towards them. She sighed. 'I bet his leg will be painful after he's been riding. I'm a physiotherapist,' she explained. 'I've advised Salvatore that horse-riding overstretches the damaged muscles in his thigh, but he doesn't care. He's determined not to allow his injury to change the way he lives his life.' She gave Darcey a rueful smile. 'Be warned: the Castellano men can be very stubborn.'

Darcey watched the horse and rider thundering across

the field towards them. The horse's powerful flanks glistened with sweat and its mahogany-coloured mane streamed behind like a flag. The rider was no less impressive. Dressed entirely in black, with a bandana tied around his head to keep back the dark hair that fell around his shoulders, Salvatore looked like a pirate—ruthless, dangerous, and so devastatingly sexy that Darcey's heart thudded.

He dismounted and walked through the gate to the pool area, moving with an innate grace despite the stiffness in his right leg. Darcey felt herself blush and was aware that Kristen was looking curiously at her. Terrified that she might betray the effect Salvatore had on her, she jumped up and mumbled, 'I'll go and help Sergio with the children.'

As she walked down the steps into the pool her eyes were drawn to Salvatore, who greeted his sister-in-law with one of his rare smiles. Fortunately the water cooled Darcey's heated skin, and she concentrated on playing with Rosa and Nico, but she was conscious of Salvatore's penetrating gaze every time she darted him a glance.

Eventually Sergio called a halt to the swimming session and he and Kristen shepherded the children into the changing cubicles. Realising that she would have to wait for a cubicle, Darcey had no choice but to walk back to the sun lounger where she had left her towel—which happened to be where Salvatore had sat down.

'Rosa looked as though she was having fun.'

His gravelly voice did strange things to Darcey's insides. She blushed as she remembered in vivid detail the passion that had flared between them, and against her will her eyes were drawn to him. He looked incredibly sexy, with his swarthy complexion and a day's growth of dark stubble shading his jaw. His shirt was half-open,

and the sight of his bare bronzed chest covered with wiry
black hair evoked a flood of warmth between her thighs.
She felt acutely self-conscious in her bikini, especially
when she felt her nipples harden in response to Salvatore's devastating virility.

'I hope you don't mind that I brought Rosa swimming. I guessed you would be busy today.' She recalled
Kristen saying that one of the winery workers had died
in the fire. 'I'm sorry that your head vintner lost his life.'

'The funeral will take place tomorrow.' Salvatore's
jaw clenched.

Darcey's gentle sympathy undermined his iron control over his emotions and he felt an inexplicable need
to hold her in his arms and allow her sweet nature to
ease his pain.

'Pietro was an excellent vintner who taught me everything I know about winemaking, and he was an even
better friend,' he said gruffly. 'Thank you for looking
after Rosa. I watched you playing with her in the pool
and she clearly enjoys being with you.'

Darcey bit her lip. 'I realise that she could grow attached to me, and I to her. I have been thinking that I
should go home and you should appoint another speech
therapist.'

His dark brows lowered. 'Why do you want to leave?'

She flushed. 'Well, in light of what happened last
night…I'm afraid it will be awkward for me to stay.'

Her wariness was understandable after his behaviour last night, Salvatore thought grimly. He should not
have come on to her the way he had. But the passion
that had exploded between them had been mutual, he reminded himself. Darcey had wanted him as much as he
had wanted her. It was imperative for Rosa's sake that he
persuaded Darcey to remain at the castle, but his daugh-

ter's need for speech therapy was not the only reason he hoped she would stay, he acknowledged.

'I do not see why it should be awkward. You are here in your professional capacity. The fact that there's a spark between us is immaterial. It happens between men and women all the time. I am sure we are both mature enough to be able to ignore an inconvenient attraction.' His eyes narrowed on her face. 'But perhaps there is another reason why you want to leave. Since your divorce there must have been other men in your life. Is there a lover back in England whom you are missing?'

'No,' Darcey said fiercely. 'I wouldn't have kissed you if I had a…a boyfriend.' She coloured hotly, thinking how naive she must sound. But she believed strongly in fidelity. It was a pity that Marcus had not shared her values, she thought wryly.

She dropped her gaze from Salvatore. The air around the pool was hot and still, broken only by the song of the cicadas in the bougainvillaea bushes.

'Why did your marriage end?' he asked abruptly.

She shrugged. 'We discovered that we weren't compatible. But the nail in the coffin of our relationship was when I discovered Marcus in bed with another woman.'

The moment the words were out Darcey regretted revealing something so personal and still so painful. She was over Marcus, but he had left her with a host of insecurities that Salvatore had opened up when he had rejected her the previous night. She looked away from him, hoping he would drop the conversation.

Salvatore watched Darcey gnaw her bottom lip with her teeth and felt an irrational rush of anger towards Marcus Rivers. From the moment he had introduced Darcey to his daughter he had been impressed by her kindness. Her soft heart did not deserve to be broken.

'The guy was obviously a jerk,' he said quietly.

Darcey bent her head so that her hair swung forward to partially hide her face. Her breath hitched in her throat as Salvatore lifted his hand and tucked a few strands behind her ear. His soft voice was unexpected and tugged on emotions she'd thought she had buried.

'I suppose it wasn't Marcus's fault that I'm not...' She flushed. 'That I didn't...excite him.'

'What do you mean?'

Oh, Lord, why had she started along this route? Darcey sighed. 'I'm hardly a sex siren. Marcus likes voluptuous women, and I'm not very well endowed in that department—as you no doubt noticed last night.'

For a few seconds Salvatore did not follow her, but as he stared into her eyes and recognised self-doubt, understanding dawned.

'What I noticed last night, and from the moment I first met you, is that you are very beautiful. How can you not know how lovely you are?' he asked intently when she looked disbelieving. 'You have a gorgeous figure.' An image flashed into his mind of her small, firm breasts with their pink, tightly puckered nipples. 'I've never been so turned on as I was last night,' he admitted roughly.

Darcey shot him a startled look. 'Then why did you stop...?'

'I heard Rosa make a sound, and I was concerned that she might wake up.'

It was the partial truth. Hearing his daughter had released Salvatore from Darcey's sensual spell and forced him back to cold reality. He was not free to make love to her while his amnesia continued to conceal his past. *Dio*, it was his fault that Adriana had died and Rosa was growing up without a mother. His guilt was a poison inside him and he did not want to taint Darcey with the blackness in his heart.

His eyes roamed her slender figure in a yellow bikini that was all the more sexy because it wasn't overtly revealing and desire knotted his stomach. She was so lovely, but she could not be his, and it was only fair that he should put some distance between them.

He stood up and began to walk away from her. 'We have agreed to ignore the attraction between us, and it will be best for Rosa if we stick to that arrangement,' he said curtly. 'I have some work to do in the vineyards and I might not get back to the castle until late. Armond will serve you dinner at eight o'clock.'

CHAPTER SIX

AT FIVE TO EIGHT Darcey walked into the dining room and felt her heart perform a somersault when she saw Salvatore standing by the window, his powerful frame silhouetted against the golden sunset. She had half expected him not to be back for dinner, and the sight of him shook her composure.

The bandana had gone, and he had changed out of jeans and riding boots into tailored black trousers and a collarless white shirt made of such fine silk that she could see the shadow of his dark chest hair through it. She was aware of her body's instant reaction to him—the way her nipples tingled and sprang to attention—and was thankful that the chiffon shawl which matched her dress hid the evidence of his effect on her.

'Good evening, Darcey.' Salvatore's hard-boned face showed no expression, but his eyes narrowed as he swept his gaze over her, taking in her slender figure in a jade-coloured jersey-silk dress. He wondered why she was hugging her shawl around her like a security blanket. 'Lydia will be joining us for dinner—but she is usually late,' he said wryly. 'Can I get you a drink while we wait?'

Dismissing the temptation to have something strong and alcoholic, hopefully to dull her senses and her fierce awareness of him, Darcey instead asked for fruit juice. She had no option but to walk across the room to him, but when he handed her a glass of pomegranate juice she moved over to the window to watch the dying rays of the sun streak the sky blood-red. Above the castle's highest tower the dark shadow of an eagle circled. Even from a distance Darcey could see that it was holding something in its hooked beak. Probably a mouse or a rabbit that it had just killed, she thought, and a shiver ran down her spine. There was a ruthless cruelty to the rugged land-scape that she sensed suited the mood of the master of Torre d'Aquila.

Salvatore reminded himself that he deserved Darcey's coolness. But he missed her bright smile. After he had left her by the pool he had visited the mortuary for a final time to pay his respects to Pietro and had felt the unfa-miliar sting of tears in his eyes. He had not cried since he was a small boy, when his father had told him his mother had left and would not be coming back.

His headache had begun soon after he had left the mortuary and now throbbed dully behind his temples. His consultant had explained that in some amnesia cases the sufferer's memory returned suddenly. His startling insight that Adriana had disliked living at the castle had given him hope that the past was about to reveal itself to him. But to his frustration a black curtain still obscured his memory.

His savage mood was not improved by the company of his mother-in-law. Lydia arrived twenty minutes late for dinner and spent the entire meal talking about Adriana.

'The birth of their child cemented my daughter's rela-tionship with Salvatore,' Lydia told Darcey. 'It was just a pity that Rosa turned out to be flawed.'

Darcey frowned. 'How do you mean, flawed?'

'Well, the fact that she's deaf and dumb.' Lydia sniffed. 'Her defective hearing doesn't come from *our* side of the family. Adriana had perfect hearing.'

'Rosa's deafness has nothing to do with a genetic link.'

Darcey had not taken to Lydia when she had first met her, and now she felt a surge of dislike for the woman. She had hoped that Rosa's grandmother would support the little girl through speech therapy, but when she had spoken to Lydia before dinner and mentioned that she might like to take part in therapy sessions Lydia had refused, saying that she would be bored.

'Rosa is a very intelligent child, and I have no doubt that she will learn to speak very quickly,' she told Lydia firmly. 'But it is crucial that she has encouragement from her family.'

She looked across the table at Salvatore. 'I've already explained that for speech therapy to be successful it must be continual, and I will incorporate it into Rosa's daily life. But I think she will benefit from an hour to an hour and a half of intensive therapy every day, which I would like you to attend. Afternoons would be best, and I thought that after the session you could take her swimming. It's something she loves and will look forward to.'

She held his gaze, challenging him to refuse her request.

'I realise that you will have to take time away from work, but Rosa needs your support.'

'And she will have it,' Salvatore assured her. He had been impressed by Darcey's fierce defence of Rosa and the way she had put Lydia in her place. 'Your idea of taking Rosa to the pool afterwards is a good one. I hope you will swim with us? I realise that you should be on your holiday, and I want you to have some relaxation time.'

The chances of her feeling relaxed around Salvatore

were zero, Darcey thought wryly. Just the idea of him wearing nothing but a pair of swim shorts made her feel hot and bothered. He had stated that it would be best if they ignored the chemistry they both felt, but his eyes sought hers and she felt as though she was drowning in his liquid dark gaze. Her awareness of her surroundings faded and she was aware only of Salvatore—master of his castle, a sorcerer who had trapped her in his sensual spell.

Shaken by the simmering sexual tension between them, she unconsciously lifted her hand to the pendant around her neck and traced the four-leaf clover, taking comfort from its familiar shape and the reminder of her father who had given it to her. Home and her family seemed a long way away, and she wished fervently that she was in France at the villa at Le Lavandou, where she had spent so many happy family holidays.

'Oh!' She stared at the pendant in her hand and re-alised that the chain had broken.

'That's the trouble with cheap jewellery.' Lydia's voice broke the silence and released Darcey from Salvatore's bewitchment. 'It's a pretty trinket, I'll grant you, but peridots aren't particularly valuable.'

Darcey placed the necklace on the tablecloth. 'It has sentimental value.'

Lydia shrugged. 'The engagement ring that Salvatore gave to Adriana is a ten-carat diamond solitaire. After her death I kept it as a memento of my darling.' She looked at Salvatore. 'Adriana told me you proposed to her at a five-star hotel in Rome. It must have been *so* romantic.'

Salvatore's jaw tightened as he glanced up at the wall, where another photograph of his wife hung at his mother-in-law's request. No memory came to him of when he had proposed to Adriana. He stared at the picture, will-ing the curtain blocking his mind to open. How could he

not remember the woman who, according to Lydia, he
had adored? he wondered grimly. Was his love so fickle
that it could so easily be forgotten? Or was he flawed,
emotionally deficient and unable to love deeply—or be
loved? Frustration surged up inside him and he jerked to
his feet, conscious of the surprised looks from Darcey
and Lydia.

'Excuse me,' he growled.

As he strode out of the dining room it occurred to him
that usually when he was in a black mood he would visit
Pietro. His old friend had always known how to calm
him. But Pietro was dead. He thought briefly of going to
see his father. Recently there had been a *rapprochement*
between him and Tito, helped by Sergio who, since his
marriage to Kristen, had become closer to their father.
But Tito was in poor health and went to bed early. He
did not want to disturb his brother. Sergio had enough to
worry about with the imminent birth of his second child.

When had he ever needed anyone? Salvatore asked
himself mockingly. All his life he had felt alone, and he
did not understand why tonight he longed for the company of a girl with green eyes and a sweet smile that
made his guts ache.

Darcey entered her bedroom and closed the door with a
sigh of relief. After Salvatore had abruptly walked out
of the dining room halfway through dinner his mother-
in-law had spent the rest of the evening talking incessantly about her daughter. Adriana had apparently been
a paragon of beauty and sophistication.

'My late husband, Adriana's father, was an Italian
count,' Lydia had explained. 'He was much older than
me and he died when Adriana was a child. But it is evident in her photographs that she was of noble blood.'

It was little wonder that Salvatore had been so deeply in love with Adriana, Lydia had said. Considering that the castle was filled with photographs of the beautiful brunette, Darcey guessed that Lydia was right and Salvatore was still mourning his wife. She frowned as she recalled that several times during their conversation Lydia had hinted that Salvatore felt guilty about Adriana's death. But why on earth should he? she wondered. She did not actually know how his wife had died. That was another mystery hidden within the castle's thick walls.

Someone had turned back the covers on the bed and the crisp white sheets looked inviting. Yawning, Darcey slipped off her shawl, but as she went to take off her necklace she remembered that the chain had broken at dinner and the pendant must still be on the dining table where she had left it.

The stone floors echoed beneath her feet as she hurried back downstairs, but when she walked into the dining room her heart sank as she saw that the table had been cleared. The butler was standing by a cabinet, polishing a silver candleholder. He looked round when he heard Darcey's footsteps.

'Armond, I left a necklace on the table.'

'*Sì.*' He nodded. 'Signore Castellano found it and took it with him.'

'Thank you.'

Why had Salvatore walked out during dinner? Darcey mused as she retraced her steps back upstairs. Had Lydia's constant references to Adriana been too painful? She knew his room was along the corridor from hers, and when she walked past she saw a light filtering beneath the door. Anxious to retrieve her pendant, she hesitated for a few seconds and then knocked.

Moments later the door opened and Salvatore's pow-

erful frame filled the opening. His shirt was partially
undone, and Darcey's eyes were drawn to the exposed
bronzed skin overlaid with black chest hair.

'Darcey?'

His deep, sensual voice sent a shiver of awareness
through her. She swallowed. 'Armond said you have my
necklace?'

'I was trying to mend the broken clasp.' He opened the
door wider. 'Come in while I finish the repair.'

The master suite's large sitting room was simply furnished, almost austere, with its rough plastered walls
covered with faded tapestries that Darcey guessed were
as old as the castle. The antique sofas had scrolled arms
and rich blue brocade cushions which matched the rug
that lay on top of the polished floorboards. Through a
half-open door she could see that the bedroom was dom-
inated by a huge four-poster bed with brocade drapes,
and a brick fireplace that was so tall she could practically stand in the recess. She wondered if the castle had
a modern heating system, or if in the winter a fire would
blaze in the hearth. Now a vase of sunflowers stood in
the grate and provided a bold splash of colour.

Quickly looking away from the bed, she moved across
to the table, where her necklace lay next to some delicate-
looking tools.

'I use these instruments to repair the clocks in the
castle,' Salvatore explained. 'There are over a hundred
clocks. All of them are incredibly old, and none actually
keep the right time,' he said wryly.

'Why do you keep them, then?'

He shrugged. 'They belong here.'

Just as Salvatore belonged at Torre d'Aquila, Darcey
thought. Tonight he reminded her more than ever of a
knight from a previous century: a fearless warrior with

an impressive physique that made her feel weak at the knees when she imagined his strong arms around her, crushing her against his broad chest as he ravaged her mouth with demanding passion.

She let out her breath on a shaky sigh, wishing she had never entered his room, but as she reached to take her necklace he scooped it up.

'I've adjusted the clasp and it should fasten securely now. Turn around and lift up your hair.'

Darcey's heart thudded as she turned away from him and gathered her hair in one hand to expose her neck. Salvatore draped the necklace around her so that the pendant rested in the valley between her breasts. She held her breath while he fastened the chain's clasp. His warm breath stirred the tendrils of hair at her nape and her heart beat faster. Why was he taking so long?

'Your skin is so pale and soft,' he murmured as he skimmed his hand along the line of her slender shoulder. 'You said the necklace holds sentimental value? Is that because it reminds you of your marriage?'

Darcey remembered that she had told him her father had given her the four-leaf-clover pendant to wish her good luck on her wedding day.

'Why would you want a reminder of the jerk who hurt you?' Salvatore said roughly. 'Are you still in love with him?'

'Of course not.' Darcey swallowed, certain that she had felt Salvatore's lips briefly brush against her neck. Her common sense told her to run from his room, but her feet seemed to be stuck to the floor. 'My feelings for the necklace have nothing to do with Marcus. I love it because it was a gift from my father. It once belonged to his mother, who he was very close to, and I was touched that he chose to give the pendant to me.'

She felt another fleeting caress on her bare shoulder and her stomach muscles clenched with sexual longing.

'Did you have a happy childhood?'

'Very.' Despite her father's unpredictable and sometimes difficult nature, Darcey knew that Joshua cared deeply for his children. 'My family mean the world to me.'

'You are fortunate.' Abruptly Salvatore dropped his hands and stepped away from her. 'My childhood memories are not so happy.'

'Kristen said that you were separated from your twin brother when you were young. Why did your parents decide to do that?'

'When my mother left my father she snatched Sergio and took him to America, but she left me behind. I don't know why,' Salvatore added, anticipating Darcey's next question. 'I grew up believing that she loved my brother but not me. Recently Sergio revealed that our mother beat him when he was a child. She had a problem with alcohol and he bore the brunt of her violent mood swings.'

He gave a humourless laugh when he saw her shocked expression.

'I guess I was lucky that she abandoned me. I was never subjected to physical abuse. In fact I rarely saw my father. I was away in England for long periods of time, but my boarding school was not an unpleasant place, and at least I learned to be self-sufficient from an early age.'

Love had been the missing factor from Salvatore's upbringing, Darcey mused, and she was sure it was the reason he found it difficult to connect on an emotional level with his daughter. But presumably he must have had a loving relationship with his wife. According to Lydia, Salvatore and Adriana's marriage had been blissfully happy, despite Lydia's vague hints that Salvatore was somehow responsible for Adriana's death.

Troubled by her conversation with Lydia, Darcey suddenly felt chilled as she glanced at Salvatore. He had moved across the room and was sitting on a stone window seat that had been hewn out of the castle walls. The curtains were open, revealing the black night sky, and the moon gleamed with cold brilliance and cast shadows over his hard-boned face.

Uncovering Salvatore's past might help her to understand him better, and perhaps give her an insight into how she could help him bond with Rosa.

Taking a deep breath, Darcey asked softly, 'How did Adriana die?'

For what seemed an age he did not answer, and when he did finally turn to face her his expression was unfathomable.

'I killed her.'

'What…what do you mean?' She was sure she could not have heard him correctly. Instinctively she crossed her arms in front of her as a shiver ran down her spine.

Something flashed in his dark eyes—a momentary glint of emotion that disappeared before she could define it.

'Adriana died when the car we were travelling in crashed down a mountainside.' Salvatore's jaw clenched. 'I was driving. We were both thrown out of an open-topped sports car. Adriana was pronounced dead at the scene of the accident. I regained consciousness a few days later to the news that I had lost my wife and there was a good chance I would lose my leg. Obviously my injuries, serious though they were, did not compare with the fact that Adriana had been killed,' he said grimly. 'It is entirely my fault that a young woman had her life cut

cruelly short, and my fault that my daughter is growing
up without her mother.'

The torment in his eyes made Darcey's heart ache, and
without thinking about what she was doing she hurried
across the room to stand in front of him.

'It was an accident—a terrible tragedy, but still an
accident,' she told him intently. 'Sometimes events happen and we can't understand the reason for them.' She
placed her hand on his arm, instinctively trying to offer
him the comfort of contact with another human being.
'Do you know why you lost control of the car? Perhaps
it was raining and you skidded?'

'What a soft heart you have, Darcey,' Salvatore said
mockingly. He looked down at her pale hand, lying on
his tanned forearm, and lifted his own hand to cup her
chin. 'Why are you so determined to find excuses for me?
Nothing can absolve me and I can never forgive myself
for causing my wife's death.' He shrugged. 'Perhaps there
were extenuating circumstances that had some bearing
on the crash. I don't know because I don't remember.'

'Do you mean you suffered memory loss due to the
crash?'

'I have no memory of the accident, or much of my
life before it. I can't remember Adriana.' He stared into
Darcey's shocked eyes. 'Since the accident I have had
amnesia. I don't remember a goddamned thing about my
marriage—or the love I felt for my wife.'

Darcey's head was reeling from the dramatic revelations of the past few minutes. 'You must have loved her,'
she said shakily.

She unconsciously clasped Salvatore's arm tighter. His
hard features were no longer expressionless. He looked
haunted. The man behind the mask was finally exposed,
and the burden of being unable to remember the car crash

that had had such devastating consequences was reflected in his tortured eyes.

'There are photographs of Adriana everywhere in the castle,' Darcey said. 'Last night at dinner when you looked at her picture I assumed you were thinking of how much you missed her. '

'Lydia put the pictures up. I look at them, hoping they will jog my memory, but nothing comes. It's as if my mind is blocked by an impenetrable wall that hides the recent past from me. I can recall my childhood, but nothing of how I met Adriana, our wedding day—or, worst of all, Rosa's birth. Sometimes I look at my daughter and I feel that she is a stranger,' Salvatore admitted with raw honesty.

'Oh, that's awful.' Darcey bit her lip.

Salvatore's words explained why he shunned a close relationship with Rosa, and the real tragedy was that both father and daughter were suffering because of his memory loss.

'Isn't there something you could do to try to bring your memory back? Some form of psychotherapy?'

'Do you think I haven't tried?' he said roughly. 'I've met numerous psychoanalysts and they all say the same thing—that I have to be patient and hope that in time my memory will return. But no one can guarantee that I will *ever* regain my memory.' He frowned. 'When we arrived at the castle I experienced a flashback. You had just asked me if Adriana liked living here and I remembered that she hadn't. She found the place too remote and quiet. But I don't know how or why I know that.' His voice was taut with frustration. 'I hoped I would recall more about her, *feel* some sort of connection to her, but my mind is blank.

He tightened his grip on Darcey's chin and tilted her

head so that she was forced to meet his gaze. 'I assume that I must have loved and desired my wife. But the truth is I can't believe I ever felt the fierce desire for her that I feel for you, *mia belleza*. Ever since I walked into your office I have been burning up with wanting you, consumed with the need to kiss you...' his voice dropped to a husky drawl that sent liquid heat coursing through Darcey's veins '...make love to you.'

'You...you shouldn't say things like that.' She desperately tried to ignore the bolt of sexual excitement that shot through her. Salvatore had moved so that she was trapped between his legs, and because he was sitting on the window seat her face was on level with his. She swallowed when she saw the sultry gleam in his eyes. 'We agreed that I came here for Rosa's sake,' she whispered.

'What if I told you that I want you for *my* sake?' he said thickly. 'What if I told you that I can't sleep at night for thinking about you? Would your heart soften towards me, sweet Darcey?'

She was mesmerised by the raw need in his voice, shocked by the hunger that he made no effort to hide. His desire for her acted as a panacea to the hurt and humiliation she had felt when she had discovered Marcus's infidelity. Even so, her heart thudded with panic when his arm snaked around her waist and he jerked her towards him. She had never had casual sex before. *Perhaps it's time you started*, whispered a wicked voice inside her head.

A tremor ran through her as she watched Salvatore's head descend, but her desire to flee from him was overruled by a far more primitive desire to succumb to his sensual mastery. Time seemed to be suspended. She could hear her blood thundering in her ears, and from outside in the darkness there came the harsh screech of an owl on its nightly hunt for prey.

At the last second her common sense urged her to pull away from him—but it was too late.

'Salvatore…don't—'

The rest of her words were obliterated as he slanted his mouth over hers. The firm pressure of his lips instantly enslaved her and she trembled as he slid his hand from her chin to her nape and angled her head so that he could plunder her mouth mercilessly.

She had not expected him to be gentle, but the force of his passion shocked and thrilled her.

'Open your mouth,' he demanded, and with a low moan she complied.

His answering groan of satisfaction as he probed his tongue between her lips shattered the last of her defences, and she cupped his face in her hands and kissed him back with fierce urgency.

He had told her he was consumed with need, and now Darcey understood as molten heat surged through her veins and the ache low in her pelvis became an insistent throb. The rights or wrongs of making love with a man she barely knew no longer mattered. In a strange way she felt that she had been waiting for Salvatore all her life.

He trailed his mouth over her throat and along the fragile line of her collarbone. Darcey caught her breath when he slid the strap of her dress over her shoulder and her heart slammed against her ribcage as he peeled the top of her dress down, lower and lower, until he had bared her breast. Her nipple reacted instantly to the brush of his fingers. His warm breath teased her senses and she could not restrain a soft cry as he flicked his tongue over the dusky peak he had exposed.

'*Santa Madonna!* You are so beautiful,' Salvatore said

hoarsely. 'I took one look at you in your prim suit and I imagined doing this.'

He proceeded to demonstrate what he had imagined doing by drawing her nipple into his mouth and tugging gently, causing a shaft of pleasure to arc from Darcey's breasts to her pelvis. She trembled as he curled his fingers possessively around her other breast, and felt impatient for him to strip off her dress completely so that he could caress her naked flesh.

'You know how this is going to end, *cara*?'

His voice was thick with sexual tension and the glitter in his eyes warned her of his intention to make love to her. It was what she wanted, Darcey acknowledged. In fact she would surely die if he did not take her to bed right now. But lingering doubts from her disastrous marriage to Marcus meant that she did not have the nerve to tell Salvatore that her need was as great as his. Instead she slid her hands behind his neck and pulled his mouth down to hers to initiate a kiss that was sweetly passionate.

Her clumsy eagerness touched something deep inside Salvatore. His conscience told him it was wrong to desire her when he was still chained to his hidden past. But he could not deny his need for her any longer. He stood up, intending to lift her into his arms and carry her through to the bedroom, but a sudden searing pain shot down his thigh. He grabbed hold of the bureau to prevent himself from falling and the porcelain vase standing on its polished surface fell to the floor, shattering into dozens of shards.

Darcey gave a startled cry. She stared at Salvatore, shocked that his eyes were no longer warm with sensual promise but hard and bitter. His face might have been carved from granite, but she had no idea what had caused his transformation from passionate lover to cold stranger.

'What's wrong?' she whispered.

Beads of sweat formed on Salvatore's brow as agonising pain ripped through his thigh. He knew there was nothing he could do but wait for the muscle spasms to ease. Until they did, walking was impossible.

The gentle concern in Darcey's eyes poisoned his soul. His Sicilian pride could not bear for her to witness his physical weakness. His jaw clenched. She was so beautiful. Even though she had pulled her dress back into place he pictured her small, firm breasts and his body ached with sexual need. But he could not make love to her now. The cramp in his leg was a timely reminder of the accident that he had been responsible for. He could not bear to see Darcey's expression when he took off his trousers and revealed the horrific mess of his scarred thigh. She might be revolted—or, even worse, she might feel sorry for him.

Darcey put her hand on Salvatore's arm, desperate to understand the torment in his eyes. 'Let me help you...'

Her sweetness brought bile to Salvatore's throat. He fought the temptation to hold her in his arms and accept the comfort she offered. He felt unmanned, and he channelled his pain into anger.

'You cannot help me,' he told her savagely.

The flare of hurt in her eyes almost stopped him, but the truth was that he was no good for her. His instincts told him that she was not very sexually experienced; certainly she was not like the casual mistresses he had from time to time, who understood that there was no possibility of him ever wanting a deeper relationship. He knew that Darcey was fascinated by him; he was aware of the way she watched him when she thought he did not notice. But he could never be the sort of man she hoped for or deserved.

He gripped her chin and brought her face close to his. 'I am not the man for you, sweet Darcey. You are curiously innocent, but there is a blackness in my soul that I fear would destroy you.'

He dropped a hard kiss on her mouth and his gut clenched when he felt her immediate response. He closed his eyes briefly and thrust her away from him.

'Get out. Run from me, Darcey. Because if you don't I will take your lovely body and crush your gentle heart.'

His eyes glittered when she did not move. The pain in his leg felt as though he was being stabbed with hot knives, but he compressed his mouth, determined not to let her see his weakness.

'Did you hear me?' he snarled. 'If you know what's good for you—*get out*!'

Slowly, Darcey backed towards the door. She could hardly believe the transformation in Salvatore. A few moments ago he had wanted to make love to her, but now he clearly resented her presence. He was rejecting her—as her father sometimes still did when he was more interested in his work, and as her ex-husband had done when he'd discovered that marrying her had not helped his acting career. The two men she had loved in her life had both been disappointed with her, and now Salvatore was sending her away. But she did not know why he had changed his mind.

Mystery surrounded him. She sensed he was haunted by the fact that he could not remember the accident in which his wife had died. Perhaps his subconscious had stopped him from making love to her because he still loved Adriana. Darcey shivered. It was mortifying enough to think that Salvatore did not desire her, but even worse was the idea that while he had been kissing her he had imagined her to be the ghost of his dead wife.

To her shame, her body still ached with unfulfilled desire—but Salvatore's face was as hard as stone and the coldness in his black eyes was the final humiliation. Uttering a low cry, Darcey spun round and fled from the room.

CHAPTER SEVEN

TAORMINA WAS PERCHED high on the cliffs and offered spectacular views of the sea and the beach resorts of Mazzaro
and Isola Bella. The town had a mixture of beautifully restored medieval buildings as well as modern shops, bars
and restaurants which catered for the many tourists who
came to explore the myriad winding streets. Darcey admired the varied architecture left behind by the Greeks,
Romans and Byzantines, to name but a few of the con-
quering armies who had occupied Taormina in the past,
but if she was honest she was just as impressed by the
numerous boutiques and shoe shops.

Standing with her nose almost pressed against the
glass, she couldn't decide whether she preferred the
strappy tan leather sandals with a wedge heel or the eye-
catching red shoes with four-inch stiletto heels.

Rosa tugged on her hand to gain her attention. *Which
ones do you like?* she signed.

Darcey gave a rueful smile as she signed back, *All of
them! But I don't need any more shoes.* She glanced up
the street and her heart did a familiar flip when she saw
Salvatore walking towards them. *Look, there's Papa*, she
signed, and pointed him out to Rosa.

As he drew nearer she purposefully turned back to
study the shoes displayed in the shop window. Two weeks

had passed since the night she had fled from his room, and during that time they had treated each other with cool politeness—at least on the surface. Occasionally when she darted him a glance she glimpsed a flare of sexual desire in his eyes that evoked an ache of longing inside her. But pride made her resist showing any sign of warmth to him. She reminded herself that she had come to Sicily in her professional capacity and strove to focus on Rosa, trying to ignore her inconvenient attraction to the little girl's father.

But, although she did everything she could to avoid him at the castle, she could not stop thinking about his situation and in particular his difficult relationship with Rosa. She had come to the conclusion that until Salvatore recovered from his amnesia he would never be able to move forward with his life or be able to bond with his daughter. If only he could remember what had caused the car accident four years ago he might be able to forgive himself for Adriana's death. But his memory showed no sign of returning, and Darcey sensed his frustration.

She stiffened as she realised that he was standing behind her. The scent of sandalwood cologne teased her senses and she hated her body's treacherous reaction to him. Salvatore's problems were none of her business, Darcey reminded herself. She was determined to maintain an emotional and physical distance from him, but perversely, in the last few days, he seemed just as determined to engineer a thaw in their relationship. At dinner he had stopped being grim-faced and uncommunicative and had drawn her into conversation, asking about her work and her life in London. And today, to her surprise, he had joined her and Rosa for breakfast and suggested that they should spend the day in Taormina.

'Surely you don't need another pair of shoes?' he murmured now, and the gentle teasing in his voice tugged on Darcey's heart. 'I've seen you wear at least ten different pairs since you arrived in Sicily.'

Taking a deep breath, she pinned a cool smile on her face before spinning round to him. 'A woman can never have enough shoes. But I'm not going to buy any of these—they're too expensive.'

'Perhaps you will allow me to buy them for you?' Salvatore glanced at Rosa and signed, *Which shoes does Darcey like best?*

The little girl immediately responded—*The red ones.*

The joke had gone far enough. Darcey glared at him as he pulled out his wallet. 'Of course I won't let you buy me shoes. If you're so determined to spend money, Rosa has seen some pretty hairbands in the shop just along the street. Why don't you let her show them to you while I pop to the chemist?'

What he would like to do, Salvatore mused as he skimmed his eyes over Darcey's slender shape, in figure-hugging white pedal-pushers and a gingham blouse, was pull her into his arms and kiss her stubborn mouth until she melted. He was sick to death of her imitation of the Ice Queen from one of Rosa's storybooks, and the knowledge that he deserved her frostiness did nothing to lessen his frustration. None of his feelings showed on his face, however.

'Good idea,' he said steadily, and held out his hand to Rosa. 'We'll meet you at the café on the other side of the *piazza.*'

As Darcey walked along the street she refused to speculate on the change in Salvatore's attitude towards her. He had been easier to deal with when he had treated her with cold indifference, she thought ruefully. At least then she'd been able to pretend that she wasn't interested in him.

Her thoughts were distracted by the sound of a distinctive high-pitched voice and, glancing down a narrow alleyway, she was surprised to see Lydia talking to
a man. Darcey had no wish to meet Salvatore's mother-
in-law and was about to continue on her way. But she
paused when she realised that Lydia and her companion
were arguing. They were speaking in Italian, and Darcey
could not understand what was being said, but it was
clear that the conversation was heated. Several times she
heard Lydia address the man as Ettore. They continued
their discussion for several more minutes, and then, to
Darcey's shock, Lydia burst into tears and rushed away.

What had all that been about? she wondered. Even
more puzzling was the fact that Lydia was in town when
she had made a point of telling Darcey that morning that
she planned to spend the day at the castle.

She was still musing over the scene she had witnessed
in the alleyway as she crossed the attractive black and
white paving of the Piazza XI Aprile in the centre of
Taormina. Rosa ran to meet her and excitedly showed
off her new hair accessories.

'Did you get everything you needed?' Salvatore asked
as they strolled towards a café.

'Yes.' Darcey hesitated. 'Do you know someone
called Ettore? I saw Lydia talking with a man—well,
they seemed to be arguing. She called him Ettore.'

'It might have been Ettore Varsi.' Salvatore frowned.
'Ettore was the first person to arrive at the scene of the
accident four years ago. He was driving a little way behind me and saw me lose control of the car on a sharp
bend. After the crash he managed to scramble down the
mountainside and he pulled Adriana and I away from
the wreckage seconds before the car caught fire. I don't
know why Lydia might have been arguing with Ettore,'

Salvatore continued. 'Perhaps you misunderstood. Lydia has always been grateful to him for trying to save her daughter.' A bleak expression crossed his face.

'Have you discussed with Ettore what happed that night? If you spoke to him, something might trigger your memory...' Darcey's voice faltered when she saw the grimness in Salvatore's eyes.

'Ettore Varsi gave a full statement of the facts to the police and at Adriana's inquest,' he said curtly. 'He had been at the party which Adriana and I had attended, and he saw us leave. His evidence states that I got into the driver's seat of the car and Adriana into the passenger seat. He followed behind us and believed that I was driving too fast as I approached a bend in the road. According to Ettore, the car spun and crashed through the roadside barrier. He stopped and called the emergency services before he climbed down the mountainside to try to rescue us.'

'I still think you should talk to him,' Darcey insisted. 'He might know more...'

'Enough!' Salvatore said harshly. 'There *is* nothing more. Ettore explained what he saw. Nothing can exonerate me from the fact that I am responsible for my wife's death.'

Darcey stared at him in frustration. 'You're so stubborn.'

'Me! Look at yourself, *cara.* Take my advice and stop poking your nose where it doesn't belong.'

So furious that she did not trust herself to speak, Darcey spun round and stalked into the café where Rosa had found a vacant table. She only wanted to help, she thought hotly, but Salvatore had made it clear that he did not want anything from her. The memory of how he had ordered her to get out of his room was still horribly embarrassing and she vowed that from now on she would not talk to him about anything other than how Rosa's speech therapy was progressing—which, after all, was the only reason she had come to Sicily.

She ordered fruit juice for Rosa, a cappuccino for herself and an espresso for Salvatore—although she wondered if he would join them now that she had put him in one of his black moods. But to her surprise he was smiling when he walked into the café a few minutes later.

'I've just had a call from Sergio,' he told her. 'Kristen went into labour early this morning and gave birth to a healthy baby boy half an hour ago.'

'Oh, that's wonderful!' Darcey waited for Salvatore to sign the news to Rosa that she had a new cousin. 'Your brother must be so relieved,' she said, recalling how Sergio had become increasingly tense as his wife's due date had approached.

'He's overjoyed.' Salvatore glanced at the coffee in front of him. 'I think we should celebrate baby Leo Castellano's birth with champagne.'

'Rosa can't drink champagne,' Darcey pointed out. *Shall we have ice cream?* she signed to the little girl, and was rewarded with a smile and a fervent nod.

Salvatore passed on a sweet treat, but as he watched Darcey and his daughter enjoying ice cream sundaes he was struck yet again by the close friendship they had formed. Darcey's kindness was apparent in everything she did, and she made Rosa's speech therapy sessions full of fun. He knew she did not understand why he found it hard to bond with Rosa. How could she comprehend the guilt he felt that his child was growing up without a mother—just as he had done? His amnesia had created a barrier between him and Rosa. *Dio!* He could not even remember her birth, or holding his newborn daughter in his arms.

The blankness in his mind evoked blackness in his heart. He had been right to send Darcey away instead of making love to her, Salvatore told himself. He knew he had hurt her feelings, but it was better than dragging her into his dark world. He had no right to taint her bright smile and cheerful nature with his despair. One day she would meet a man who would love her as she deserved to be loved, and she would love him back with all the generosity in her heart.

In brooding silence Salvatore drank his coffee and noted with heavy irony that its bitter taste matched the bitterness of his thoughts.

'Okay, that's enough for today.' Darcey simultaneously spoke and signed to Rosa. She gathered up the phonetics cards they had been using and smiled at the little girl. 'Well done! You spoke all the sounds we've been practising perfectly. I'm very pleased with you, and so is your *papa*.' She glanced at Salvatore, silently willing him to praise Rosa.

He had been as good as his word and joined in the speech therapy sessions every afternoon, but although he appeared relaxed and gave plenty of encouragement, Darcey still sensed a faintly reserved air with his daughter. To her relief he gave one of his rare smiles.

'You did very well today,' he told Rosa. 'Go and get ready for swimming.'

Darcey had decided to hold the therapy sessions in the summerhouse by the pool, so that Rosa could have her reward of a swim with her father immediately afterwards. Salvatore watched her run off to the changing cubicle.

'She seems to be making good progress.'

'She certainly is,' Darcey assured him. 'I realised when I met Rosa that she is a very bright child, and I'm confident she will quickly develop speech and language skills.'

'Thanks to you and your skill and dedication.' Salvatore rested his brooding gaze on her flushed face. 'Are you going to join us in the pool today?'

He frowned when Darcey shook her head.

'I need to use the time that you swim with Rosa to get on with some work. There's a lot to do to set up my private speech therapy practice,' she explained.

The excuse was partly true, for she *had* been researching possible venues where she could run her business. But she also used her free time to study the role she was to portray in her father's play. Reading Joshua's script, Darcey was amazed by his great talent as a playwright. She was so proud of her father, and pleased that he chosen her for the lead role, but she was plagued by self-doubt, and for that reason she had decided not to tell anyone outside of her family that she was going to be in the play until she was certain she could justify her father's faith in her.

'Why don't you be honest?'

Salvatore's terse voice dragged Darcey from her thoughts.

'I know you are revolted by the sight of my scars, but you've watched me swimming with Rosa every day since you arrived here—surely you've had time to get used to the mess my leg is in by now?'

'I'm *not* revolted by your scars!' She was shocked by the conclusion he had come to about her refusal to join him in the pool. 'I just think it's important that you and Rosa spend some time together,' she insisted.

Salvatore's gaze held a momentary look of doubt before he walked off to get changed.

Darcey pulled up her father's script on her laptop and tried to focus. The play was set in the time of the Second World War and was based on a true story about Joshua's mother, Edith, who had married a Frenchman and worked with the French Resistance until she was caught by the Nazis and tortured. Amazingly, Edith had managed to escape and had returned to Ireland, where her husband had later joined her, and the couple had gone on to have five children.

It was an inspiring story, and Joshua Hart's play was a moving tribute to his mother's bravery. But Darcey could not concentrate when her eyes were drawn to the pool. The sight of Salvatore's bronzed, athletic body proved a major distraction. It was true that the deep scars on his thigh were unmissable, but they certainly did not lessen the impact of his potent virility. He was the sexiest man she had ever met and Darcey gave a heavy sigh as she forced her eyes back to her laptop screen.

The sound of footsteps on the decking of the summerhouse made her look up, and she was surprised to see Rosa standing in front of her. The little girl took a deep breath.

'Dar-cey!' she said clearly.

'Oh, Rosa—you clever girl!' Darcey's eyes filled with tears of emotion that Rosa had spoken her first word. It was a breakthrough moment and she threw her arms around the child and hugged her.

'She has been practising saying your name with me,' Salvatore explained as he joined them in the summerhouse. 'Rosa is hoping that you will swim with us.'

Darcey gave him a suspicious look, which he countered with a bland expression. He knew she would not refuse, she thought ruefully. She smiled at Rosa and spoke whilst signing—*'I'll go and put my swimsuit on.'*

Stepping out of the changing cubicle a few minutes later, Darcey told herself it was ridiculous to feel self-conscious. Her yellow bikini was perfectly respectable. But she was supremely aware of Salvatore's intent gaze as she walked down the pool steps, and she quickly ducked under the water and swam away from him. She concentrated on Rosa, but although she did her best to ignore Salvatore she found her eyes straying to him, and her heart gave a jolt when she discovered he was watching her. Sexual tension simmered between them, fuelled by every furtive glance and the accidental contact of their bodies as they played in the pool with Rosa.

Darcey was relieved when Nico arrived, accompanied by the English nanny that Sergio and Kristen had hired to help with their growing family. Margaret was able to use sign language, and Salvatore had arranged for her to share her time between caring for Nico and Rosa.

'Nico has already been swimming in the pool at Casa Camelia,' Margaret explained. 'I'll take the children to play in the sandpit.'

Left alone with Salvatore, after Rosa had run off to play with her cousin, Darcey wrapped a towel around her shoulders, intending to go and change back into her clothes. But his deep voice stopped her.

'Surely you can take a break from working on your laptop and enjoy the sunshine?' His dark eyes gleamed with unexpected warmth. 'I already feel bad that you have missed your holiday in France.' Seeing Darcey hesitate, he added, 'While Margaret is taking care of the children I'd like you to give me an update on Rosa's progress.'

She could hardly refuse, but Darcey ignored the sun-lounger he had pulled up for her and went to sit beneath a parasol. 'I'll burn if I sit in the sun for more than a minute,' she told him. 'My mother has had a recent scare with a malignant melanoma so, much as I'd love a tan, I'm better off staying in the shade.'

'That's wise, with your fair skin, but you can be affected by UV rays even in the shade and it would be a good idea to use sunscreen.' Salvatore picked up the bottle of lotion, but instead of handing it to Darcey he tipped a blob of cream onto his palm and walked behind her.

She gasped at the feel of the cool lotion on her warm skin, but what made her heart beat even faster was the sensation of Salvatore's hands massaging her shoulders. Her body reacted instantly, and she was mortified when she looked down and saw the hard points of her nipples jutting beneath her bikini top.

'This is not appropriate,' she choked.

He bent his head and his soft laughter tickled her ear. 'Maybe not, but it's enjoyable—for both of us. Relax, *cara*, you're very tense.'

What did he expect? His touch was intensely sensual, and she could feel herself beginning to melt as desire pooled between her thighs.

'You wanted to discuss Rosa,' she reminded him desperately. 'Her confidence is growing daily, and it is vital that you continue to attend the speech therapy sessions to encourage her.' Darcey hesitated, wondering how she could help Salvatore to connect emotionally with his daughter. 'You are the most important person in Rosa's life,' she told him softly. 'She adores you.'

He abruptly snatched his hands from her shoulders. 'I wonder if she will when she discovers that it is my fault she does not have a mother.'

Knowing by now that he hated revealing his emotions,

Darcey expected him to walk away, but after a moment he pulled out a chair and sat down next to her beneath the parasol.

'Have you any idea what it feels like to know that I robbed my daughter of her mother?' he said harshly. 'Sometimes I've even wondered——' He broke off and swallowed hard.

Shocked by the pain she glimpsed in his eyes, Darcey said gently, 'You've wondered what?'

'Whether it is my fault she is deaf. I know that the medical reason was an ear infection, but perhaps the trauma of suddenly being separated from her mother contributed to Rosa's deafness.'

Darcey's heart ached for him, and she reached out and put her hand on his arm.

'I've read Rosa's medical notes. The most probable reason for her deafness is that during her birth excess fluid was trapped in the cochlea and damaged the tiny hair cells inside. It's called sensorineural hearing loss. It is possible that Rosa had moderate cochlear damage at birth and then a severe infection when she was a year old caused further damage and left her profoundly deaf, but I can assure you that the death of her mother, although traumatic, could not have caused Rosa to lose her hearing. You are not to blame, Salvatore,' she told him urgently. 'I don't know why or how the car accident happened, but I'm convinced that you would not have acted in a way that put Adriana's life at risk.'

He shook his head. 'What puzzles me most is that we were thrown out of the car, which means that we couldn't have been wearing seat belts. But I *always* wear a belt. I keep asking myself why I didn't wear one that night and insist that Adriana put a seat belt on?—especially when I was driving with the roof open.'

Salvatore closed his eyes as a searing pain shot through his head. Snatches of memory suddenly came into his mind.

He could see the sharp bend in the road ahead. He could feel the wind rushing through his hair. The car was travelling too fast. Fear churned in his stomach. He must turn the wheel and steer the car away from the edge of the road. But his hands were not on the wheel. He wasn't in control—and now it was too late...

'Salvatore?' Darcey's voice jerked him back to the present. 'What's wrong? Do you have a migraine?'

'No...' He raked a hand through his hair. 'Nothing is wrong.'

He was tempted to tell her about the images in his head, but what he had seen did not make sense. *Why* hadn't he been in control of the car just before it crashed?

He stared into Darcey's green eyes and felt a gentle tug on his heart. 'Thank you for putting my mind at rest about the cause of Rosa's deafness. I've always felt guilty,' he admitted roughly. 'A father is supposed to protect his child, but I believed I had caused her harm.'

Darcey's breath hitched in her throat as he lowered his head towards her. The atmosphere had altered subtly and sexual awareness throbbed between them as he brushed his mouth over hers. The kiss was frustratingly brief, but its sweetness pierced her heart and its promise of sensual ecstasy made her tremble.

'Rosa is coming,' he warned softly.

Darcey saw the regret she felt herself that he could not kiss her properly reflected in his eyes. Dragging oxygen into her lungs, she reached for her sunglasses to hide the devastating effect he had on her equilibrium.

Rosa dashed up to her father but then hesitated, as if she was unsure of her reception. Her wariness evoked a shaft of pain inside Salvatore. He had been so weighted down with his feelings of guilt that he had unwittingly pushed Rosa away, he realised heavily. Darcey had shown him that his little girl needed him and loved him. It was down to him to show Rosa that she meant the world to him.

Smiling, he opened his arms to her. For a second she looked surprised, but then she stepped into the circle of his arms and he hugged her tight.

Would you like to come to the stables with me? he signed. He was glad for once that he did not need to speak, because his throat burned with unfamiliar tears that he swallowed hastily as Rosa nodded eagerly. Salvatore glanced at Darcey and knew from the softness in her eyes that she had guessed his emotions were choking him.

'I'll spend some time with Rosa and meet you back at the castle later. Remember I'm hosting a business dinner party tonight? You'll join me, of course,' he said, forestalling the argument he could see she was about to make.

Without giving her a chance to reply he lifted his daughter onto his shoulders and strode away.

The path between the pool area and the castle ran beside the cliff-edge and provided wonderful views of the private bay belonging to the Castellano Estate. The colour of the sea reflected the azure blue of the sky, Darcey noted, and the pretty pink wildflowers growing along the edge of the path made a stunning contrast.

The late-afternoon sunshine felt hot on her shoulders and she was glad of the protection of her wide-brimmed hat. She was falling in love with Sicily, she thought, trying to ignore the voice inside her head which taunted that it was not only Sicily that had captured her heart.

With her mind on Salvatore, she took scant notice of the man who had stepped onto the path a little way ahead of her. She guessed he had walked up from the beach. She was used to seeing estate workers walking around the vast Castellano property, and would not have thought any more of it if the man hadn't looked over his shoulder. He was clearly startled when he saw her, and immediately turned back down the path leading to the beach. Darcey watched his rapidly retreating figure, feeling puzzled. She recognised him as the man she had seen arguing with Lydia in Taormina. But if Ettore Varsi worked on the Castellano estate surely Salvatore would have said so?

She was still wondering about the man on the path when she reached the castle. But as she entered the cool flagstoned hallway her thoughts turned to the dinner party tonight. Salvatore had said it was a business dinner for several wine importers from Eastern Europe whom he hoped to persuade to sell Castellano wine. It sounded a formal affair, and Darcey wondered what she should wear. Certainly the white cotton sundress she was wearing at the moment would not do.

She would ask Armond's advice, she decided. She had struck up a firm friendship with the butler, who seemed to belong at Torre d'Aquila as much as Salvatore did.

Armond could often be found in the dining room, but when Darcey walked into the room she was surprised to see Lydia, standing by the cabinet where the silverware was kept.

'*Oh*—I thought everyone was out,' Lydia said sharply. She seemed flustered. Especially when Darcey glanced at a silver snuff box sticking out of the large bag on the floor. 'I was just packing up some of the silverware to take it to be professionally polished,' she explained. 'My daughter liked everything in the castle to be properly cared for, and now that she is no longer here I have arranged with Salvatore that I will take on the responsibility of maintaining the castle's valuable antiques. Adriana loved the castle as much as Salvatore does.'

Yet Salvatore's only memory of his wife was that she had disliked living at Torre d'Aquila. Darcey did not say so to Lydia. 'I was looking for Armond,' she murmured.

'It's his afternoon off.' Lydia pushed the snuff box into the bag and closed the zip. 'He won't be back until dinner this evening.'

Just before eight o'clock Darcey entered the salon where she knew that cocktails would be served before dinner. None of the guests had yet arrived, and she hoped that if Salvatore thought her dress was unsuitable she would have time to run back upstairs and change.

He was standing by the bar, an imposing figure in a black tuxedo and so unfairly sexy that Darcey felt her stomach swoop. She noticed that he was clean-shaven for once. Without his customary black stubble shading his jaw he looked less like a pirate and more like a billionaire business tycoon.

He watched her walk into the room and his silence was telling.

'My dress is over the top, isn't it?' she said ruefully. 'I wasn't sure how formal the dinner party would be but I couldn't resist wearing the evening dress I bought to take to France.' She headed for the door. 'I'll go and put something else on.'

'Don't you dare!' Salvatore growled. He strode across the room with surprising speed, considering his injured leg, and stood in front of the door, blocking her path. 'You look beautiful.'

He studied her slender figure in the floor-length lilac

silk dress that skimmed her soft curves. The dress was strapless, showing off her bare shoulders and the upper slopes of her breasts. Her creamy skin was as smooth as fine porcelain, and closer inspection revealed a scattering of tiny golden freckles which matched the colour of the sun-lightened hair that framed her face.

He slowly shook his head. 'You always look beautiful. But tonight you are breathtaking, *mia bella*. Your dress is perfect.' He trapped her gaze and Darcey's heart beat a frantic tattoo when she saw molten desire in his eyes. '*You* are perfect, sweet Darcey, and I am going to spend the entire dinner fantasising about the gorgeous body beneath your dress.'

She blushed and wished she could make some witty, flirtatious response, but she felt tongue-tied and incredibly vulnerable, wondering if he was simply amusing himself with her. 'I wish you wouldn't tease me,' she mumbled.

'*Santa Madre!* You think I am teasing?' His voice deepened. 'I have never been more serious in my life, nor wanted any woman as urgently as I want you.' Salvatore's jaw clenched when he glimpsed the uncertainty in her eyes. 'I'd like to meet your ex-husband and let him know what I think of him for hurting you so badly,' he said harshly.

Darcey bit her lip. 'I was a fool to trust Marcus. Maybe I would be foolish to trust you too,' she said huskily. 'Lydia says you will never love another woman after Adriana, and that the women you have affairs with mean nothing to you. I…I don't think I could be happy to sleep with you knowing that in your eyes I am nothing.'

Her words grated on Salvatore's conscience. It was true that the few affairs he'd had since he had been widowed had been conducted almost exclusively in the bedroom. Sex without strings was fine when both parties agreed to it, and he had made sure his mistresses had been under no illusion that he might want a more meaningful relationship, but he had always known that Darcey was different from the women he'd had those casual affairs with.

'It is not true that you mean nothing to me,' he said harshly. 'I respect and admire you.'

The sentiments sounded hollow even to his own ears. Frustration surged through him as he fought the urge to pull Darcey into his arms and show her how goddamned good sex without the complication of emotions could be.

He jerked his eyes from her face as the salon door opened and Armond appeared to inform him that the guests had arrived.

Salvatore hated parties at the best of times, and tonight he wished he could send his guests away. But, if his father had done nothing else, Tito had at least drilled a sense of duty and a strong work ethic into him. Stifling his irritation, he instructed the butler to usher the guests in.

'We will continue this conversation later,' he told Darcey gruffly.

Her pink-glossed mouth was an irresistible temptation, and with an oath he slanted his lips over hers in a brief, unsatisfactory kiss that left him aching for more.

CHAPTER EIGHT

DARCEY WAS FORCED to call on all her acting skills to appear calm and collected as Salvatore introduced her to his dinner guests. He gave no explanation of her role at the castle, and she was sure his business associates assumed she was his mistress—especially when he slipped his arm possessively around her waist as they walked through to the dining room.

Lydia was late, as usual, and as they took their places at the table Armond informed Salvatore that she would not be joining them at all because she was feeling unwell. Thinking of Salvatore's mother-in-law reminded Darcey of the man she had seen when she had walked back from the pool: the same man who had been arguing with Lydia in Taormina a few days ago.

'Did Ettore Varsi come to visit Lydia?' she asked. 'I saw him earlier today, on the path by the beach.'

Salvatore frowned. 'I was not informed by the security guards that Ettore had visited the estate. Perhaps you mistook one of the workers for him?'

'No, it was definitely him.' Darcey was absolutely certain it *had* been Ettore she had seen, and felt irritated that Salvatore clearly did not believe her.

The conversation around the dinner table quickly turned to business, but Darcey did not mind. She was preoccupied with her thoughts. Salvatore made an effort to be a charming host, but she sensed his impatience with social niceties and knew he would rather be at the winery or out in the vineyards than making polite small talk. He was a man of action rather than words, and she had a feeling that the same would be true in the bedroom.

Thinking about making love with him brought a flush to her cheeks, and her colour deepened when she felt his brooding gaze on her. Did she dare respond to the glittering desire in his eyes? Why shouldn't she enjoy a brief fling with him? She smiled ruefully to herself when she remembered her mother's advice to have a sizzling affair with a sexy Sicilian. She had told her mother that Salvatore was dangerous, and now she knew it to be true. He was a serious threat to her heart, and for that reason she was hesitant about them becoming lovers.

It was late when the guests departed. Darcey stood with Salvatore on the steps of the castle and watched the taillights of the cars disappear down the driveway. There was no moon or stars tonight, and the darkness closed around them like an impenetrable cloak.

'A storm is brewing,' he predicted. 'Can you feel the electricity in the air?'

Something was certainly making the hairs on the back of her neck prickle, but she had a feeling it was the smouldering sensuality of the man beside her rather than the atmospheric conditions. Darcey's heart-rate accelerated as Salvatore slipped his arm around her waist and led her back into the castle. An unspoken question hovered between them, but she was no closer to the answer than she had been during dinner. Her body ached with longing for him to take her to bed, but the voice of caution inside her head was determined not to be ignored.

Salvatore lifted his hand and tucked a few silky strands of copper-brown hair behind Darcey's ear.

'Sweet Darcey, what am I going to do about you?' he murmured, half beneath his breath.

He was on fire for her and the throb of his arousal could only be assuaged by making love to her. If she had been any other woman he would have whisked her off to bed long ago, but the indecision in her green eyes stalled him and the faint tremor of her mouth tugged on his conscience.

The sound of brisk footsteps on the stone floor shattered the tense silence. Salvatore frowned as he glanced towards the butler, who had appeared in the doorway.

'You may retire for the night, Armond. I will turn off the lights when I go to bed.'

'I must speak to you about an urgent matter, *signore*.' The butler was clearly troubled. 'Some items of silverware are missing from the cabinet in the dining room. I only noticed when I replaced the cutlery after dinner and saw that some pieces at the back of the cabinet were out of place. When I looked I realised several valuable antiques have disappeared. The items concerned are not used regularly and I cannot say when they went missing,' he added regretfully.

Armond looked deeply upset. Darcey knew he took great pride in his duties at the castle and she quickly reassured him. 'It's all right, Armond. Lydia—Signora Putzi—took some of the silver ornaments away to be professionally polished. I saw her take them out of the cabinet this afternoon. I assumed you knew,' she said slowly, when the butler looked puzzled.

'I assure you that I take excellent care of the silverware and polish all the pieces regularly,' Armond said in an affronted voice.

'No doubt there is an explanation,' Salvatore murmured. 'Armond, will you go and ask Signora Putzi to come down to my study? She is forever telling me that she has trouble sleeping, so she is probably still awake,' he told Darcey drily.

Ten minutes later Armond ushered an irate Lydia into the study. 'What on earth is going on?' she demanded. 'Why have you disturbed me at this time of night?'

Her anger turned to outrage when Salvatore briefly explained about the missing silver and she shot Darcey a furious look.

'Of *course* I didn't take anything out of the cabinet. I've never heard such nonsense. Darcey is obviously lying and trying to put the blame for the disappearance of the silver on to me, when in actual fact *she* must have taken the items.'

'But...I saw you in the dining room earlier, taking things from the cabinet,' Darcey faltered, stunned by Lydia's denial. 'You told me—'

'I was in my room all afternoon, reading,' Lydia snapped.

'Did you meet up with Ettore Varsi? I saw him in the grounds of the estate this afternoon, and I saw you talking to him in Taormina the other day.'

For a moment Lydia looked startled, but she quickly recovered and turned to face Salvatore. 'I have no idea what Darcey is talking about. I haven't seen Ettore for months. I'm going back to bed,' she said regally. She flicked a scathing glance at Darcey. 'I understand your game, Miss Rivers. You've set your sights on Salvatore and you want me out of the way because I am a reminder of the love he had for my daughter. Don't bother to deny it. I've seen the way you look at my son-in-law. But you are not the first stupid girl to have a crush on him and I

don't suppose you will be the last. Just don't fool yourself into thinking that you will ever be more than a convenient outlet for his physical needs—'

'That's enough!' Salvatore interrupted the older
woman sharply. 'You know nothing about my relationship with Darcey.'

'I'm simply telling her the truth.' Lydia glared at him,
but then her face crumpled. 'I adored my Adriana but she
was stolen from me. You were responsible for her death,
Salvatore, and the least you can do is to remain faithful
to her memory.'

Lydia swept out of the room, and in the ensuing silence
her ugly accusations seemed to echo around the study.

'I *did* see her take the silverware from the cabinet,'
Darcey insisted. 'I don't understand why she denied it.'
Nor did she understand why Lydia had denied speaking
to Ettore Varsi in Taormina. She glanced at Salvatore,
but his hard features revealed nothing of his thoughts.
'You do believe me...don't you?'

His reply did nothing to reassure her. 'I'm sure there is
a reasonable explanation for everything,' he said curtly.
'I suggest you go to bed and we will discuss the situation in the morning.'

Salvatore stared at Darcey's hurt expression and felt
a surge of frustration. His instincts told him she was
speaking the truth about the missing silver, yet it made
no sense. Why would Lydia take the things? And why
did Darcey insist that she had seen Ettore Varsi?

'The man you saw today cannot have been Ettore.
The only access to the estate is through the main gates,
which are guarded around the clock. I asked the security guards to check through the CCTV footage, in case
they had forgotten about his visit, but his car doesn't appear on the film.'

'Do you think I'm lying?' she demanded hotly.

Salvatore shook his head. 'I think you were mistaken.'

Which was as good as saying he thought she was lying, Darcey thought grimly as she marched out of the study. Too much was going on that she did not understand, and Lydia's inexplicable behaviour tonight further fuelled the mystery. As she ran upstairs to her bedroom she recalled Lydia's accusation that she had a crush on Salvatore and her face burned with mortification. Had she really been so obvious? Maybe Salvatore had believed she would fall into his bed with little persuasion. But now he thought she was a liar and a thief and that was why he had looked at her with cold disdain.

Angry tears stung her eyes. Things would have been so much easier if he had never strolled into her office in London and turned her life upside down. She wished she had not come to Sicily, but deep in her heart she wished even more that she was not destined to leave Torre d'Aquila at the end of the summer. The painful truth was that she had fallen fathoms deep in love with Salvatore, but his heart was buried with his dead wife.

The storm broke over the castle with a lightning flare outside the window that briefly lit up the bedroom before it died away to leave the room in complete darkness. A giant thunderclap shook the ancient walls and Darcey jerked awake. She fumbled to switch on the bedside lamp and realised that the castle must have suffered a power cut.

Remembering the candles on the chest of drawers, she slid off the bed, grimacing at the thought that her dress was probably creased because she had fallen asleep fully clothed. Lightning flared again, and the ensuing darkness was so black that for a moment she felt disorientated. She immediately thought of Rosa. The little girl would not be disturbed by the thunder, because her cochlear implant device was switched off, but if the lightning woke her she would be terrified of the dark and would not understand why the nightlight in her room did not work.

Another flare of lightning enabled Darcey to locate and light a candle, but as she hurried down the corridor the feeble light it emitted threatened to sputter out. At least she could reassure the child if she woke up, she thought. But as she pushed open Rosa's bedroom door she bumped into something big and solid and could not restrain a squeak of surprise.

Salvatore was holding an old-fashioned oil lamp, and the flame cast flickering shadows on the walls and over the chiselled contours of his face.

'I should have known that your first concern would be Rosa,' he said in a curious tone. 'As you have no doubt realised, the power is out. Unfortunately the castle does not have a backup generator, but the oil lamps are always kept filled. I've lit one in Rosa's room and it should last until morning.' He glanced at the dim light from Darcey's candle and blew across the flame gently to extinguish it. 'I'd better come and light a lamp in your room.'

He led her back along the corridor and ushered her into her room, holding the lamp high to guide her. As the lamplight flickered across her face Salvatore frowned.

'Why have you been crying? It's pointless to deny it—your eyes look like shimmering green pools,' he said roughly.

'What did you expect after I've been unjustly accused of being a thief?' Darcey's voice trembled. 'You made it plain that you believe Lydia rather than me.'

Recalling his cold expression down in the study, she gave a choked cry and whirled around, wanting to get away from him. He was still blocking her path to the door, and with no clear thought in her head as to what she was doing she ran across to the French doors leading to the balcony.

The storm was in full fury and the rain was falling so hard that it lashed her bare arms when she stepped outside. Darcey's emotions were in tatters. The scene in Salvatore's study, when his silence had implied that he thought she had stolen the silverware, had left her feeling as hurt and humiliated as she had been when she had walked in on Marcus having sex with his mistress.

She lifted her face to the sky, so that the rain disguised her tears, but Salvatore had followed her onto the balcony and he caught hold of her shoulder and spun her round to him.

'I never thought for a second that you took the silver,' he said fiercely. 'I don't know why Lydia lied, but I've no doubt the truth will be revealed. I certainly do not doubt your honesty. How could I, when I have witnessed every day since I brought you to Torre d'Aquila your sweet nature, your kindness and your abundant compassion?'

His voice deepened, caressing Darcey's senses and soothing her hurt pride.

'I would trust you with my life, *mia bella*.'

His dark eyes blazed, as if he was determined to make her believe him. He cupped her cheek, and to Darcey's amazement his hand was unsteady.

'You accuse me of regarding you as unimportant, but that is not true.' His mouth twisted. 'My amnesia makes me feel that I am trapped in a dark tunnel with no beginning or end. The truth is that I don't know *what* I feel, but I am certain that I have never felt this way about any other woman. It's not just sexual attraction,' he insisted as she opened her mouth to speak. 'For most of my life after my mother abandoned me I put up barriers and pushed people away. Even my twin brother and my own daughter could not thaw the coldness inside me. But I don't want to push *you* away, *carissima*.'

He threaded his other hand through her hair and lowered his head so that Darcey could feel his warm breath on her rain-soaked face.

'I want to hold you close and make love to you. I want to show you how perfect it will be for us.'

How could she deny him when she wanted him with all her heart? Darcey thought. Salvatore had made no promises. He had admitted honestly that he did not know how he felt. But the fact that he felt *something*, and had opened up his emotions as much as he had, allayed her doubts. She understood that his difficult upbringing meant he found it hard to give his trust, and she was deeply moved by his avowal that he would trust her with his life.

'I want to make love with you too,' she told him huskily.

The confession brought a sense of release, as if she had been set free from the past. She was no longer the naive girl she had been during her marriage. Salvatore had restored the self-confidence that her ex-husband had destroyed and she wasn't ashamed to admit that she desired him. But she would come to him as his equal, she vowed. She was not a timid virgin.

Lifting her hands to his face, she urged his mouth down on hers.

It was like putting a match to dry tinder. The first touch of his lips on hers set their passion alight, as if all the weeks of sexual frustration, the secretive glances and sleepless nights tormented by longing, were bound up in the kiss. Darcey parted her lips as Salvatore deepened the kiss until she was aware of nothing but him, the slight roughness of his jaw against her cheek and the sheer eroticism of his tongue pushing into her mouth. She knew there would be no turning back now. Soon she and Salvatore would be lovers.

The prospect caused her heart to skitter with a mixture of nervous excitement and anticipation, and when he wrapped his arms around her and crushed her against his broad chest she melted into his embrace.

He had known Darcey was trouble the minute he'd walked into her office, Salvatore thought. His instincts had told him that beneath her prim suit she was a sensual, exciting—he glanced up at the torrential rain falling from the heavens and gave a wry smile—and unpredictable woman.

'You're soaked through,' he growled, running his hands over her sodden dress, which was sticking to her body like a second skin.

'So are you.'

With a boldness he had not expected she tugged open the buttons of his shirt and parted the wet material to skim her hands over his naked chest. Desire corkscrewed through him when she flicked her tongue over one of his nipples, and without another word he lifted her into his arms and carried her back into the bedroom.

The light from the oil lamp cast a gentle glow over the room and softened Salvatore's hard features a little. The first time she had seen him he had reminded her of a medieval knight, Darcey remembered. But at that first meeting his eyes had been cold and expressionless, whereas now they were lit with a sultry heat that set her heart pounding.

'You're shivering,' he said softly. 'Are you cold?'

She met his gaze and Salvatore noticed that her eyes had darkened to jade.

'No, I'm not cold.'

Another tremor ran through her, and he understood. The same urgent desire was making his body shake.

'You need to get out of your wet dress,' he murmured.

Stepping behind her, he ran the zip down her spine.

Darcey caught her breath when the strapless silk bodice slithered down. Her eyes were drawn to the floor-length mirror on the wall opposite them as Salvatore slid his arms around her and cupped her bare breasts in his hands. The contrast of his tanned fingers with her pale flesh was incredibly erotic. He towered above her, this dark, enigmatic man, master of Torre d'Aquila, keeper of her heart.

Her pulse quickened as she watched their reflection, watched him stroke his thumb-pads across her nipples and then roll them between his fingers until they swelled to hard points. The pleasure was so intense that she gave a little moan and tried to turn to face him, but he tightened his arms around her so that she was trapped against him.

'Do you like that, *mia bella*?' he whispered in her ear.

When she nodded he squeezed her nipples harder, seeming to know instinctively the fine line between pleasure and pain.

Liquid heat pooled between Darcey's thighs when she felt the hard ridge of his arousal push against the cleft of her bottom. She was desperate for him to touch her intimately, and he must have sensed her impatience for he gripped her dress and tugged it down over her hips so that it fell to the floor, leaving her in just a pair of lilac lace knickers. Darcey's mouth ran dry as she watched in the mirror as Salvatore skimmed his hand down over her flat stomach to the edge of her panties. She swallowed when he eased his fingers beneath the fragile barrier of silk and stroked the tight cluster of copper-coloured curls that hid her femininity.

Mesmerised by the erotic image reflected in the mirror, she widened her eyes as she felt him part her and slide his finger inside her. He gave a feral groan as he discovered the slick heat of her arousal. His eyes met hers in the mirror as he began to caress her, and almost instantly she felt her body tighten.

'Salvatore…' She breathed his name, warning him that she was close to orgasm. She did not want him to stop what he was doing with his fingers, but he had aroused a greater need in her that only his full possession could satisfy.

Finally he allowed her to turn around, and immediately lowered his head to take first one dusky nipple and then the other into his mouth. Darcey gasped with the exquisite sensations he was arousing. With feverish haste she pushed his shirt over his shoulders so that she could run her hands over his naked chest. Boldly she moved lower and unfastened his belt buckle.

'Don't stop, *carissima*,' Salvatore bade her roughly when she hesitated.

She stared at his face, all angles and planes in the flickering lamplight, and her stomach clenched when she saw the primitive desire in his eyes. Returning to her task, she freed his zip and pushed his trousers over his hips, realising that he was barefoot. He stepped out of his trousers with easy grace, but instead of touching her he waited, his expression hidden beneath heavy eyelids, while her gaze moved to the mass of deep scars on his thigh. Darcey had seen them before in the pool, but up close the purple welts were a shocking reminder of the terrible injuries he had sustained in the car accident.

Gently she ran her fingerers over the scars and felt him flinch.

'I'm sorry. I didn't mean to hurt you,' she whispered.

'You didn't,' he assured her. 'But if you carry on touching me I hope you are prepared for the consequences.'

'If I touch you like this, do you mean?' she asked innocently, slipping her hand beneath the hem of one leg of his boxer shorts and lightly stroking his swollen penis.

'Madonna!' Salvatore's restraint shattered and he dragged her against him, capturing her mouth in a fiercely possessive kiss. With a deft movement he pulled off his boxers and stood before her, proudly naked and magnificently aroused.

Darcey drew a startled breath when she saw the size of him, but her faint trepidation was forgotten when he slanted his lips over hers and kissed her with sensual passion. The room tilted as he lifted her into his arms and laid her on the bed.

The hard glitter in his eyes told her the time for teasing and foreplay was over. A shadow of her old self-doubt returned when he pulled her panties off and ran his eyes slowly over her naked body. She thought of the photographs she had seen of his gorgeous wife. Adriana had possessed a voluptuous figure. Did Salvatore wish that her breasts were fuller and her hips more rounded? Darcey wondered.

He stroked his hand lightly over her stomach and gave a hoarse groan as he caressed the soft skin of her inner thighs. 'You take my breath away, *mia bella*. The instant I met you I imagined making love to you, and now I can't wait any longer.'

She shared his impatience and offered no resistance when he pushed her legs apart. It was new to her, this uncontrollable hunger that consumed her, and it was a little frightening to find herself at the mercy of her need for sexual fulfilment. But she was enslaved by her need for Salvatore, and when he lifted himself above her she arched her hips, trembling, eager, as the tip of his manhood pressed against her core. As he eased forward she opened for him, catching her breath when her internal muscles had to stretch to accommodate him.

He stilled and stared into her eyes. 'Are you all right? I don't want to hurt you.'

'I'm fine,' she assured him. This pirate was as dangerous as she had guessed him to be, but his tenderness was unexpected.

He kissed her again, gently at first, and she felt a pull on her emotions. But as he deepened the kiss she stopped thinking and gave herself up to the firestorm of passion building inside her as he penetrated her fully and filled her with his swollen length.

Salvatore withdrew and then drove into her again, slowly at first, increasing Darcey's excitement with each measured stroke. It felt so unbelievably good, and she sensed from his quickened breathing that his pleasure was as intense as hers. His dark hair fell forward and she brushed it back from his face before tracing the shape of his chiselled features with shaking fingers. Some deeply primitive instinct insisted that this was her man. The moment she'd met him she'd had a strange sense that she belonged to him, and now, as he thrust into her again and again, she felt that they were joined body and soul.

It couldn't last. Their mutual hunger was too intense. Darcey tensed as she felt ripples of sensation begin deep in her pelvis, and she clung to Salvatore's sweat-sheened shoulders as he quickened his pace. She gasped as he slid his hands beneath her bottom and angled her to take an even deeper thrust. She should have guessed that to be possessed by a pirate would be more compelling, more intense than anything she had ever experienced, she thought. But then her mind went blank and sensation took over. Her climax was hard and fast—pulse-waves of pleasure throbbing through her body. At the same time she heard Salvatore make a harsh sound as his orgasm overpowered him.

For a long time afterwards they remained still joined, breathing hard. In the aftermath of the most passionate lovemaking Salvatore had ever known he felt a sense of contentment that he had never experienced before. For the first time in his life he felt truly relaxed and at peace.

He watched Darcey's copper-gold eyelashes drift closed. Her creamy skin was flushed rose-pink, both on her face and her breasts, he noted, feeling a swift resurgence of desire. He resisted the urge to wake her and take her again. He'd guessed from the slight resistance of her internal muscles when he had initially thrust into her that she had not had sex for a while, and he told himself to be patient. She had agreed to stay at the castle until the end of summer. There would be plenty of opportunities to make love to her. It occurred to him that maybe he could persuade her to extend her stay, and that thought was followed by the realisation that he was in no hurry for her to leave.

Lying back on the pillows, he turned his mind to his niggling concerns about the missing silver antiques and his mother-in-law's curious behaviour. He did not doubt that Darcey had seen Lydia take the silver from the cabinet, but if there was a simple explanation why had Lydia reacted so strangely?

There was also the question of Ettore Varsi. Again, Salvatore believed Darcey. There was no reason why she would have made up the story that she had seen Ettore on the Castellano Estate. But why had he been here? And why had he been careful to avoid the security guards?

Ettore had been on his mind a lot recently. After the accident Salvatore had been grateful to the man who had saved his life by dragging him away from the car before it burst into flames. He had given Ettore a significant financial reward. But for reasons he could not explain to himself he had never liked the man. When Darcey had tried to persuade him to talk to Ettore about the accident, in the hope that something would kick-start his memory, he had shot her down, convinced that there could be no absolution for him. He had been driving the car and he must have been responsible for the crash. But in his last few flashbacks, his wisps of memory were frustratingly incomplete, and if they were true they did not make sense.

Salvatore closed his eyes, hoping that the dull throb behind his temples that had begun a few minutes ago would lessen. But the pain intensified until his head felt as though it would explode. He was almost tempted to wake Darcey and seek solace in the gentle compassion he knew she would offer. He pushed the thought away. He had never asked anyone for help in his life and he wasn't about to start now. Instead he gritted his teeth and waited for the headache to pass. The oil lamp had gone out, and as he stared into the darkness the shadows that had clouded his mind for so long shifted.

Darcey opened her eyes to find her bedroom was filled with bright sunlight. For a moment she wondered if she had dreamed the storm of the previous night. The rumpled sheets and the slight soreness between her legs warned her that she had not imagined making love with Salvatore. He had spent the night in her bed, or at least part of the night. She had no idea when he had left her room—or why he had chosen not to stay with her. Did he regret what had happened? She bit her lip as her old insecurities surfaced. Perhaps he regretted betraying the memory of his wife?

She was distracted from her thoughts when Rosa skipped into the bedroom, carrying a pile of storybooks. Salvatore was aware that Rosa came to her room most mornings, and it was understandable that he would not have wanted his daughter to discover him in bed with her, Darcey's common sense pointed out.

'I'd better get up,' she said, and signed to the little girl. 'I'll read to you after breakfast.'

Darcey took a quick shower and dressed in a white cotton skirt and a green strap top, pleased to see that her usually pale skin had gained a light golden tan during the time she had been in Sicily. It only took a couple of minutes to dry her hair, and with no other excuse to avoid meeting Salvatore she went to find Rosa and take her down to the dining room for breakfast.

The English nanny, Margaret, was in the nursery. 'I think it might be a good idea if I take Rosa to Casa Camelia to play with Nico,' the nanny said. 'There seems to be an argument going on downstairs between Signora Putzi and Signore Castellano. It's probably best if Rosa is kept away from the situation. Things sound rather heated.'

Puzzled by what Margaret had said, Darcey realised she could hear raised voices when she went downstairs. She hesitated when she saw Salvatore and Lydia in the entrance hall and felt a jolt of shock as she recognised the man with them as Ettore Varsi—whom Lydia had sworn she had not seen for months.

Wearing black jeans, shirt and riding boots, and with a grim expression on his face, Salvatore looked formidable as he faced Lydia. 'Explain why you took the silver antiques,' he demanded.

'So you believe the word of that little tart?' Lydia snapped. 'You fool, Salvatore. It's obvious that Darcey is hoping to snare a rich lover and she doesn't want me around to interfere with her plans.'

'Leave Darcey out of this,' he said in a dangerously soft voice. 'Of course I believe her. She is the most honest and honourable person I have ever met. But the same cannot be said of *you*, Lydia. You were caught on the security cameras leaving the castle early this morning, carrying the bag Darcey described, which she had seen you filling with silverware. At the same time Ettore was caught by my security guards landing his boat on the Castellano Estate's private beach.'

Suddenly sensing Darcey's presence, Salvatore glanced towards the stairs.

'I'll—I'll go,' she stammered, her heart sinking as she stared at his stern features. It was impossible to believe that he had made love to her with such tender passion last night.

'No, I want you to stay.'

He sought her gaze, and for a second she glimpsed a flare of emotion in his dark eyes that shook her.

He returned his attention to his mother-in-law and the man with her, who looked as if he would rather be somewhere else. 'I suspect you took the silver to give to Ettore,' Salvatore told Lydia. 'But I want you to tell me why.'

'This is ridiculous—treating me like a criminal,' Lydia blustered. 'I admit I...*borrowed*...some silverware, but I don't know why Ettore came to the Castellano Estate.'

'I was fishing,' Ettore muttered. 'I had trouble with

my boat and I was forced to land on the beach. I don't know—'

'Enough!' Salvatore's voice cracked like a whip and both Lydia and Ettore stared at him nervously. 'Before you tell me any more lies you need to know that I have regained my memory—and I remember *everything* about the accident.'

CHAPTER NINE

DARCEY'S SENSE OF shock was mirrored on Lydia's face. Salvatore's mother-in-law turned pale and covered her face with her hands. 'Oh, my God. I didn't think it could happen after all this time…'

Ettore Varsi had also paled. He spun round and ran across the hall to the front door, but was apprehended by two security guards waiting outside. Salvatore strode over to him and grabbed him by the lapels of his jacket.

'You lied, didn't you?' he said harshly. 'I *wasn't* driving the car when it crashed. Adriana was driving. For the past four years all I could remember was getting behind the steering wheel when we left the party. But now I remember that on the journey home I stopped. Adriana and I were having a row and I knew it wasn't safe to drive when I had lost my temper.'

He tightened his grip on Ettore.

'I remember seeing you drive past while we were standing at the side of the road arguing. Adriana suddenly jumped into the driver's seat of my car. She was drunk and I was scared for her safety. As she pulled away I managed to leap into the passenger seat. I was pleading with her to slow down when we overtook you on the road.'

Salvatore's voice roughened.

'I remember approaching the bend and knowing that we weren't going to make it. Adriana was going too fast. I tried to grab the wheel, but it was too late. The last memory I have is of the car smashing through the barrier and hurtling down the mountainside. *Why did you lie to the police?*' he asked Ettore savagely. 'Why did you allow me to believe that the accident was my fault?'

'She told me to do it.' Ettore pointed to Lydia.

He looked terrified, and when Darcey glanced at Salvatore's murderous expression she wasn't surprised.

'It was her idea.'

Salvatore flung Ettore away, as if he felt contaminated by the other man's presence. 'I don't believe you. It can't be true.' He looked at his mother-in-law and frowned as Lydia burst into tears.

'It *is* true,' she wept. 'There's no point pretending any more. I was staying here at the castle the night the accident happened, and as soon as I heard the news I rushed to the scene of the crash. I wanted to save my baby, but Adriana was already dead.'

She gave a tearing sob that wrenched Darcey's heart.

'I saw Ettore,' she continued. 'He was waiting to give a statement to the police. He told me what had happened—how he had seen Adriana driving erratically just before the crash.' She looked pleadingly at Salvatore. 'I guessed she would have got drunk at the party. She loved champagne. Adriana was a top model and you are a member of the renowned Castellano family, so I knew the crash would be headline news around the world. I couldn't bear the thought of my daughter being blamed for the accident and the media tearing her reputation to shreds. I loved my darling girl and I…I wanted to protect her name.'

Lydia took a shuddering breath.

'So I offered money to Ettore if he would give a false

statement to the police. He had pulled you and Adriana away from the car before it caught fire. There was no way of proving who had been driving—there was just Ettore's word.'

'*Santa Madre,*' Salvatore said raggedly. 'All this time you let me think I had killed Adriana and robbed Rosa of her mother. You *knew* I was tortured with guilt...'

'You didn't love Adriana,' Lydia said bitterly. 'You only married her because she was pregnant and you wanted the child. You deserved to suffer like I was suffering.' Taking another shuddering breath, she continued. 'At first everything worked out. I paid Ettore to keep quiet about what he knew. But he kept asking for more money and I couldn't meet his demands. I am not wealthy. My husband lost a fortune in a bad business deal and when he died I inherited very little. Luckily your guilt over Adriana meant that you allowed me to stay at the castle, which cut down my living expenses.'

'So that's why you kept telling me how much I had loved Adriana. You played on my conscience.'

The raw pain in Salvatore's voice was too much for Darcey to bear and she hurried over to him and gripped his hand. He did not look at her, but he squeezed her fingers in acknowledgement of her support.

'You must have prayed that I would never regain my memory,' he said grimly to Lydia.

'You were different when you came back from England.' She glanced at Darcey. 'It's not hard to guess why. I knew that if you had an affair with Darcey you might not want me around. I told Ettore I couldn't give him any more money, but he insisted. In desperation I agreed to take some of the silver antiques, so that he could sell them. There are so many valuable items in the castle I didn't think anyone would notice if a few went missing.'

'Armond has catalogued every item,' Darcey murmured.

She looked towards the front door as a commotion broke out. Ettore had managed to escape from the security guards and was tearing down the front steps of the castle.

'Let him go,' Salvatore advised the guards. 'He won't get far now that the security staff have moved his boat from the beach. He'll be arrested when I tell the police that he gave a false statement and has been involved in blackmail. I hope he rots in jail, and if I get hold of him he'll think he's in hell,' he said bitterly.

His expression turned to disgust as he studied Lydia, who was still crying. He was patently unmoved by her tears. 'I'll give you five minutes to pack and then I want you to leave my home for good.'

'But...surely you will allow me to visit my granddaughter occasionally?' Lydia whispered.

'After what you have done you're lucky I have decided not to press charges against you. But you will never be welcome at Torre d'Aquila again.'

Lydia gasped and her shoulders shook as more sobs tore through her. Darcey's soft heart ached for the older woman, despite all that she had done.

She put a comforting hand on Lydia's arm and stared at Salvatore, her green eyes bright with emotion. 'That's too cruel,' she said softly.

His jaw clenched. 'How can you defend her after she let me suffer for four hellish years?'

'I know what she did was terrible, but she has lost her only daughter. Rosa is her only link with Adriana.'

Darcey bit her lip as Salvatore's dark eyes burned into her. She knew he thought she was being disloyal by sympathising with Lydia. His mouth twisted and he growled something ugly before he swung away from her and strode out of the castle. She longed to run after him, but Lydia collapsed onto the floor and Darcey hurriedly called to Armond for help.

'I can't believe Lydia and Ettore did such a terrible thing,' Kristen said for about the tenth time. She shook her head. 'Lying to Salvatore and letting him think he was responsible for Adriana's death was unforgivable. No wonder he was so angry when he came and told Sergio this morning. But at least he has regained his memory at last.'

Darcey glanced across the charming sitting room at Casa Camelia, where she had spent the day. Kristen was picking up the toys that Nico and Rosa had been playing with before the nanny had taken them outside to the garden.

'I'm glad Salvatore confided in Sergio. When he left the castle after Lydia had confessed, he looked—' Darcey broke off, unable to explain Salvatore's savage expression or the flash of hurt in his eyes when she was sympathetic to Lydia.

Kristen nodded. 'It was tragic that the brothers were separated when they were young boys and didn't share the bond many twins have. But they are closer now. Salvatore has always seemed so self-contained, but recently I've noticed a change in him, and Sergio has mentioned it too.' She gave Darcey a speculative look. 'Salvatore seems more relaxed since you have been staying at the castle. What *is* going on between the two of you?'

Darcey felt heat rise in her face. 'Nothing,' she said quickly. 'At least nothing serious.' She bit her lip as she recalled their passionate lovemaking the previous night. For all she knew he might have regarded having sex with her as a one-night stand. 'Salvatore doesn't allow anyone too close.'

'And yet I sense that he would like to get close to you,' Kristen's bright blue eyes softened when she saw that Darcey was uncomfortable with the conversation. 'I wonder when the men will be back. They went out on the horses hours ago.' She focused on the tiny baby in Darcey's arms. 'Talking of men—how is my little man?'

'He's still asleep.' Darcey looked down at baby Leo's angelic face and felt a deep pull of maternal longing in the pit of her stomach. 'He's gorgeous,' she murmured.

Kristen laughed. 'Like all the Castellano men.' She glanced out of the window at her older son Nico, who was racing across the patio with Rosa. 'I think our five minutes of peace is about to end,' she said ruefully.

Darcey took Rosa back to the castle in the early evening. The little girl was tired after spending the day with her energetic cousin, and fell asleep within minutes of Darcey tucking her into bed. She had not seen or heard from Salvatore all day, but a few minutes after she had walked into her bedroom Armond knocked on the door.

'Signore Castellano has asked me to inform you that dinner will be served in the tower room this evening.' The butler handed her a large flat box. 'He also asked me to give you this.'

Puzzled, she carried the box over to the bed and gasped when she opened it and lifted out an exquisite dress. The floor-length cream chiffon gown was beautifully understated and she recognised the logo on the box as belonging to a top design house. The last time she had seen Salvatore he had seemed bitterly angry with her. She had no idea why he had given her the dress, or why he had arranged for them to eat in her favourite room in the castle.

With an hour to spare before dinner she indulged in a pampering session, and after a long soak, fragrant with bath crystals, she smoothed scented oil onto her skin and dried her hair into a glossy bob before slipping the dress over her head. The low-cut neckline revealed the smooth upper slopes of her breasts and the narrow shoulder straps embellished with crystals added sparkle to the elegant gown.

Her heart was thudding by the time she reached the tower room, and although she told herself she was breathless because she had climbed four flights of stairs, the truth was that she felt nervous at the prospect of being alone with Salvatore for the first time since she had been naked in his arms.

She opened the door and stepped into the circular room, which had windows all the way round the walls, giving stunning vistas of the Sicilian countryside and the smouldering volcano Etna towering in the distance. But Darcey barely noticed the view. Her eyes were drawn to Salvatore.

Silhouetted against the evening sunshine streaming through the windows, his face was in shadow. She was aware of his exceptional height and the power of his formidable build. Wearing close-fitting black trousers and a fine white shirt, his dark hair brushing his shoulders, he would not have looked out of place in a previous century, she thought ruefully.

He studied her for long moments, while Darcey's tension grew, but then, to her amazement, his mouth curved into a warm smile that trapped her breath in her lungs.

'You look even more beautiful in the dress than I imagined when I chose it for you,' he murmured.

'It's the loveliest dress I've ever worn.' She swallowed. 'I...I thought you would still be angry with me.'

'Angry with *you*?' he sounded genuinely surprised. 'Why would you think that, *carissima*?'

'Because I asked you to show leniency to Lydia.'

Her heart missed a beat as Salvatore crossed the room and stood in front of her. He slid his hand beneath her chin and she felt a jolt of shock when she saw that the warmth of his smile was reflected in his eyes. The change in him was remarkable. His face was no longer set in a stern expression and there was a new softness to his chiselled features that made Darcey's insides melt.

'I knew even as I stormed out of the castle this morning that I should not have expected anything less from you. Your compassionate heart puts me to shame.'

'You have every right to be furious and bitter,' she said huskily. 'Lydia and Ettore did a terrible thing. Ettore lied purely for financial gain, and I hope he is sent to prison, but I can understand why Lydia wanted to protect her daughter even after her death. She loved Adriana so much.' Darcey hesitated. 'Lydia accused you of not loving Adriana. If that is true, why did you marry her?'

Salvatore exhaled heavily. 'I find it amazing that after four years of blankness I am suddenly able to remember everything about my past—including my relationship with Adriana. I met her in Rome. I was there on business and she was modelling at a charity fashion show that I was invited to.' He shrugged. 'I found her attractive and we became lovers. But to be honest I had no intention of prolonging our affair after I returned to Sicily. That was until three months later, when Adriana turned up at the castle and announced she was expecting my baby. A DNA test proved it *was* my child. She insisted that the condom must have been faulty, but I suspect she aimed to fall pregnant as a means of gaining financial security once she realised the extent of my wealth. It's not an unusual story, is it? Rich guy gets trapped by unscrupulous gold-digger,' he said sardonically. 'But I immediately accepted responsibility for my child and did the only thing I could do under the circumstances—married Adriana. It was certainly no love-match, but I was determined to try to make the marriage work for the sake of our child. And when Rosa was born I fell in love.

'Not with Adriana,' he said in answer to Darcey's questioning look. 'The moment I held my daughter in my arms I was overwhelmed by an emotion I had never felt before. My loveless childhood had not prepared me for the intense love I felt for Rosa, and it was for her sake that I did my best to make Adriana happy so that we could provide a secure family for our daughter.'

Salvatore moved to the window and stared out at the estate's vineyards, stretching away to the horizon. He was proud of his Sicilian heritage. Perhaps it was because his father had sent him away to school that he loved his home so deeply, he thought. He sensed that Darcey was waiting for him to explain more about his marriage, and in a way it was a relief to be able to talk about the past that for four years had been blocked out by his amnesia.

'Adriana hated living at Torre d'Aquila and wanted us to move to Rome. It was the one thing I could not bear to do, even to save my marriage. My heart belongs here,' he said gruffly. 'The vineyards, the rich soil that produces the best grapes—this land is part of me. When I was a boy and my father sent me away to school I felt dead inside, and I did not feel alive again until I returned to the estate. After I finished studying viticulture at university I came back to take charge of the winery and I vowed I would never live anywhere else.'

Salvatore glanced at Darcey and felt his stomach clench with desire. She looked incredibly sexy in the dress he had chosen and his mind was distracted by the erotic fantasy of undressing her. But she deserved to hear the full story, so he continued.

'Adriana returned to her modelling career when Rosa was a few months old. She frequently went away on assignments and left Rosa behind at the castle with me and a nanny. I was concerned that as Rosa grew older she would miss her mother. And then through modelling Adriana came to the notice of a film director who offered her a role in a film. She was determined to move to California to pursue an acting career.'

His jaw tightened. 'It seemed a grim irony that history was repeating itself. My mother had abandoned me to be an actress in America, and now my wife planned to do the same thing and abandon our daughter. That's what we were arguing about when we drove away from the party. For Rosa's sake I begged Adriana to reconsider her plans. She accused me of being selfish and trying to ruin her chance to be an actress—and she was right,' he said heavily. 'If I had been more understanding of Adriana's dreams, if I had agreed to leave Sicily and go to California with her, then she would not have driven off in a temper and lost control of the car—and Rosa would still have a mother.'

'You can't keep blaming yourself,' Darcey said softly. She walked over to Salvatore and placed her hand on his arm. 'For Rosa's sake you have to let go of the past and move on with your life.'

'It will be easier to do so now that I can remember what happened that night.'

He covered her hand with his much larger one and the contact of his warm skin sent a quiver of sensation along

Darcey's arm as she remembered the feel of his naked body on hers when he had made love to her.

'It is thanks to you that I discovered how Lydia and Ettore had tricked me into believing that I was responsible for Adriana's death,' Salvatore told her. 'After we made love last night my amnesia lifted. You have given me my life back. For the first time in four years I can look forward to the future, and I plan to be the best father I can be to Rosa.' He lifted his hand to Darcey's face and looked deeply into her eyes. 'But my immediate plan is to take you to bed and spend the night making love to you, my sweet Darcey.'

He did not mention what would happen *after* they had spent the night together. Darcey had no idea whether she featured in his plans for the future or whether he simply wanted to have sex with her. But her treacherous body did not care. Last night Salvatore had revealed her deeply sensual nature and she had surprised herself with her wanton response to him. Now, as he brushed his lips along her collarbone and found the pulse beating erratically at the base of her throat, molten desire swept through her and the heavy ache in the pit of her stomach became an insistent throb of need.

His lips continued upwards, trailing feather-soft kisses over her face, her eyelids, until finally he claimed her mouth in a fiercely passionate kiss that sent fire coursing through Darcey's veins. She responded to him mindlessly, parting her lips so that he could explore her with his tongue. Nothing mattered except that he should make love to her. Salvatore had not made any promises of wanting a meaningful relationship. But her ex-husband had broken every one of his marriage vows, she thought ruefully. She did not know if she could completely trust any man ever again. Promises were easy to make and easy to break, whereas sexual desire was simple and uncomplicated.

'*Dio*, you drive me insane,' Salvatore said thickly.

But instead of kissing her again, as Darcey had hoped, he stepped away from her and raked a hand through his hair.

'I had the evening planned, but I only have to look at you and all my good intentions disappear.' He lifted her hand to his mouth and brushed his lips across her fingers before leading her over to the table that she saw had been decorated with flowers and candles. 'I planned this evening to be a date,' Salvatore explained. 'Over dinner I thought we could get to know each other better. I don't just want to have sex with you,' he said softly. 'I want to find out more about Darcey Rivers while we eat good food and drink fine wine—but I warn you that we might not make it as far as dessert before my need to make love to you wins over my attempts to be chivalrous,' he admitted ruefully.

Her smile stole his breath. 'I would love to go on a date with you,' Darcey assured him. 'And I'll be quite happy to forgo dessert,' she added, her green eyes shimmering with sensual promise.

A selection of salad dishes, accompanied by cold meats, seafood and cheeses, had been prepared for them, and to go with the food Salvatore served a rich red wine from the Castellano vineyards. The view from the tower of the sun sinking below the horizon was spectacular and Darcey felt relaxed—yet at the same time she felt a shiver of anticipation when she caught the sultry gleam in Salvatore's eyes.

'Tell me more about your family,' he invited. 'You said you are close to your parents? What do they do for a living?'

She hesitated. It was unlikely that her famous family were well known in Sicily, but she had met Salvatore in London and there was a good chance he might have heard of the Hart acting dynasty. If she told him who she was he would probably ask why she had not followed the family tradition and become an actress. She did not want to admit that one reason why she hadn't was because of her lack of self-confidence and her fear that she was not as talented as her parents and siblings. Performing in her father's play would be a big test. Even though the opening night was months away she felt nervous every time she thought about it, and she did not feel confident enough with Salvatore to reveal her insecurities to him.

'My parents own their own business,' she murmured. It was the truth, for her parents still took an active part in running the theatre company they had established when Darcey was a child. 'My father makes wine for a hobby and he has a vineyard at our house in France.' She nudged the conversation in a different direction.

'Really?' Salvatore was immediately curious. 'How many hectares of vines does he have?'

'Um…about three.'

He looked amused. 'Ah, so it's a small-scale winery? There are one hundred hectares of vines on the Castellano Estate. But France certainly produces some of the best wine in the world.'

'*This* is a lovely wine.' Darcey took a sip of the red wine and found it delightfully smooth. 'I think it would be easy to drink too much of it.' She felt light-headed after half a glass, although that might have more to do with the tangible sexual awareness simmering in the tower room, she acknowledged.

She looked across the table at Salvatore and her stomach muscles tightened when she saw the undisguised hunger in his eyes.

'Darcey!'

His feral growl sent a shiver of excitement through her. He stood up and walked around the table. Holding out his hand, he drew her to her feet and pulled her into his arms.

'Carissima, I have never needed anyone in my life, but I need you,' he said roughly. 'I adore talking to you, but if I don't make love to you right now I think I'll explode.'

His raw honesty moved her. He had tried to keep his tone light, but beneath it she had heard something in his voice that made her imagine him as a lonely boy, abandoned by his mother and sent away to school in a foreign country by his father.

'I think conversation is overrated,' she whispered as she reached up and wound her arms around his neck.

Laughter rumbled in his chest, but there was nothing teasing about his kiss when he claimed her mouth. He pushed his tongue between her lips in an erotic imitation of how he would soon push his powerful erection into her receptive body. Heat pulsed between Darcey's legs and she kissed him with a desperate fervency, trying to show him that her need was as great as his.

While they had been having dinner night had fallen, and outside the sky had darkened to indigo, lit by a huge moon that filled the tower room with silver shadows. Salvatore led Darcey over to an antique *chaise longue* upholstered in rich burgundy velvet and her pulse quickened when she realised that he intended to make love to her on it. He slid the straps of her dress over her shoulders, and when her breasts spilled into his hands he cupped the soft mounds and stroked her nipples until they hardened.

'You are so beautiful,' he whispered against her skin as he trailed his lips over her trembling body.

He took one taut peak into his mouth and suckled her. The sensation was so intense that Darcey gave a soft cry, and when he turned his attention to her other breast she felt molten heat pool between her legs. She was impatient for him to push her down onto the sofa, but he seemed determined to kiss every inch of her body and tugged her dress down so that it settled in a froth of chiffon at her feet. The sight of her lacy thong brought a growl of approval from him as he knelt in front of her and kissed her flat stomach, the soft skin of her inner thighs.

'Salvatore...!' She gave a startled cry when he pressed his mouth to the tiny strip of lace between her legs and then eased the thong to one side so that he could run his tongue up and down her moist opening.

She clutched his shoulders as she felt him gently part her and push his tongue into her to bestow the most intimate caress of all. It was a new experience for Darcey, but her shock quickly turned to pleasure as he brought her to the edge of ecstasy.

'Please...' she gasped, feeling the coiling sensation in her pelvis tighten as Salvatore flicked his tongue across her clitoris.

Her husky plea tugged on Salvatore's heart. Darcey was so sweetly responsive. She had crept under his guard and warmed the coldness inside him, and his sole aim was to please her. Ignoring the urgent need to seek his own satisfaction, he pressed his mouth against the heart of her femininity and tasted the sensual musk of her arousal.

The storm inside her was building, and Darcey could feel her control slipping. She dug her nails into Salvatore's shoulders as he continued to pleasure her with his wickedly invasive tongue. She needed to tell him that if he didn't stop she would—

'Oh...'

Her thought-processes juddered to a halt as the first ripples of orgasm swiftly intensified until her entire body pulsed with pleasure. Only then, when she was gasping and her legs buckled, did Salvatore lift her in his arms and place her on the velvet cushions of the *chaise longue*. She watched him strip, her heart thumping, and when he stood between her legs she arched her hips and gave a choked cry as he plunged his powerful erection deep into her.

He filled her, completed her, and with every hard stroke he claimed possession of her body and her soul. Her second orgasm was even more intense than her first, and as she wrapped her legs around his back he gave the hardest thrust yet and his body shuddered with the force of his release.

A long time afterwards Salvatore lifted his head from the soft pillow of Darcey's breasts and looked into her bright green eyes. 'Not only was your husband a jerk, but he was evidently a selfish lover too. Didn't he ever take the time to discover ways to give you pleasure?'

She flushed, feeling embarrassed that he had guessed oral sex was a new experience for her. 'The truth is my marriage was shaky right from the start,' she admitted. 'I found out soon after the wedding that Marcus had only married me because...'

Her voice faltered. She felt reluctant to admit the humiliating truth that Marcus had married her because he had wanted to get close to her famous family.

'I wasn't the person Marcus thought I was,' she said at last. 'We met while we were staying at the same beach resort, and I think we were both seduced by the romantic atmosphere. But I should have known that holiday romances don't last. The reality of living together revealed how unsuited we were. I wasn't exciting enough for Marcus.'

The faint tremor in her voice made Salvatore wonder if she still had feelings for her ex-husband, and he was surprised by how strongly he disliked the idea. He knew Darcey was an intensely loyal person, but he was certain that any residual feelings she might feel for the man she had married were misplaced.

'Let me show you how very exciting I find you, *mia bella*,' he murmured, shifting his position so that his erection nudged between her legs.

He loved the way her eyes darkened to jade with desire. Her soft smile as she took him inside her tugged on his heart. He was still coming to terms with regaining his memory and finally discovering the truth about the accident. But for the first time in four years he was able to look forward, and the future suddenly seemed full of promise.

CHAPTER TEN

Salvatore felt a surge of pleasure when he walked across the lawn and saw Darcey sitting beneath the shade of a parasol. She was wearing a simple white shift dress that showed off her light golden tan. Her silky bob of copper-brown hair framed her lovely face and she looked elegant, innocent, and incredibly sexy all at once.

His sense of well-being increased when he leaned down to claim her mouth and she parted her lips for him to deepen the kiss.

'You seem to be permanently attached to your laptop.' His light tone did not fully disguise his curiosity about why she spent so much of her free time when she wasn't with Rosa working on her computer.

Darcey considered explaining that for the past few weeks she had been studying the role she was to take in her father's play, but talking about it would make it real, and for the sake of her edgy nerves she preferred not to think about the opening night, when she would walk onto the stage for the first time. Looking beyond the play, she had written a business proposal that she hoped would convince the bank to give her a loan so she could set up a private speech therapy practice.

Salvatore glanced over her shoulder at the columns of figures on the screen.

'I need to make my business plan impressive so that the bank will agree to lend me enough money to cover the initial expense of setting up a private speech therapy clinic,' she told him. 'I've never run my own business before and it's all a bit daunting.'

'I'll take a look at your proposal, if you like. I'm busy at the moment, with the grape harvest, but there's no hurry, is there? I thought you were planning to start your business some time next year?'

The shutters had come down on Salvatore's expression so that Darcey had no idea what he was thinking. She wondered why he had offered to look at the proposal when he clearly wasn't interested. His tone was cool, almost off-hand, reminding her of how aloof he had been when she had first met him.

'I need to have my plans ready. Time passes so quickly. It's September already, and I'll be going home at the end of the month.' The thought made her heart ache, and in an effort to disguise the huskiness in her voice she said quickly, 'I've been thinking about who you could employ to replace me as Rosa's speech therapist, and I've had an idea. A colleague I used to work with retired from her job last year, but she still does some private work. Pamela doesn't have any family ties and I'm sure she would agree to come to Sicily and work with Rosa.'

'We'll discuss the matter another time,' Salvatore told her in a noncommittal voice. 'Has Rosa told you that she is going to stay at Casa Camelia for a couple of days, while I go to Rome for a business meeting?'

'Yes, she's very excited about her first sleepover with her cousin. Although I'm not sure how much sleep the children will actually get—or Sergio and Kristen, for that matter.' Darcey gave him a rueful look. 'If you had asked me, I would have been happy to look after Rosa. I didn't know until she told me at breakfast that you were going away.'

She could not hide the note of hurt in her voice that Salvatore hadn't informed her of his plans. His desire for her showed no sign of fading, and he made love to her every night with tenderness as well as passion, so that she had started to hope that perhaps he cared for her, but the fact that he had not deemed it necessary to tell her about his trip to Rome was a clear indication that he did not have any regard for her or her feelings.

He brushed a few strands of hair back from her face and his expression softened. 'That is because Rosa was sworn to secrecy. I arranged for her to stay with Sergio and Kristen because you are coming to Rome with me.'

The warmth in his eyes set her pulse racing. 'Why would you want to take me to a business meeting?'

'I'll leave you while I meet with my export manager, but the meeting shouldn't take more than a couple of hours—enough time for you to investigate the shoe shops on Via Condotti. We'll have lunch at a restaurant and spend the afternoon exploring the city. I overheard you telling Armond that you would love to visit the Colosseum,' he murmured.

'But you are so busy with the harvest. I'm sure you don't have time to take me on a sightseeing trip.'

'I always have time for you, *carissima*.' Salvatore could not resist the temptation of Darcey's soft lips and he kissed her again, a slow, drugging kiss tinged with the tenderness he felt for her. 'It will be good for us to spend some time together. There's something I want to talk to you about.'

Whatever he wanted to talk about sounded serious, Darcey thought nervously. 'Rosa has already gone to Casa Camelia. We have time to talk now,' she suggested.

'No, we don't. We're leaving on the helicopter in fifteen minutes.'

'But I need to pack for the trip...'

She jumped to her feet, but as she was about to race into the castle Salvatore slipped his arm around her waist.

'Everything has been taken care of. I asked the maid to pack for you. All you have to do is relax and enjoy yourself. You've worked so hard with Rosa, and her speech is improving amazingly fast. This trip is a way for me to show you how much I appreciate all that you have done for my daughter—and for me,' Salvatore said, his voice roughening with emotions that until he had met Darcey had been unfamiliar to him. 'For the next few days and nights I intend to devote myself to you, *mia bella*. Especially the nights,' he added, giving her a wolfish smile that made her pulse-rate rocket.

It was Darcey's first visit to Rome, and she discovered a bustling, cosmopolitan city with a fascinating historical heritage. She had assured Salvatore that she would be fine on her own while he attended his business meeting.

On his way out of their hotel room he'd pulled her into his arms and kissed her hard, as if he was reluctant to leave her. 'I'll cancel my meeting,' he'd said gruffly.

'You can't. Your business is important.' She had pushed away the thought that she would miss him even for a few hours. 'I'll be waiting for you,' she'd told him, with a sweet smile that tugged on Salvatore's insides.

At lunchtime she found the restaurant close to the landmark Spanish Steps where she had arranged to meet him and was informed that Salvatore had not yet arrived, but their table was ready. As she followed the waiter outside to a pretty courtyard filled with the scent of roses and orange blossom she guessed his meeting had overrun, but she was happy to sit and sip a glass of lemonade while she studied the restaurant's clientele.

It was obviously a popular place for local Romans to dine. The women were sophisticated, and most of the men were wearing suits and looked like successful business-men. Take the man who had just stepped into the court-yard. He was impeccably dressed in a pale grey suit and dark blue silk shirt, and was so stunningly handsome that it was impossible not to notice him. His almost black hair gleamed like raw silk and was cut short in a style that emphasised his chiselled cheekbones and square jaw.

Darcey's heart missed a beat as the man headed pur-posefully in her direction and she realised why he seemed familiar.

'I'm sorry I'm late, *carissima.*'

She could not stop staring at Salvatore. 'You look…' she had been going to say *different* '…gorgeous,' she said huskily. 'Why did you cut your hair?'

His smile blew her away. 'I decided it was time I smartened up my appearance. I have finally put the past behind me. It's time to make a fresh start and look to the future.'

'I'm glad for you.' It was the truth, but Darcey felt as if an arrow had pierced her heart when she thought about *her* future. In a couple of weeks she would go back to London and it was likely that she would never see Salvatore again. He had not suggested that he wanted their affair to continue, and anyway the logis-tics of a long-distance relationship would be difficult— especially while she was rehearsing for her father's play, she thought dully.

She told herself to enjoy the time she had left with him, but although the baked sea bass she had ordered was delicious her appetite had disappeared. After lunch, when they strolled around Rome visiting the popular tourist sites, she was aware of the interested glances other women sent him and jealousy burned in her stomach. If Salvatore's hopes for the future included marrying again he would have no shortage of candidates willing to share his life and his bed at Torre d'Aquila.

They returned to the hotel in the early evening.

'I've booked a table for dinner here at the hotel's restaurant for eight o'clock,' Salvatore said as he followed Darcey into the bedroom of their luxury suite. He watched her kick off her shoes and frowned when he noticed her face was unusually pale. 'Why don't you lie down for a while? It was hot walking around the city and you're probably tired.'

Salvatore had been a wonderful tour guide, showing her the famous sights of Rome, and he had gone to a lot of effort to make the day enjoyable. Darcey did not want him to think she was unappreciative. It wasn't his fault she had fallen so deeply in love with him that the thought of leaving him was tearing her apart, she acknowledged.

She dredged up a smile. 'I'm not at all tired.'

Her heart thudded when he drew her into his arms. 'In that case you definitely need to lie down, *cara*,' he murmured, his voice as sensuous as crushed velvet. 'We have a few hours to spare until dinner and I have an excellent idea for how we can use the time.'

He bent his head and claimed her mouth, the kiss quickly changing from gentle to fiercely passionate as Darcey responded to him with an urgency that set them both alight. She could not resist him—not when she knew that soon there would be no more chances to make love with him. She would go back to London and he would remain at his castle, free at last from the darkness of his past and ready to move on with his life.

Perhaps you should tell him how you feel about him, prompted a voice inside her head. The idea caused Darcey's stomach to lurch. Salvatore had always known that she would be going home at the end of September and he had never asked her to extend her stay. She was no longer worried that he was in love with his dead wife. He had admitted that he had never been in love with Adriana. That was what troubled her. Salvatore had revealed that as a result of his unhappy childhood he found it hard to get close to anyone. If he felt anything at all for her he was keeping his feelings well hidden.

He moved his hands round to her back and ran the zip down her spine. Her dress slithered to the floor, quickly followed by her bra and knickers.

'*Dio*, have you any idea what you do to me?' he demanded hoarsely. 'All day I have thought about holding you like this, undressing you and feeling your naked skin against mine.'

Salvatore might be a master at hiding his emotions, but his undisguised desire for her was balm to Darcey's aching heart. She helped him out of his clothes with unashamed eagerness and they fell onto the bed in a tangle of limbs, their breathing quickening as they touched and stroked each other until the waiting became intolerable and he pulled her beneath him.

He made love to her hard and fast and they climaxed simultaneously. A little while later he rolled onto his back and guided her down onto him. This time the loving was slower and more intense, and as Salvatore groaned and buried his face in Darcey's neck he wondered what the hell was happening to him.

'I don't want your retired friend to take your place as Rosa's speech therapist.'

Darcey was half-asleep, her body utterly relaxed in

the sensuous aftermath of passion. Salvatore had made love to her with such tenderness and exquisite care that tears had filled her eyes and love had filled her heart.

She opened her eyes to find him propped on one elbow, leaning over her. She couldn't get over how gorgeous he looked with his short hair and clean-shaven jaw. But the biggest change was the warmth in his eyes. He had looked so cold and stern when she had first met him, she mused. But now he looked relaxed and unbelievably sexy.

She tried to concentrate on what he had said.

'Pamela Dickens has years of experience in speech therapy, and she is a very kind person. I think Rosa would like her,' she said, guessing that he was concerned about how Rosa would react to a new therapist.

'You don't understand.'

He held her gaze, and something in his expression made Darcey's heart miss a beat.

'I don't want you to go back to London. I want you to stay at Torre d'Aquila with Rosa—and with me.'

'Salvatore, I…' She was prevented from saying anything more when he placed his finger across her lips.

'I was going to say this over dinner, but as usual you have turned my plans upside down,' he said wryly. 'I know you want to set up a private practice, but maybe you could put your plans on hold. I understand that your career is important to you.' His voice deepened. 'But *you* are important to me, Darcey.'

Salvatore could feel his heart slamming against his ribs. He could not remember ever feeling nervous in his life and it was not a comfortable experience. But he had realised that he could not let Darcey walk out of his life.

'There is something special between us. I think,' he said. 'I'd hoped that you feel it too, *carissima*.'

Darcey's breath was trapped in her lungs and her voice emerged as a whisper. 'What exactly are you saying?'

'I'm asking you if you will live at the castle with me instead of going back to England and let's see how our relationship develops.'

His hand was unsteady as he brushed Darcey's hair back from her face. The emotions she evoked in him were unlike anything he had felt for any other woman and he was still trying to assimilate what it was he felt for her.

'I don't know what is ahead for us,' he told her honestly. 'All I know is that before I met you I gave no thought to the future, but now I don't want to contemplate a future without you.'

It was not a declaration of love, but Salvatore's confession that she was special to him was more than Darcey had dared to hope for. Was it enough for her to alter her career plans and leave her family and friends to move to Sicily? It could be the biggest gamble of her life, she acknowledged. But if she walked away from him without giving their relationship a chance she knew she would regret it for the rest of her life.

She curled her arms around his neck and pulled his mouth down to hers. 'I'll stay on one condition,' she murmured.

His shoulders tensed. 'And what is that?'

'That you promise to make love to me as beautifully as you did a few minutes ago at least once a night.'

Salvatore felt a gentle tug on his heart as he stared into her bright green eyes. 'I give you my word, *cara*.' He grinned, feeling more carefree than he had ever done. 'And there's a good chance I'll manage mornings and possibly afternoons too,' he murmured.

The teasing and the underlying tenderness between them was new to him. His upbringing had taught him not to analyse his emotions, but if he'd had to describe how he felt right now, *happy* summed up his feelings perfectly, Salvatore mused.

'I will still have to go home for a couple of months,' Darcey said ruefully. 'I can't let my father down. But I'll come back to Torre d'Aquila after...' She hesitated.

'After what?' Salvatore trailed his lips over her throat. He did not want to talk, he wanted to make love to her, but something in her tone made him lift his head and look at her. 'Why do you need to return to London?'

'Well...' Darcey took a deep breath. Salvatore would be the only person outside of her family to know that she was going to perform in her father's play, and it was a measure of how much she trusted him that she felt comfortable to talk to him about it. 'I'm going to take the lead role in a play my father has written. You might have heard of the actor and playwright Joshua Hart?'

Salvatore frowned. 'He is a renowned English Shakespearean actor. I actually saw him play Hamlet at the Globe Theatre last year, when I was in London.' He gave her a puzzled look. 'The Hart family are well known in the theatrical world. But what does that have to do with you?'

'Joshua is my father. Hart was my maiden name.'

He stared at her. His brain seemed to have frozen. He couldn't think and he was sure he could not have heard Darcey correctly.

'Are you saying that you're family are *actors*?' His brain unfroze. 'And *you* are going to act in a play?'

It did not make sense. She was a speech therapist, for God's sake!

He sat up and raked a hand through his hair. 'Let me get this straight. *You intend to leave me because you want to pursue a career as an actress.*' He gave a bitter laugh. 'Well, there's nothing new there. First my mother left because she dreamed of becoming a film star, then my wife, and now you.'

'*No*, it's not like that at all,' Darcey said urgently. It had not crossed her mind that Salvatore would link her decision to perform in the play with his mother's and Adriana's determination to be an actress. But now that he had pointed it out she felt guilty that she had not told him about her connection to the acting world. 'I don't want to be a film star. I'm not even a proper actress, although I did a bit of acting when I was younger. I decided that I wanted a different career to the rest of my family.'

Darcey's voice faded as she watched get up from the bed and pull his trousers on. His jaw was set, but she did not understand why he was angry. The happiness she had felt a few moments ago was trickling away as fast as sand in an egg-timer.

'I agreed to take this particular role because the play is about my grandmother and is very personal to my father,' she explained hurriedly. 'The production is only booked to run for two months.'

'What will happen if the play is a success and continues to run?'

'I suppose another actress will take the lead role.'

'And your father wouldn't persuade you to carry on playing the part indefinitely? There is a play in the West End that has run for more than twenty years.'

'I think it's unlikely that Dad's play will be as successful as *The Mousetrap*.' Darcey sighed. 'Look, I realise this is a surprise…'

'That's something of an understatement,' Salvatore said with savage sarcasm. 'Why didn't you mention before about your connection to the acting profession? You deliberately kept it a secret. You even lied to me when

I asked you what your parents did for a living. You said they own a business.'

She flushed. 'I didn't lie. My parents run a theatre company called Speak Out, which aims to bring drama to the deaf community. When I was growing up I used to perform with the company. My father was disappointed when I decided not to carry on acting. I agreed to be in this play because…well, to be honest I wanted to please him,' Darcey admitted huskily. 'Dad and I have had a bit of a rocky relationship since I decided to train as a speech therapist rather than go to drama school. I hoped that working together on the play would bring us closer.'

Salvatore's eyes were as black and hard as basalt spewed from Mount Etna. 'All this time you have hidden who you really are.'

'I didn't tell you about my family because I've had past experiences where people have tried to befriend me just because my name is Hart. That was especially true of my ex-husband.' She took a deep breath. She had never told anyone the humiliating truth about her marriage, but she wanted to be honest with Salvatore. 'Marcus is an actor, with his sights set on stardom. He told me he was in love with me, but I found out after the wedding that he had only pretended to be interested in me because he thought that having Joshua Hart as a father-in-law would help his career.'

'So you didn't trust me?'

Salvatore's words fell into the room like pebbles hitting the surface of a pool.

'I…' Darcey swallowed, unable to deny the accusation.

'Dio!' he exploded. 'I have turned my insides out and bared my soul to you, and you couldn't even tell me your goddamned *name*.'

'I'm sorry,' she mumbled. 'After what Marcus did I

have found it hard to trust people. But I *do* trust you, and I very much want to come back to Sicily when the play is finished and…and live with you and Rosa.'

'You say now that you'll come back, but my past experiences suggest that the lure of fame is hard to resist,' Salvatore said bitterly. 'Perhaps you would find living at the castle boring after being on the stage?'

His jaw clenched.

'My mother abandoned me when I was five years old because she wanted to be a famous film star, and for the same reason my wife planned to abandon our baby daughter. Rosa has already grown close to you. How can you simply walk away from her and let her think that you don't care? But maybe you don't give a damn about her?'

Maybe she didn't give a damn about *him*, Salvatore thought grimly. Maybe she had been acting all these weeks that they had been lovers. Perhaps her soft smile and the way she whispered his name when he made love to her hadn't been signs that she cared for him—*as he cared for her*. The realisation of how much he cared hit him so hard that it sucked the breath out of him.

'Of course I care about Rosa,' Darcey said strongly.

'Then why are you going to abandon her?'

Why are you going to abandon me?

The unspoken question circled in his mind and memories of his childhood came rushing back. He remembered when he was five years old. Remembered his father telling him that his mother had gone away for ever and taken his twin brother with her.

Salvatore hadn't believed it. His mother had gone away before, to act in films, but she had always come back. He had run upstairs to her bedroom and flung open the wardrobes. Each one had been empty. Patti's clothes had all gone and all that had remained in the room was the lingering scent of her perfume. To this day the fragrance of lilies brought a lump to his throat.

He had gone to find Sergio, to tell him that Mamma had left them. His father must have been playing a trick on him when he'd said that his brother had gone too. But Sergio had not been in the nursery, or in the garden. Salvatore had searched the whole estate for his brother before he'd realised that he really was alone, abandoned, and his heart had felt as if it was breaking.

But it had not broken, of course. Hearts did not really break—it was just an expression people used.

'You're not being fair to Rosa. Even if you came back to the castle after this play you might go away again if another role came up. She has had enough instability in her life. I can't risk you hurting her.'

'I swear that won't happen,' Darcey told him intently.

'Then tell your father that you can't take this role.'

'I can't do that. I made a promise to him and I won't let him down.'

'But you don't care about letting *me* down?' Salvatore said harshly. 'A few moments ago you agreed to stay with me and give our relationship a chance, but you are determined to put your father's wishes above mine.'

'It is not only for my father's sake that I want to do the play,' Darcey admitted. 'I want to do it for me. I was never as self-confident as the other members of my family. After my divorce I felt even worse because Marcus had made a fool of me. The play is a chance to prove to myself that I can be strong and brave and face my fears. But that is nothing compared to the bravery my grandmother showed during the war, and I feel honoured that my father chose me to tell her story.'

She met Salvatore's bitter black gaze and her heart sank. 'I promise I'll come back to you.'

She could feel him putting up barriers and shutting her out.

'Trust works both ways,' she said quietly. 'You have to trust that I will keep my word, and if you can't, then...'

'Then what, Darcey?' he challenged.

The question hung in the air between them. Darcey recalled Kristen's warning that Castellano men could be very stubborn. It seemed that Salvatore only wanted a relationship with her on his terms and wasn't prepared to compromise.

'If you can't trust me, then there can be no future for us.'

Her mouth felt dry with the fear that she was killing their relationship stone-dead. If she agreed to pull out of the play everything would be all right, but what would happen the next time they disagreed about something? Would she have to give in to him to keep the peace between them?

Salvatore was such a strong character, and sometimes she felt overwhelmed by him. He could very easily dominate her and she was scared by how desperately she loved him. She wanted to please him—just as she had always wanted to please her father, she thought with a flash of insight. The truth was she needed to go away for a while and put some distance between her and Salvatore while she came to terms with her feelings for him. But, even though she knew it was the right thing to do, her heart ached at the idea of leaving him and Rosa even for a few weeks.

'I have explained why doing the play is important to me,' she said huskily. 'But if you won't even wait for me for a couple of months then it makes me wonder if I am really as special to you as you said, or whether that's a line you spin to all your mistresses.'

Salvatore stiffened. So she still intended to leave? He shouldn't be surprised, he told himself. She had obviously never cared about him. It was lucky he hadn't told her that he—*Dio!* What a fool he had been to think that she might have loved him.

He shrugged. 'It seems that neither of us have been completely honest, doesn't it, *cara*?'

He made the endearment sound like an insult. It was impossible to believe that his eyes had ever gleamed with sensual passion, let alone tenderness, Darcey thought dully.

She felt numb inside as she watched him stride over to the door. 'Where are you going?'

'I need some air.' He glanced back at her and his hard features did not alter when he saw her lower lip tremble. 'You need to make a choice, Darcey. Stay with me—or walk away for ever.'

CHAPTER ELEVEN

HE WALKED WITHOUT knowing where he was going, without caring. The crowds on the streets were thinning in the evening; the restaurants and bars were busy. By the Trevi Fountain he saw two lovers entwined in each other's arms, oblivious to the world. *Enjoy it while it lasts,* he thought cynically. And the ache inside him grew heavier.

When he reached the river the sun was sinking below the horizon and the lamps that lined the riverbank cast their golden light on the dark water. There was peace here—solitude for a man who was always alone. Maybe it was his destiny, but it felt like a curse.

His steps slowed as he recalled the past weeks, when he hadn't been lonely. Darcey had lit up the castle and his life with her beautiful smile and her sheer joy in living. He had never laughed so much as he had since she had come to Torre d'Aquila. He had not laughed much at all before he had met her, Salvatore acknowledged. He had not known what it truly meant to make love until he had looked into her eyes as their two bodies became one and felt complete for the first time in his life.

He carried on walking, but without the same urgency, without the anger. Why was he so angry because she wanted to go back to England for a few weeks? he asked himself. She had said that performing in her father's play was important to her, and rather than assuring her that he understood he had tried to manipulate her and control her instead of listening to her.

The truth was that he *was* afraid that if she left she would not come back—as his mother hadn't. He was afraid of being hurt. And so to disguise his fear he had said awful things to her and told her she had to choose between what she wanted and what he wanted. Instead of opening his heart to her he had issued her with a goddamned ultimatum.

Madonna—what had he done? He turned on his heel and began to walk back the way he had come, back to the hotel.

'If you can't trust me...'

Her words echoed inside his head and the black shadows from his past lifted. Of course he trusted her. She had proved over and over that she kept her word. She had worked diligently to help his daughter learn to speak, and her patience and loving care had already transformed Rosa into a happy and confident child. His heart clenched. Darcey would not abandon Rosa, and she would not abandon him, but he feared that he might have driven her away.

He began to run, ignoring the pain in his injured leg. He ran all the way back to the hotel. When he entered their suite and saw that the wardrobe where she had hung her clothes was empty the pain of his heart breaking was the worst agony he'd ever experienced, and the lingering scent of jasmine and old-fashioned roses brought a lump to his throat.

Darcey's father had once told her that sitting alone in a dressing room in the final minutes before a performance were the longest and loneliest moments of an actor's life. Now she knew how true his words were, she brooded as she watched the hands on the clock move excruciatingly slowly.

Her nerves were jangling and she just wanted to get the first night over with. She must have been mad to agree to do this. She must have been crazy to walk away from Salvatore. She loved him, so why hadn't she stayed?

Because he doesn't love you, said the voice in her head. He had proved that when he had told her to choose. *'Stay with me—or walk away for ever.'*

The weeks since she had returned to London had flown past. She was glad that rehearsals had taken up so much of her time, because concentrating on her role had prevented her from thinking about Salvatore. But it was a different matter when she went home every evening. She had spent the first few days after she'd arrived home clinging to the hope that he would phone. That hope had long since died, and her anger at his intransigence had also faded. Now she simply felt guilty that she had not told him sooner about her intention to perform in the play, and her heart felt like a lead weight in her chest.

Her father had commented on her weight loss, which had left her looking gaunt, while her sleepless nights were evident in the dark circles beneath her eyes.

'I know your grandmother often went without food when she worked for the French Resistance, and I commend your dedication to portraying Edith realistically, but I really wish you would eat properly,' Joshua had said in concern.

Salvatore might retract his accusation that she hankered for fame and glamour if he saw her in the drab trench coat she wore for most of the performance, Darcey thought ruefully. The play was not a West End produc-

CHANTELLE SHAW 179

tion and was being staged at a fringe theatre in Islington. But a Joshua Hart play was guaranteed to draw interest from the media, and Darcey knew that several respected theatre critics were in the audience.

A knock on the dressing room door caused her stomach to cramp with nerves. Taking a deep breath, she managed to smile at the assistant stage manager.

'This was delivered for you,' he said, handing her a long cardboard box.

Her parents and other family members had already sent her bouquets of flowers to wish her luck. Darcey fumbled with the ribbon and opened the box to reveal a single red rose.

'Do you know who sent it?' she asked shakily. 'There's no note with the box.'

The ASM shook his head. 'All I know it that someone left it at the front desk a few minutes ago. They were cutting it fine—the play is about to start.' He smiled at her. 'Are you ready, Miss Hart?'

She lifted the rose and smelled its exquisite perfume. Strangely, she did not feel nervous any more. She could do this, Darcey told herself. For her father, but more importantly, for herself.

'Yes,' she said steadily. 'I'm ready.'

'Did you know that the critics from most of the national papers were here tonight, and all of them have given your performance fantastic reviews?' Joshua Hart told Darcey as he steered her across the packed room where the after-show party was taking place. 'I've always known you are a gifted actress. It's in your blood. And tonight you've proved that you are a true Hart.' His tone became serious. 'You could have a wonderful acting career. But it's not what you want, is it?' he said intuitively.

Darcey shook her head. 'I'm happy with the career I've chosen. I'm sorry, Dad.'

Her father looked surprised. 'You have nothing to apologise for. I'm proud of you—*and* the job you do.' He looked at her closely. 'Are you all right? Your mother thought there was some chap in Sicily…'

'I'm fine,' she said quickly.

It was untrue, of course. From the moment she had walked onto the stage and searched along the front row of the audience she had been far from fine. Her hopes that Salvatore had sent her the red rose and come to see the play had been dashed and she had been dangerously close to tears for the whole performance. She had been stupid to think that he might use the ticket she had posted to him, she told herself.

The brief note she had sent with it to the castle had been her only communication with him since he had stormed out of their hotel room in Rome. Furious at his uncompromising attitude, she had gone straight down to the reception desk and arranged to catch the next flight back to London.

If she had stayed would they have been able to discuss things rationally once they had cooled down? She would never know, and regret deepened Darcey's misery so that it took all her acting skills to smile and chat with the other members of the cast.

The party ended eventually, but the prospect of driving through the dank November night to her empty house was so depressing that she hung around until she was the last person left in the theatre.

She walked across the stage and stared out at the dark auditorium. There was no one there to see her tears and she could not hold them back any longer. She had a lot to look forward to, she tried to convince herself. The bank had agreed to give her a loan, and in the new year she intended to look for premises where she could establish a private speech therapy clinic.

Footsteps rang out hollowly in the empty theatre. Alfred, the caretaker, probably wanted to lock up.

'I thought you would be celebrating your success.'

The gravelly, achingly familiar voice tore at her heart. Her eyes flew open and she blinked to clear her blurred vision.

'Wh…what are *you* doing here?'

Salvatore stepped out of the shadows and Darcey felt a sharp pang of physical awareness as she studied his chiselled features. His hair was cut short, like the last time she had seen him, and the grey wool overcoat he was wearing over a black silk shirt emphasised his powerful athletic build. He looked less like a pirate and more like a billionaire businessman. Darcey thought he looked utterly gorgeous.

'Where else would I be?' he murmured. 'I wouldn't have missed your first night for the world.'

'That wasn't the impression you gave in Rome.'

She brushed her tears away, unaware that Salvatore's gut clenched as he saw the betraying tremble of her hand.

'I was a bloody fool in Rome.'

He walked down the centre aisle of the auditorium and Darcey noticed that he limped heavily.

'Your leg…?'

He shrugged. 'The damp weather plays hell with the metal pins holding my thigh bone together, but I'll live,' he said drily. 'The opening night of your play coincided with a trip I'd planned to make to London. I'm selling the house on Park Lane.'

'I suppose there's no point in keeping it now that Rosa no longer needs to see the audiologist at the hospital?'

'I intend to buy another house—preferably on the out-skirts of London. I'm looking for a family home.' He gave her a wry look. 'With less marble features and a garden for Rosa to play in. She misses you,' he said quietly.

Darcey bit her lip. 'I miss her too.'

'Actually, I have a shortlist of properties to view,' Salvatore continued. 'I was hoping you would come and look at them with me.'

Being so close to him was sheer torture—especially when all he seemed to want to discuss was the property market. Darcey closed her eyes and felt hot tears seep beneath her lashes.

'I'm sure an estate agent will be able to advise you much better than I can.' Her voice cracked. 'Look, I don't know why you want to buy a house in London when your home and your heart are in Sicily.'

She could not stop crying, and she felt such an idiot. Angry with herself, she turned to walk into the wings. But Salvatore leapt up onto the stage and caught hold of her, spinning her round to face him. His dark eyes blazed with an expression that made her catch her breath.

'My heart is wherever you are,' he said fiercely. 'I'm buying a house in England for you, *carissima*, for *us*—if you will have me.'

'I don't understand.' Her voice was choked with tears.

'You were so furious. I understand why you thought I had betrayed you. I should have told you that I come from a famous acting family, and that I had accepted a role in my father's play. I should have trusted that you are nothing like Marcus. But in the past people have wanted to get close to me just because of my family, and I liked the fact that you wanted to be with me for who I am.'

Salvatore exhaled heavily. 'When you said you were returning to London to be an actress it felt like history was repeating itself yet again. All I could think of was that you were going to leave me, like my mother had left and Adriana had planned to do, because the life I had offered you in Sicily was not as exciting as a career as a film star. It hurt to know that you had kept secrets from me,' he admitted roughly. 'It shames me to say that my anger made me want to hurt you. After I'd stormed out of the hotel I regretted behaving the way I had, and especially giving you an ultimatum to choose between me and performing in the play. I had behaved like an arrogant jerk and I realised that I needed to do some serious thinking about our relationship and how I really felt about you.'

He brushed the tears from her cheeks with gentle fingers. Darcey's heart gave a jolt when she saw his soft expression. How *did* he really feel about her? She refused to allow herself to hope that just because he had come to see the play she meant something to him. She wished he would be honest, even if that meant telling her that there was no future for them. Then he could go away and leave her alone to deal with her broken heart.

'When I went back to the hotel and found you had gone it was clear that you had made your choice. I knew I could only blame myself for driving you away.' Salvatore's voice cracked as he recalled feeling as if a knife had sliced his heart open when he had discovered that she had left him.

'Since then I have been putting plans into place. I've appointed a manager to run the Castellano winery, and I have helped the castle staff to find new jobs. Only Armond will remain to look after Torre d'Aquila.'

Darcey gave him a startled look. 'But…why won't you be living there? You love the castle and the vineyards.

You told me once that you belong to the land and that you would never live anywhere but the castle.'

'There is no joy at Torre d'Aquila since you left. It's just a pile of ancient bricks—soulless and lifeless without you there.' Salvatore cupped Darcey's chin and tilted her face so that he could look into her tear-bright green eyes. 'When I watched your performance tonight I realised what an incredible talent you have. Your compassion and sensitivity make you a gifted actress, and I don't doubt that after the reviews you've received offers for other acting roles will flood in. That is why I am willing to move to London, or LA—wherever you need to be to develop your acting career.'

Darcey's heart thudded as his words slowly sank in. 'Do you mean you would leave Sicily for me?'

'I would follow you to the ends of the earth if you asked me to.' Salvatore drew a ragged breath. 'Haven't you worked it out by now, sweet Darcey? I love you. Nothing means more to me than your happiness. I don't care where we live so long as your beautiful smile is the first thing I see every morning and I can hold you in my arms every night and make love to you with all the love that is in my heart.'

His mouth twisted when he saw her stunned expression.

'I never knew I could feel like this. I didn't believe I could fall in love. But within five minutes of walking into your office I was determined to take you to Sicily, and even back then I sensed that I would never want to let you go.'

Her silence filled Salvatore with black despair.

'I appreciate your offer to leave Torre d'Aquila—' she began.

He could not bear to hear the rest of her sentence.

'But you don't feel the same way about me—that's what you're going to say, isn't it?' His throat ached and he had to force the words out. 'I should have expected it. I am not an easy man to love.'

'Oh, I don't know,' she said softly. 'I fell in love with you very easily about twenty seconds after you strolled into my office and immediately reorganised my life.'

'Darcey?' Salvatore closed his eyes briefly and when he opened them again his lashes were wet. '*Tesoro*…do you really love me?'

She heard the lonely boy he had once been and her heart cracked open.

'You are everything…my world, the love of my life.' Lost for words to tell him what he meant to her, she framed his face with her hands and drew his mouth down to hers.

It was a kiss unlike any they had shared before. Almost tentative at first, and achingly tender, a silent vow of unending love and the promise of passion as Salvatore took control and kissed her with fierce desire.

'I left because I was scared of how much I love you,' she admitted painfully. 'I thought that if we were apart for a while I would be able to control my feelings for you.' Her voice wobbled. 'But I have missed you so much.'

'*Carissima*, I have missed you desperately, but I wanted you to be able to concentrate on the play and I told myself I must be patient and wait for you. But I can't wait any longer. Will you marry me?' he said urgently. 'We'll need to discuss where we will live, and if you take film roles you'll probably have to go away on location, but I know we can work things out. I love you, and all I want is to make you happy.'

Darcey stood on tiptoe and linked her arms around his neck. 'Then take me home to your castle. I'm pleased to have done this play, but when it finishes I have no intention of taking any more roles. You belong at Torre d'Aquila and I belong with you,' she told him softly. 'What I want more than anything is to be your wife and Rosa's mother. She is going to need speech therapy for a while yet, and I love her as if she were my own child.'

Her smile made Salvatore catch his breath.

'My answer to your question is yes, I'd love to marry you. I hope we'll fill the castle with our children, who will never doubt that we love them as deeply as we love each other.'

Salvatore drew Darcey into his arms and held her close, wondering if she could feel the thunderous beat of his heart. *'Ti amo,'* he said, in a voice choked with emotion.

After a lifetime of burying his feelings he did not find it easy to express how he felt. But he showed her as he claimed her mouth and kissed her with all the love in his heart.

The play finished its run two days before Christmas. Salvatore and Rosa had moved into Darcey's tiny house in London with her and they had lived together as a family. On Christmas Eve they woke to find a thick layer of snow on the ground. It was the first time Rosa had seen snow, and she was wide-eyed with excitement as the car taking her and Darcey to the church drove through the white streets.

Being a bridesmaid was a big responsibility, and the little girl clutched her basket of white rosebuds tightly as she followed Darcey down the aisle to where Papa was waiting. Papa had said that today Darcey was going to become his wife and Rosa's *mamma*. Rosa felt so happy that she gave a little skip and waved to her cousin Nico, who was watching the proceedings with his parents and baby brother.

At the altar Salvatore could not resist turning his head to watch the two people he loved more than anything in the world walk towards him. Rosa looked adorable in her red velvet cloak, but his eyes were drawn to the woman who had stolen his heart. Darcey was breathtaking in a white silk bridal gown edged with pearls at the neckline and the hems of the long sleeves. In her hands she carried a bouquet of red roses, and her only jewellery was the heart-shaped diamond pendant he had given to her, which sparkled in the rays of the winter sunshine.

The wedding ceremony was simple but deeply moving, and the groom's deep voice was unsteady as he made his vows and promised to love his bride for eternity. Soon they would be returning to the castle in Sicily, but Salvatore's heart no longer belonged to Torre d'Aquila. It belonged to Darcey, who was the love of his life, and as he slid a gold band on her finger he whispered the words against her lips.

'I will love you for ever. My heart and soul are yours and there will never be any secrets between us.'

Darcey rested her hand on her stomach and smiled as she thought of the secret she would tell him later, when they were alone. She knew he would love their child unconditionally, as she would, and as they loved Rosa. But her heart belonged to Salvatore.

'I love you too,' she murmured and, reaching up on tiptoe, she kissed him.

* * * * *

SEDUCED BY
THE CEO

PAMELA YAYE

This book is dedicated to single mothers everywhere. I hope you find a sexy, romantic man like Nicco Morretti who sweeps you off your feet and cherishes you every day of your life. I wrote this one for you mums, so enjoy!!!

Chapter 1

Famed restaurateur, Nicco Morretti, watched celebrity party planner Claudia Jefferies-Medina sail through the doors of Javalicious and noted that as usual, she was right on time. Smiling broadly, he stood and pulled out a chair for her at their table. Celebrating the grand reopening of his restaurant lounge, Dolce Vita, last night left Nicco feeling sluggish. But he quickly shook off his fatigue and smiled. "Good morning, Claudia."

"It's great to see you again." Kissing him on both cheeks, Claudia greeted him as if they'd known each other all of their lives rather than just a month.

"Thanks for agreeing to meet me on such short notice. I really appreciate it."

"No problem," Claudia said as she sat down, took off her white blazer and draped it behind her chair. "I was already in town on business, so squeezing you in this morning was a cinch."

"I ordered you a cappuccino when the waiter came by earlier. I hope that's okay."

"You remembered what kind of coffee I like," she said,

touching a hand to her chest. "Thank you, Nicco. That was very thoughtful of you."

The waiter arrived, tray in hand, and placed two steaming mugs on the round wooden table. "Would you like to order something from the breakfast menu?"

"Nothing for me," Nicco said, reaching for his coffee mug. "I'm good."

While Claudia chatted with the waiter about the morning specials, Nicco studied the thin, long-haired women seated beside the front window. They grinned lasciviously, and he did, too, making a mental note to introduce himself to the blond babes after his meeting with Claudia ended. He glanced around the sparsely decorated café, surprised to see that it was filled to capacity. The quaint coffee shop attracted locals and tourists alike, and although it was only nine o'clock in the morning, a steady stream of casually dressed people shuffled through the open door. The scent of sea water mingled with the aromas wafting around the café, and the sound of squawking birds and laughter filled the air.

"Have you had a chance to review the notes I sent you last week?"

Nicco wanted to laugh, but didn't. Claudia sat on the edge of her seat, her eyes bright and her excitement sky high. "I think my mom will get a kick out of the live band, and the vintage photo booth, but the rest of the report didn't wow me."

Claudia frowned as if confused by his words, but she didn't speak.

"The party's too small, too low-key. It needs to be grand, flashy and over-the-top."

"Nicco, it doesn't get much bigger than the grand ballroom at the Biltmore Hotel," she said, sounding as animated as a high school cheerleader. "I've done several events at the Biltmore, and they outdo themselves every single time. If you'd like, I could email you some pictures of the pre-Grammy party I did back in January."

Nicco shook his head. "That won't be necessary."

"Are you sure? I think if you saw some pictures you'd feel differently about us booking the Biltmore. It's a gorgeous hotel rich in history and culture, and one of my personal favorites."

"I'm just not feeling it, Claudia, so please keep searching for another venue." His mind was made up. Nicco tasted his coffee, and leaned back comfortably in his chair. He loved the Biltmore Hotel, and thought the food and service was outstanding. But he didn't want to have his parents' anniversary party in a hotel where he'd had numerous sexual liaisons. But he couldn't tell Claudia that, not without looking like a sleaze ball. He wanted the celebrity party planner to think he was a mature, upstanding guy. So, spilling the beans about his past escapades at the historic hotel was definitely out of the question. "My parents worked hard to give me and my brothers a great life in this country, and I want to throw them the most expensive, outrageous anniversary bash Miami has ever seen!"

Claudia was silent for a moment. "What about a mega yacht?"

"Will three hundred people fit comfortably inside?"

"When did the guest list balloon to three hundred people?" she asked, raising an eyebrow.

"Once word got out that my parents were celebrating their twenty-fifth wedding anniversary, our relatives in Venice and Florence insisted on making the trip to Miami."

"The more the merrier, right?"

"That's the Morretti way!"

"Trust me, it's the Mexican way, too. A small family dinner at my in-laws' place usually involves hundreds of people, and more food and alcohol than a Carnival Cruise ship!" Claudia laughed out loud, but quickly sobered and continued her spiel. "A mega yacht can comfortably hold up to five hundred people, and has everything you can think of—lavish staterooms, a lounge, a formal dining room, a pool and even a personal theater. You name it, the yacht's got it."

"Interesting," Nicco said, stroking the length of his jaw. "That could work."

"I'll look into it and get back to you once I find out more information. Can I get your assistant's new number?" she asked, her pen poised to write. "I rang her yesterday to confirm our meeting this morning, but her cell phone has been disconnected."

"Gracie no longer works for Morretti Inc."

"That's too bad. I really liked Ms. O'Connor. Have you found a replacement yet?"

"No, but my HR director is in the process of interviewing suitable candidates as we speak." Nicco raised his mug to his lips and took a swig of coffee. "Hopefully she'll find someone soon, but in the meantime you can reach me by phone or email."

"That works for me."

"One last thing. I want the party to be a surprise, so I'd appreciate if you kept everything quiet." Leaning forward in his chair, he glanced conspicuously around the café to ensure no one was listening in. "The only people who know about the anniversary bash are my brothers, Demetri and Rafael, and I'd like to keep it that way."

"I can do that!" She fervently nodded her head. "Covert is my middle name!"

Laughing, they clinked coffee mugs.

Claudia's cell phone vibrated, and when she glanced at the screen, her face brightened. "I apologize for the interruption," she said, swiping her cell phone off the table. "Do you mind if I take this call? It's my husband, and I'm worried he's still stuck at the Orlando airport."

"Please, by all means, go ahead."

Claudia pressed her cell phone to her ear. *"Santiago, bebé, ¿estás bien?"*

For the second time in minutes, Nicco swallowed a laugh. Claudia sounded more like a love-struck teenager, than an accomplished businesswoman who'd recently been featured in top magazines. With her cell phone at her ear, she swept through the café, speaking in a hushed tone. Nicco scoured the café for the blonds in the daisy dukes he'd spotted earlier, but couldn't find them anywhere. And that sucked, because he needed a woman in his bed *bad*. Like yesterday. Sex was his favorite pastime, the only thing ever worth missing a round of golf with his brothers for. And Nicco couldn't think of anything better than having a gorgeous woman—or two—between his black satin sheets.

Punching in his cell phone password, he fired off a quick text to his older brother, Rafael, and waited anxiously for his reply. For months, Nicco had been debating whether or not to buy Javalicious, and as he sat in his corner table watching the staff fly around the room like busy bees, he decided investing in the coffee shop would be a smart, solid business move. And if Rafael agreed, he'd be one step closer to owning the popular Ocean Drive café just steps away from Miami Beach.

"Wesley, I don't need you to take care of me. I'm a strong, intelligent woman who can take care of herself. Got it?"

Frowning, Nicco shot a glance over his shoulder, curious to see who was responsible for the loud, angry outburst. Seated directly behind him, a woman with short black hair and dressed in pink workout gear spoke on her cell phone. Nicco couldn't see her face, but there was no mistaking her frustration, or the contempt in her voice for the person on the line.

"Please, you wouldn't know the truth if it walked up and slapped you!"

Nicco cracked up. But when he saw the puzzled expressions on the faces of the patrons seated nearby, he killed his laughter and pretended to read the menu card propped up against the napkin holder.

"Sorry about that." Claudia took her seat and rested her cell phone on the table. "My husband was calling to give me an update on his schedule. He'll be in Miami within the hour."

"Then don't let me keep you," Nicco said. "We're finished, so go meet your husband."

"Are you sure?"

"I'm positive."

Up on her feet, her eyes twinkling like diamonds, she collected her things and flashed a friendly wave. "Take care of yourself, Nicco. I'll be in touch."

The second Claudia rushed out the café doors, Nicco searched the room for the woman in the pink workout gear. He found her standing in line, typing furiously on her cell phone, wearing a cheeky grin. Nicco stood in the middle of the café, staring at her. Her facial features were perfect, and so was her taut derriere. Last night, at the grand reopening of Dolce Vita, he'd met scores of women, but they all looked the same—long, silky hair, coats of thick makeup, wearing tiny dresses that left nothing to the imagination. But the woman in front of him now with the killer curves and big brown eyes instantly seized his attention. *She's a stunner, nothing short of magnificent, the most striking woman on the face of the earth.*

Nicco moved forward, toward her. Couldn't help it. Couldn't stop himself. His hands itched to touch her, to squeeze, to caress and stroke her delectable, hourglass shape. Her tank top showed off toned arms, her leggings fit her body like a second skin, and her neon-pink sneakers drew his gaze down the length of her long, sculptured legs.

God bless the man who invented spandex! The woman had a body that made him salivate. Her looks were jaw-dropping, clear off the Richter scale, and Nicco found it impossible to turn away from her. He more than liked what he saw—her dimpled cheeks, the beauty mark above her mouth and most importantly her fine, feminine figure. His thoughts were all over the place, jumping from one illicit image to the next. Battling the needs of his flesh, he stood transfixed, unable to move.

The woman glanced up from her cell phone and caught his eye. Nicco's heart rate sped up, beating at a wild, fanatic pace. For a moment, all he could do was stare helplessly at the beauty standing across the room. That's it. Breathing required every single drop of energy he had left.

Her glossy, pink lips slowly curled into a smile, one that hit him straight in the heart. And when his eyes zeroed in on her moist, lush mouth, Nicco imagined himself planting one on her. A long, sensuous kiss that would turn her on.

Nicco watched the woman pay her bill, and when she headed in his direction, he surfaced from his sexual haze. Clearing his throat, he racked his brain for the right pick-up line, one that would capture her attention and buy him a few precious minutes of her time.

"How was your workout?" Nicco winced when he heard the question slide past his lips.

How was your workout? mocked his inner voice. *Surely you can do better than that. Quit staring at her cleavage, man, and get your head in the game!*

Her feet slowed and a frown bruised her lips. "My workout?" she repeated, regarding him closely. "Were you in my Bootie Camp class this morning?"

Nicco chuckled. "No, unfortunately I missed it. Where do you teach?"

"Why? Are you looking to drop a few pounds?"

"Do I need to?" Raising an eyebrow, he cocked his head to the right. Nicco wanted her to get a good look at him, so he stood tall and squared his shoulders. He saw her eyelashes widen and flutter, and heard her quick intake of breath. She darted a glance down at his shoes and a sly grin claimed his mouth. *That's right, baby. I wear a size twelve shoe. How you like me now?*

"Since you're a fitness instructor, I'd love your expert opinion." Nicco rested his hands on his waist and displayed a bold, in-your-face stance. "Am I in good shape or not?"

Rolling her eyes, an exasperated expression marring her features, she heaved her gym bag over her shoulder and stepped past him as if he hadn't just asked her a question.

Nicco didn't know what possessed him to touch her, but when his hands connected with her flesh he felt a rush, a charge so powerful his knees buckled. They stood in the middle of the café, staring at each other. His desire for her so strong, his mind went blank. "Please don't go. We're not finished talking."

Leaning forward, he read the name printed on the top hand corner of her tank top. *Jariah Brooks.* Nicco tried it on for size, allowing the syllables to stroke the length of his tongue, before deciding that her name was as striking as her dark, creamy complexion. "I'd love to take you out sometime, Jariah. Can I get your phone number?"

"I'm busy."

"Every night?"

"Look," she snapped, "I'm having a really bad day, and I'm not in the mood to hear any of your slick lines, so go hit on someone else."

"Let's sit down and talk."

"Let's not and say we did."

"Do you know who I am?"

Jariah sputtered a laugh. "No, should I?"

"I think so." Bragging was usually beneath him, but to impress the saucy fitness instructor, he was willing to use every trick in the book. "I'm well-known around these parts. My picture is always in the newspapers and on TV."

She stared at him for a moment, as if trying to place his face, then fervently nodded her head. "Oh, wow," she gushed, pointing a finger at him. "I thought you looked familiar."

A grin overwhelmed Nicco's mouth. Finally. Now that Jariah recognized him—and knew that he was one of the most successful restaurateurs in the nation—they could skip the preamble and head straight to the penthouse suite at his favorite, luxury hotel. He had plans for Jariah, plans that involved whip cream, Cristal, and a box of Magnum condoms, and the sooner they got to his suite at the Hilton Bentley the better.

"You were on last night's episode of *Cheaters,* weren't you?"

Hanging his head, Nicco clutched his shirt, as if wounded by the dig, but deep down he was amused. Aroused actually. He loved their playful banter. Much like her stunning looks, Jariah's cheeky wit was a turn-on. But what Nicco liked most about the mocha-brown was her mouth. Her lips were thick, moist and plump, and looked incredibly inviting.

"Sorry, but I'm not interested."

"Not interested?" Nicco chuckled a laugh. "Can't say I've ever heard *that* one before."

"There's a first time for everything," she said in a sing-song voice.

"Are you married?"

"Why?" she quipped. "Are you looking for your *one true love?*"

Nicco choked on his tongue. *Hell, no!* he thought, sliding his hands into the back pocket of his blue Levi's jeans.

I'm only thirty-four and besides I'm far too smart to ever do something as stupid as tying the knot! Nicco caught himself, just as he felt a tidal wave of guilt. Not everyone who fell in love and got married was foolish. His kid brother, Demetri, had found love with news reporter Angela Kelly—and he'd never seen a happier, more loving couple. Since popping the question last month on live TV, Demetri and Angela had become the newest celebrity "it" couple, and every time Nicco talked to his brother he waxed poetic about his new fiancée and their upcoming wedding.

Happily ever after isn't for everyone, and it certainly isn't for me. Nicco didn't do relationships, and rarely saw the same woman twice, but he was willing to make an exception for Jariah-Curves-Galore-Brooks. One night with the saucy beauty wouldn't be enough. He'd need a week with her, shoot, maybe even two or three.

Nicco couldn't think straight. It was hard for him to stay present in the moment. He felt unsteady on his feet, as if he'd been smacked upside the head by a Roger Clemons fastball. This had never happened to him before. Ever. No one had ever affected him like this. Over the years he'd hooked up with a wide assortment of red-carpet darlings, but Jariah Brooks was the first and only woman to ever take his breath away.

His heart roared like the engine of his Harley Davidson, and when Jariah moistened her lips with her tongue, Nicco strangled a groan. *I don't know how much more of this I can take,* he thought, raking a hand through his short, curly hair.

"Mommy!"

Nicco felt someone bump the back of his legs and a cold liquid splash onto his sandals. A chubby, wide-eyed girl with pigtails jumped into Jariah's arms and giggled with delight. Her hands swung wildly, and every time she moved her drink splashed onto him.

Stepping back, Nicco snatched a wad of napkins off the breakfast counter along the front window and dabbed at the front of his black V-neck T-shirt.

"Mommy, can we go to the beach? Please? Pretty please?" the girl whined, tugging on her mother's tank top. "I promise to be a good listener."

"Not today, Ava. You have a dentist appointment at ten forty-five."

The girl stamped her foot. "But I don't want to go to the stinky dentist. I want to go to the beach! You promised I could go swimming!"

Intrigued by the exchange, Nicco glanced up. The little girl was the splitting image of Jariah. Mother and daughter shared the same dark brown complexion, wide, expressive eyes, and delicate button nose. A tanned, stocky man joined them, and kissed Jariah on each cheek. He wore a lopsided smile, and was so smitten with the fitness instructor he had stars in his eyes.

Feeling dumb for hitting on her, Nicco mentally berated himself for publicly making a fool of himself. He watched the trio exit the café, and as Jariah strode past the front window, hand-in-hand with her daughter, their eyes met. She caught him staring at her—again—but this time Nicco didn't flash his trademark grin. There was nothing to smile about. Jariah had a kid, and at least *two* men in her life. And since children and drama were a turn-off Nicco tore his gaze away from her pretty face and studied his diamond Montblanc wristwatch instead.

Nicco dumped his napkins in the garbage. He had to hurry or he'd be late. He had an eleven o'clock meeting with the head of his security team, Gerald Stanley, and was anxious to hear if the former navy SEAL had garnered any new information about the break-in at his downtown restaurant. The perpetrators had caused thousands of dollars' worth of damage, but two months later the police still had no leads. He suspected deep in his gut that his ex-assistant, Gracie O'Connor, was involved, but he wasn't ready to share his thoughts with anyone. He was going to handle it his way, and no one was going to stop him—not even his brothers.

How had things come to this? How had things gone so bad, so quickly? Nicco wondered, expelling a deep, troubled breath. A year ago, he'd been on top of the world, living the good life, but the day before his thirty-fourth birthday his whole world had fallen apart. Twelve months later, he was still picking up the pieces.

Slipping on his aviator sunglasses, he strode purposefully through the café doors. Outside, at the intersection of Ocean Drive and First Street, Nicco spotted Jariah and her daughter. The little girl was cute, every bit as beautiful as her mother, and Nicco couldn't help thinking what a great-looking family they were.

Nicco shook his head, dismissed the unsolicited thought that rose in his mind. *Jariah Brooks is a stunner, but I definitely dodged a bullet there.* Kids weren't his thing, but playing the field definitely was, and as soon as he finished his workday he was making a move on the full-figured brunette at his favorite spa. The masseuse wasn't as witty as Jariah Brooks was, but she was the ready, willing, down-for-whatever-in-the-bedroom type, and tonight, that was all that mattered to Nicco Morretti.

Chapter 2

Jariah sat at the conference room table inside Morretti Inc. mentally preparing for her interview. Her heart was beating so loud and fast she feared she would collapse. As Jariah waited for the Human Resources Director to arrive, she straightened her dress and assessed her look. Jariah was excited about the account manager position, but worried her nerves would get the best of her and she'd trip all over her words.

Glancing around the conference room, she took in the tasteful paintings, the leafy plants positioned beside the window and the low-hanging lights. *I have to nail this interview. I need this job and the salary even more.* Jariah had been out of work for months, and pounding the pavement had yet to produce any results. Teaching aerobic classes at Premier Fitness was great fun, and she loved seeing her students' progress each week, but the paycheck just wasn't cutting it. Her bills were piling up, and Jariah feared if she didn't land a full-time position soon she'd have to dip into her emergency fund.

And what will I do once that *runs out?* Jariah told herself not to imagine the worst possible scenario—the one with her losing her home and crawling back to her ex-fiancé. It didn't matter what Wesley said. She *would* make it without him, and when she did, she'd finally be able to give her daughter, Ava, the life she'd always dreamed of. And she didn't need Wesley or anyone else to help make it happen.

Turning her face toward the window, she closed her eyes and allowed the sunshine raining down from the morning sky to calm her fears. Jariah felt herself relax, felt the tension radiating through her cold, chilled body recede. Hearing her cell phone vibrate from inside her purse, Jariah slid a hand into the side pocket and took out her Black-Berry. Jariah had three new text messages from Wesley, and each one was more annoying than the last. He was furious that she had refused to get back together with him. So he'd been blowing up her phone for weeks, his cruel taunts only proved how immature he was.

Switching off her cell phone, she dropped it inside her purse, and sat back comfortably in her leather wingback chair. Jariah was sick of Wesley's superior, know-it-all attitude and she refused to take any of his calls.

Wesley Covington, the twenty-nine-year-old chief administrative deputy making waves from Orange County to Capitol Hill, was not only the father of her daughter, but an overgrown child himself. The Ivy League graduate had the power to ruin a perfectly good day, and as Jariah thought about the messages he'd sent her, she wondered for the umpteenth time what she'd ever seen in the privileged mama's boy.

Why can't I meet a nice guy? Jariah wondered, releasing a troubled sigh. Someone sweet, chivalrous and romantic, who was good with kids. Hoping the man upstairs was listening, she stared up at the ceiling pitifully, as if that would seal the deal. *A little chemistry would be nice, too,* she thought with a fervent nod of her head. Since calling it quits with Wesley eight months ago, Jariah had been on dozens of dates but none of the guys she met excited her.

A picture of a tall, gorgeous guy with intense eyes and curly hair sprang in her mind. As Jariah sat there, thinking about the hottie who'd approached her at Javalicious on Friday, she inwardly chastised herself for not giving him her phone number. *Why?* her inner voice questioned. *He's a player who's probably bedded more women than Hugh Hefner!*

Hearing a sharp knock on the door, she shot to her feet and adjusted her Donna Karen dress. The door opened, and Jariah stood there, dumbfounded. Her lips parted, but nothing came out. *What the hell? What is he doing here?* It was the guy from Javalicious. The one who'd hit on her, and probably every other woman in the popular café. On Friday, he'd looked handsome in his casual T-shirt and khaki pants, but today he looked like a Hugo Boss model fresh off the runway. Clean-cut, with thick eyebrows, and sideburns, his ebony-black hair a mass of short, tight curls, he carried himself like a man who was used to getting his way in the boardroom *and* in the bedroom. All arms and legs, he was the height of a basketball player, and had the strong, muscled physique to match.

Her eyes slid greedily down his chiseled body. His shoulders filled out every inch of his lightweight suit jacket, his sky-blue shirt showed off the powerful definition of his upper chest, and his tailored pants hung just so. The man knew how to rock a suit, and smelled as debonair as he looked. He was cool, suave and hot—just like she remembered. He wasn't the kind of man a woman forgot, and as he crossed the room toward her, Jariah felt a rush of panic. Her palms grew slick with sweat, and if her knees shook any harder her legs would give way.

"We meet again," the stranger said in a velvety smooth voice. "Jariah, right?"

Taken by his smile and his dreamy scent, all Jariah could do was nod her head. *Is this really happening?* she wondered. *Am I actually standing face-to-face with the guy I blew off two days ago?* He was too close, but Jariah didn't move. Couldn't, not when he was openly staring at her. The Italian hunk was the sexiest thing on two legs, but something about him still rubbed her the wrong way. Jariah didn't know anything about the attractive stranger, but she could spot a player a mile away, and this guy was definitely that. His cocksure stance said it all: I'm handsome and charming and I can have any woman I want.

Not me Casanova, so back off!

"I thought that was you. I glanced into the conference room, and there you were." He slid a hand casually into his pocket, stood there as if he had all the time in the world to shoot the breeze. "Shouldn't you be at the gym teaching the morning Bootie Camp class?"

"Are you stalking me?"

His eyes gleamed with mischief. "No. Would you like me to?"

Jariah couldn't think of a witty comeback to put him in his place, so she said nothing.

"I'm just kidding," he said, holding his hands up in the air, as if he was surrendering to Miami's finest. "I work here. What's your story?"

"If you must know, I'm here for a job interview."

"That's *really* great news."

Baffled by his statement and his enthusiasm, she said, "It is?"

"Absolutely. This place is filled with a bunch of boring, stuffy suits, and it'll be a nice to have a woman like you around for a change."

"A woman like me?" she repeated, raising an eyebrow. "What is that supposed to mean?"

"You've got moxie, and I find your honesty refreshing."

"You don't know me."

"Not yet," he shot back. "But I'm working on it."

He smelled of expensive cologne, and when he raked a hand through his hair, Jariah wondered what it would be like to play in his dark, thick curls.

"How's your daughter? Did everything go okay at the dentist on Friday?"

Stunned by the question, Jariah eyed him closely, trying to recall their previous conversation. *What is this guy up to? Is it possible that he is stalking me?* He didn't give off that creepy, peeping-tom vibe, but he made her nervous. His questions put her on edge, made her uncomfortable. Before she could put him in his place, the door opened and a skinny brunette wearing designer eyeglasses and a stylish gray pantsuit marched briskly inside.

Stopping abruptly, she said, "Good morning, Mr. Morretti. Is there a problem?"

Jariah didn't hear the gasp that escaped her lips, but it must have shot out of her mouth in surround-sound because the brunette gave her a funny look.

Touching a hand to her scalding-hot cheeks, Jariah choked down the lump in the back of her throat. *This young, ridiculously hot guy owns Morretti Incorporated?* Hell, no. No way. It couldn't be, she argued, refusing to believe it. He was the boss's son. Had to be. Remembering their conversation on Friday made Jariah wince. *I am so screwed. There's no way I'm getting this job. Not after the way I spoke to him at the coffee shop.*

"Please, Mrs. Reddick, call me Nicco." His eyes were narrowed, as if he was pissed off, but his mouth held a teasing grin. "Save the formalities for Rafael and my father. I'm far more laid-back. Haven't you figured that out by now?"

Jariah wanted to roll her eyes but didn't. The HR director was wearing a wedding ring the size of a jaw breaker, and was likely in her mid-forties, but she giggled like a kid watching *Finding Nemo*.

"Mrs. Reddick, if it's okay with you I'd like to sit in on this interview."

No, it's not okay! Jariah screamed inside in her head. She prayed the brunette would show Nicco Morretti the door, but when he flashed one of his wide, panty-wetting smiles at the HR director, she eagerly nodded her head.

"Of course, by all means." Mrs. Reddick gestured to the conference room table with more flair than a model at the Miami Car Show. "Please, pull up a chair and join us."

"Can I get you something to drink?" Nicco asked, sliding behind Jariah and holding out her chair. "Coffee? Tea? A glass of wine?"

Jariah felt the compulsion to laugh, but didn't. *Who drinks wine at nine-thirty in the morning?* she wondered. *I bet he does!* Nicco was testing her, but Jariah refused to let the hot-shot businessman unnerve her. Guys like Nicco Morretti—rich, arrogant, womanizers—were a dime a dozen in Miami and hardly her type. It didn't matter that he had dashing good looks, or more swagger than a championship winning bull fighter. He was just a man, and like her ex, not someone she could ever trust. Nicco Morretti was a charmer, a guy who got off on seducing women and no one could tell her otherwise. "No, thank you. I'm fine."

Girl, you better lick those lips and hike up that skirt!

Jariah was appalled by the thought that entered her mind. Yes, Nicco Morretti was attractive, and flirting with him certainly wouldn't hurt her cause, but Jariah wanted to the get the account manager's job on her own merit. Not because she'd flashed some cleavage at the boss's son. She wouldn't do it. No way, no how.

All business, the HR Director sat down with a flourish and opened the manila file folder she'd put down on the round, mahogany table. "Welcome to Morretti Inc., Ms. Brooks. I'm Mrs. Reddick. It's a pleasure to meet you."

To conceal the fact that she was shaking, Jariah crossed her legs, and clasped her hands around her knees. Taking a deep breath didn't calm her nerves, and Jariah feared if she tried to speak nothing would come out.

"Tell us about yourself, Ms. Brooks. What would you like us to know about you?"

Releasing the breath she'd been holding, she sat up straighter in her chair. This was her time to shine, to prove that there was more to her than met the eye, and Jariah held nothing back. She told the HR director about her education, her past work experience, and the joy she found in volunteering with the Meals on Wheels program.

"What makes you stand out from your peers?" Mrs. Reddick asked.

"I'm dependable, trustworthy and responsible. I take great pride in my work, and I'm committed to being the best account manager I can be."

The HR director continued. "What's your worst character trait?"

That depends on who you ask. My parents think I'm irresponsible, my ex says I'm unreasonable, and his mother is convinced I got pregnant to trap her beloved son. The accusation stung, even after all these years, but Jariah didn't have time to dwell on her troubled thoughts. "I can be stubborn at times, especially when I'm very passionate about a project, but I've never allowed my shortcomings to interfere with my ability to do my job."

Mrs. Reddick folded her arms rigidly across her chest, and Jariah knew she'd said the wrong thing, but before she could revise her response, the HR director spoke.

"Why should we hire you, Ms. Brooks?"

"Because I'm a dedicated, hard-working professional who thrives under pressure."

"Mrs. Reddick, if it's all right with you I'd like to ask Ms. Brooks a few questions."

Bewildered by Nicco Morretti's request, Jariah regarded him coolly. *This isn't good,* she thought as her heart rate sped up.

"Go ahead, Nicco." Mrs. Reddick flapped her hands like a bald eagle taking flight. "She's all yours."

Leaning forward in his chair, his eyes zeroing in on hers, he was nothing like the sly, flirtatious guy who'd hit on her two days earlier. "Why do you want to work for Morretti Inc.?"

Because I'm an out-of-work single mom, and kids are expensive! Unsure of what to say, Jariah racked her mind for a suitable answer, one that would paint her in a favorable light. Over the past three weeks she'd been on so many interviews it was hard to keep the companies straight, and though she tried, Jariah couldn't remember anything remarkable about Morretti Inc. But she couldn't tell the boss's son that, so she said the first thing that came to mind.

"This is not only a fine opportunity for personal growth and professional advancement, but Morretti Inc. is a place where I feel I can make a difference." Hearing the nervous quiver in her voice, Jariah paused to take a deep breath. "As an account manager, well versed in finance, book keeping and stock and investment options, I see this position as a perfect fit for me. Because I have excellent time management skills, I'm able to accomplish a lot in a limited amount of time and I have always led by example."

"Is your significant other supportive of your career ambitions?"

Jariah frowned, and noticed that Mrs. Reddick raised her eyebrows, too. *What an odd question. Is that his way of asking me if I have a boyfriend?* She expected Mrs. Reddick to come to her rescue, but when the HR director didn't, Jariah had no choice but to respond. "I'm single," she said brightly, though she wanted to kick Nicco in the shin for digging around in her personal life. "My daughter is my number one priority right now."

"Do you have any qualms about working at a male-dominated company?"

"Absolutely not. To be honest, I get along better with men than I do with women." The second the words left her mouth Jariah regretted them, but to her surprise, Nicco grinned. He looked amused.

"Do you have any questions for me before we conclude today's interview?"

"Yes, as a matter of fact I do." Jariah held his gaze. For some odd reason seeing the puzzled expression on his face bolstered her courage. "What makes Morretti Inc. different? What sets your company apart from the competition?"

Nicco gave her a long, searching look. "That's a great question, Ms. Brooks."

You impressed the boss's son. You go girl!

"Morretti Inc. has been the leader in the shipping industry for over fifty years, and since expanding our services in the nineties we're increased our profits by 16 percent. In addition to our shipping, moving and security divisions, we also own condominium properties, car dealerships and a wildly successful restaurant franchise. Have you heard of Dolce Vita?"

Yes, but it's too expensive for my tastes. "Yes, of course. It's a celebrity hotspot, and one of my favorite Italian restaurants in Miami."

Jariah fidgeted with her fingers and shifted uncomfortably in her chair. Lying didn't sit well with her. It troubled her conscience, made her feel like a fraud but she felt compelled to tell Nicco Morretti what he wanted to hear. The interview was going well, better than she'd expected, and she didn't want to do anything to turn him off. "Can you tell me about your employee development program?"

Mrs. Reddick spoke up. "We have a mandatory, one-week training session for all new employees, monthly webinars and workshops and a tuition reimbursement program for all full-time employees enrolled in university classes."

"That's impressive," Jariah said, meaning every word. "When will you make a decision about the account manager position?"

"By Wednesday." Mrs. Reddick closed her file folder. "Do you have any other questions?"

Shaking her head, Jariah picked her purse up off the floor and stood to her feet. "Thank you for taking time out of your very busy schedule to meet with me this morning."

"No, thank you for coming." Nicco stood and gestured to the door. "I'll walk you out."

"That won't be necessary. I remember the way."

"If you insist."

"I do."

Stepping forward, Jariah took the hand Nicco offered, and gave it a firm shake. Ignoring the warmth of his touch, she strode through the conference room door with her shoulders squared and her head held high.

Staring through the glass window, Nicco watched Jariah walk down the hallway with the grace of a woman twice her age. Her sleeveless dress, which clung to each sinuous curve of her body, made Nicco wonder if she'd ever been a model. He imagined her naked, with nothing on but her red patent leather pumps, and all but exploded in his boxers.

Jariah Brooks is all wrong for you. His conscience pointed out. *She has a kid, man trouble,* and *a serious attitude problem, remember?* Nicco did, but that didn't stop him from wanting her. Intelligent, assertive women turned him on, and he enjoyed Jariah's strong personality and the way she stood up to him. She was definitely a looker, and he liked that she was single…and available.

"What do you think?"

Remembering that he wasn't alone and that Mrs. Reddick was standing beside him, watching him like a hawk, he turned away from the window and shook off his thoughts. "I think Ms. Brooks would be a great addition to our accounting department, don't you?"

"No, I don't."

"You don't?" Nicco heard the surprise in his voice and coughed to clear his throat. After leaving Javalicious on Friday, Nicco had told himself to forget about Jariah, but the message had failed to reach his brain. All weekend, he'd thought of her and nothing else. Running into her at his office had been a stroke of good luck, and after sitting in on her interview, Nicco was even more intrigued by the single mom with the keen mind and stellar résumé. "I was impressed by her answers and the questions she asked."

"Ms. Brooks is articulate, and obviously intelligent, but I don't want to hire anyone who may cause trouble or disrupt the harmony within the accounting department—"

"And you think Ms. Brooks is trouble?"

Mrs. Reddick shoved her papers back into her manila file folder. "I can't say for sure, but I'd rather not take the chance. And besides, she's a single mother."

"What does that have to do with her ability to do the job?"

"In my thirty years of experience in HR, I've found single moms to be unreliable, undependable, and often too distracted by personal issues to effectively do their job."

"That sounds like discrimination, Mrs. Reddick."

"It's called selective hiring."

Her words troubled him, but Nicco decided not to argue with Mrs. Reddick. The HR director was new to

Morrretti Inc., but his father trusted her wholeheartedly, and he didn't want to say anything to ruffle her feathers. "You're the expert. Do what you think is best," he said with a shrug of his shoulders. "Have you hired a new executive assistant for me?"

"Unfortunately, none of the men I've interviewed yesterday were up to snuff."

Stunned, Nicco stared wide-eyed at the HR director. Was Mrs. Reddick off her rocker? What would ever possess her to hire a dude to be his right hand? "Come again?"

"In light of what happened with Ms. O'Conner, your father thought it was best I hire a male assistant to work alongside you, and I agreed."

"I don't give a damn what my father thinks," Nicco snapped, growing annoyed by her condescending tone. He knew what the HR director was implying, and he didn't like it. "I would prefer working with a woman, so please don't discriminate against female applicants."

"I'll keep your wishes in mind, but I have to do what's right for the company..."

Nicco raked a hand through his hair. It wasn't his fault his former assistant, Gracie O'Conner, had developed feelings for him and caused a scene at the company barbecue. Three days later Gracie quit, and when word had got back to company headquarters about the incident his father, Arturo, had reamed him out in English *and* Italian.

His thoughts slid back to the past. Nicco loved everything about women—their strength, their femininity, the way they smelled and looked and moved. But they were also the most cunning, calculating people on the face of the planet. One night, after too many glasses of Cristal, he'd slept with Gracie. The next morning he'd apologized and made it clear that they could never be more than friends, but like all of the other women in his past she'd foolishly thought she could change him. When that didn't work, she threatened to sue him for sexual harassment. To keep her quiet, and their family name out of the tabloids, his father had quietly paid her off.

The muscles in his jaw tightened. Every time he thought about how Gracie had screwed him over, he burned inside. Why did women view him as their meal ticket?

He didn't want to rock the boat or piss off Mrs. Reddick, but he wasn't sold on having a male executive assistant. He needed someone strong and assertive who spoke her mind. Someone like… A light went off in his head. "I want Ms. Brooks."

Mrs. Reddick gasped. "Excuse me?"

"I want Ms. Brooks to be my new executive assistant."

"But she applied for the account manager job."

"I know, but since you're not hiring her for the position, I'd like her to work for me," he said, keeping his tone casual, despite his growing excitement. "Not only does Ms. Brooks have marketing training, she also has extensive experience working with start-up companies, and I bet she has great ideas on how to trim costs without sacrificing value and quality."

Mrs. Reddick pursed her thin lips. "I've been an HR director for more than three decades," she reminded him. "My gut instinct is that Ms. Brooks isn't the right fit for this company."

Nicco dismissed her words with a shake of his head. For some unexplainable reason, he wanted to help the out-of-work single mom. Other women like Gracie enjoyed living off men, but Jariah was independent and charitable, and he admired her ambition. After reading her curriculum vitae, he felt that she'd be a great addition to the Morretti Inc. family. He didn't care what Mrs. Reddick thought. He was hiring Jariah, and that was that. "With all due respect, Mrs. Reddick, I'm quite capable of hiring my own executive assistant."

"Ms. Brooks is a university graduate, with years of experience working in finance," she said matter-of-factly. "Being an EA is beneath her. She won't take the position."

"She will." Nicco adjusted his tie and flashed a broad grin. "Because I'm going to make Ms. Brooks an offer she can't refuse."

Chapter 3

"Mom, can Dad come over for dinner?"

Absolutely not! Jariah thought, opening the fridge and taking out the Tupperware container filled with last night's leftovers. The less time she spent with her ex the better, so inviting Wesley over to break bread after another stressful day of job interviews was definitely out of the question. "Not tonight, baby."

"But I haven't seen Daddy since my birthday party."

Hearing the anguish in her daughter's voice made her heart ache, but Jariah couldn't tell Ava the real reason her father wasn't coming around anymore. He was still trying to get back at her for breaking up with him, but the only person he was hurting was their daughter. "Your dad is busy at work, but he's always thinking about you, Ava, even when you're apart."

Ava sat at the kitchen table, playing with her stuffed animals, and when she poked out her bottom lip she looked just like her father. "I miss Daddy so much," she said. "He buys me ice cream and games and always tells me funny stories…"

Like most children, Ava adored her father and could go

on for hours about how wonderful he was. Jariah wasn't in the mood to talk about Wesley, but she let her baby girl talk, and resisted the urge to change the subject. Her ex was a decent father who spoiled their daughter silly, but he was a terrible boyfriend and a selfish lover. *Considering how inept he was in the bedroom, it's a miracle we ever got pregnant.*

Jariah's gaze drifted to the window above the sink. Birds chirped in the trees, girls played jump rope in the streets and the neighborhood watchdog, Mr. Regula, stood in his driveway, buffing his Cadillac to a shine. Aventura was a safe, caring community, filled with hardworking people, and Jariah enjoyed living in such a diverse, multicultural neighborhood.

"Mom, can we go to Chuck E. Cheese's tomorrow?" Ava asked, glancing up from her toys.

Jariah popped the leftovers in the microwave and set the timer for two minutes. "You have day camp tomorrow, remember?"

"I hate summer camp. It's boring and the kids are mean."

"Still not getting along with the other girls, huh?"

Her lips twisted into a scowl. "Laquinta called me a boo-boo head and pulled my braids."

"La who?"

When Ava giggled, her pigtails tumbled around her pretty, plump face.

"It doesn't matter what anyone says. You're beautiful."

"Just like you, right, Mama?"

"That's right, and don't you forget it." Jariah walked over to the table, cupped her daughter's chin and kissed the tip of her nose. "Put your toys away. It's time for dinner."

"Are we having pizza? I hope so. I just *love* cheese pizza."

"I'll make you pizza this weekend, but tonight we're having veggie casserole."

"Again? But we had that yesterday."

Overlooking her daughter's disappointment, Jariah opened the stove and heaved the casserole dish onto the counter.

"When I'm at Dad's house he lets me eat whatever I want," Ava announced. Marching over to the pantry, she tugged open the door and rummaged around inside. "I don't want leftovers. I want Froot Loops and chocolate chip cookies."

"Ava, cut it out. You're going to eat what I made for dinner and that's final."

"Why?" she demanded, her voice a shrill shout. "Why can't I eat what I want?"

"Because eating junk food will give you a tummy ache, and I don't want you to get sick."

"You always say no. You never give me what I want."

Feeling her temperature rise, Jariah cautioned herself to remain calm. Instead of scolding Ava for acting like a spoiled brat, she picked up the stuffed animals scattered on the table, and handed them to her daughter. "These need to go back to your room."

"I hate it here," Ava shouted. "I wish I lived with Daddy!"

Of course you do, Jariah thought sourly. *Your dad gives you whatever you want, and there are no rules at his house. It's one big party over there!* Releasing a deep sigh, she fought back the tears of frustration that threatened to break free. Ava's words hurt, made her question whether or not she was a good mother. Before self-pity could set in, Jariah shook off her thoughts and regarded her strong-willed daughter. "You can sit down at the table and eat dinner with me, or you can go to your room. It's your choice."

Ava stood there for a minute, her big, brown eyes narrowed as if weighing her options. Without a word, she took the toys out of Jariah's hands and moped down the hallway toward the stairwell. Her head was down, her shoulders were bent, and she moved like someone racked with grief.

Sadness flooded Jariah's heart. She felt a tightness in her chest that made it hard to breathe. It hurt to see her daughter like this, but what could she do? It wasn't her fault Ava hadn't seen her dad in a month, was it? These days, Wesley's visits were short and sporadic and more often than not he didn't show up at all. *Should I take him back? Should I move in with him for Ava's sake? Is that the answer to all of my problems?*

Chasing away the thought, Jariah returned to the stove and resumed preparing dinner. Taking Wesley back would be a mistake. He didn't love her—not the way she needed to be loved—and more importantly she didn't love him. Years ago, when they'd started dating at Miami University she'd naively thought Wesley was "the one." But after discovering she was pregnant, she'd seen a different side of him—a weak, spineless side that chose his parents repeatedly over her. And after years of playing second fiddle to his family, Jariah realized Wesley was never going to change, and broke things off for good. Contrary to what he thought, she deserved more, and didn't need him or anyone else to take care of her.

Hearing her cell phone ring, Jariah searched the kitchen for her BlackBerry. Spotting it on the breakfast bar, she scooped it up and read the number on the display. Luckily, it wasn't Wesley or his obnoxious mother. Jariah didn't recognize the number on the screen, but as she put her cell phone to her ear, she hoped and prayed it was someone calling to offer her a job. "Hello, Jariah Brooks speaking."

"Good evening, Jariah. This is Nicco Morretti. How are you?"

The sound of his deep, smooth voice tickled the tips of her ears.

"I'm great, thanks." Jariah knew why Nicco Morretti was calling, and for the first time since losing her job last month, she smiled from ear to ear. Excitement surged through her veins, hard and fast. Jariah wanted to dance around the kitchen, but she maintained her composure.

"I hope I haven't caught you at a bad time."

"No, not at all," she rushed to say. "I'm not doing anything. Now's a great time to talk."

"I'd like to discuss a business proposition with you."

Confused, Jariah scratched her head. A business proposition? Frowning, she stared down incredulously at the phone. *Did I get the account manager position or not?* she wondered, leaning against the granite countertop. "I'm sorry, Mr. Morretti, but I'm afraid I don't understand. What is this pertaining to?"

"I'd rather not discuss it over the phone."

Discuss what? I have no clue what you're talking about!

"Let's meet at Dolce Vita for drinks at eight o'clock."

"Tonight?"

"Yes, is that a problem?"

"Mom, look, I washed my hands with soap!" Ava stood beside the pantry door, waving her hands frantically in the air, hopping up and down as if she was on a pogo stick. "Can I have some cookies now?"

To quiet her daughter, Jariah pressed a finger to her lips, and steered her over to the table. "Is it okay if I call you back in an hour? I'm kind of in the middle of something."

"That's no problem at all," he said, his tone calm. "I'll talk to you then."

Jariah hung up and rested her phone on the kitchen counter. *What was* that *all about?* she wondered. *What is Nicco Morretti up to?* As Jariah fixed Ava a plate, she replayed her conversation with the cocky CEO in her head, trying to figure out if she'd missed something. But there was nothing to miss. Their conversation had been brief, and he'd been vague and mysterious throughout. The only way to find out what Nicco Morretti wanted was to meet him tonight at his restaurant, but first she had to find a babysitter.

Once Ava was eating dinner, Jariah slipped out of the kitchen and went into her bedroom. It was times like this that Jariah wished she could talk to her parents. She longed to hear her mother's voice and her father's booming laugh, but she knew they would never take her call. They had cut her out of their lives, and their bitter rejection still stung months later.

Ignoring the heaviness in her chest, Jariah flopped down on the bed, punched in her neighbor's phone number and waited anxiously for the call to connect. Cousins, Sadie and Felicia Robinson were good old-fashioned country girls, and Jariah loved hanging out with them. And so did her daughter. The cousins fussed over her, snuck her junk food when they thought Jariah wasn't looking, and gave Ava free reign of their town house.

"Hey, Sadie, how are you?" Jariah asked, greeting the thirty-five-year-old boutique owner with the fun-loving personality.

"I'm great. I was just about to make dinner. How is my sweet little honey pie doing?"

"Ava's fine, giving me sass and attitude as usual."

"Good for her!" Sadie cheered. "She needs to stand up for herself. You're way too strict."

"I have to be. Her dad is a total pushover," Jariah explained, feeling compelled to defend herself. "Ava throws a fit and he caves like a house of cards!"

The women laughed.

"Is Felicia still at work?" Jariah asked.

"No, she has a date."

"Another one? That's the third one this week and it's only Tuesday!"

"I know, tell me about it," Sadie quipped, her voice losing its cheer. "And the guy who picked her up tonight was a total hottie. Was driving a sports car and everything."

"You sound jealous."

"Why would I be jealous? I have a date, too."

"You do? With who?"

"The remote control!" Sadie giggled. "*Dating in the City* starts in fifteen minutes, and I can't wait to see what happens between Nelson Hamilton and the chick from…"

Jariah checked the time on the digital alarm clock, saw that it was almost six o'clock, and knew she had to rush things along. "Sadie, I need a favor," she began, clearing her throat. "Can you babysit Ava for me tonight? I know its short notice, but the CEO of Morretti Incorporated just called and asked me to meet him for drinks."

"No problem, girl. I'll be right over."

"There's no rush. I don't need to leave for another hour."

"I know," she said, "but I can smell your cooking all the way over here, and I'm hungrier than a plus-sized model on a no-carb diet!"

Jariah glanced at her wristwatch, and then tossed a look over her shoulder for the third time since arriving at Dolce Vita. When she'd entered the ritzy restaurant lounge and informed the hostess that she was meeting Nicco Morretti, the freckled brunette had greeted her warmly and escorted her to a secluded table in front of the picture window.

To pass the time, Jariah logged on to the internet and resumed reading an article she'd found that afternoon about Morretti Inc. Thanks to the magazine, she knew tons of information about the company and it's handsome CEO with the bold personality. Knowing the good, the bad and the ugly about Nicco Morretti made Jariah feel prepared and more confident about meeting him for drinks at his downtown restaurant.

A rich, heady aroma sweetened the air. A waitress sashayed through the lounge pushing a dessert cart, and Jariah hungrily licked her lips. A loud cheer went up from the table behind her, but she didn't pay the group any mind.

Dolce Vita was large, boisterous and busy, but the candle-lit tables, Italian marble and sable-brown decor created an intimate vibe. The restaurant lounge was the perfect setting for a romantic date, or a surprise marriage proposal, and as Jariah sat there, bored out of her mind, she reflected on the pitiful state of her love life. *Is Wesley right? Am I going to regret dumping him one day and beg him to take me back?*

Banishing the thought to the furthest corner of her mind, Jariah picked up her cocktail glass and slowly sipped through her straw. She longed to have someone special in her life, a man who would love her unconditionally. As she glanced around the room and saw all the starry-eyed couples toasting with wine flutes held high, she felt a stab of envy. *Am I ever going to meet Mr. Right? Or am I destined to spend my nights alone with no one to keep me company but my daughter and my girlfriends?*

Her thoughts turned to her parents, but instead of pushing her memories aside, she dialed their home number. As usual, the answering machine clicked on, and when it did, she took a deep breath and mustered all the cheer she had inside her. "Hi, Mom, and Dad, it's me, Jariah. I was just thinking about you, and wanted you to know that Ava and I miss you very much. We'd love to hear from you, so please give us a call. Bye."

Jariah pressed the end button on her phone and dropped it back into her purse.

"Can I interest you in another pineapple martini?"

"No, just the bill, thank you."

The waiter's eyes were wide with alarm, but he nodded and scurried off. He was back seconds later with the hostess in tow, fidgeting nervously with his hands.

"I just got off the phone with Mr. Morretti, and he asked me to apologize on his behalf," the hostess said, her tone contrite. "Can I get you another beverage while you wait?"

"No, thank you. I'd like the bill."

"The bill?" she repeated. "But Mr. Morretti is on his way."

"That's all fine and well, but he's already wasted enough of my time tonight." Jariah checked her watch, saw that it was eight-thirty, and stood to her feet. Cuddling in bed, reading with her daughter was the highlight of her day, and if she hurried she could still make it home in time to put Ava to bed. "The check, please."

"It's on the house."

"On the house?" Jariah frowned, confused by the hostess's words. "Why?"

"Because you're a personal guest of the owner."

Oh, of course. I bet all of his female guests eat for free.

"Thank you. Good night." Jariah tucked her black clutch bag under her arm. Walking through the lounge, she noted that every table was filled and that patrons were smiling, chatting and laughing. The waiting area was jam-packed, and as she strode past the aquarium, several men wearing wedding bands winked at her. Jariah rolled her eyes and kept on moving. Getting involved with a married man was asking for trouble, and Jariah avoided drama at all costs.

The evening air was thick and held the scent of rain. *Where had the summer gone?* Jariah wondered, striding through the restaurant parking lot. In a few short weeks, Ava would be back in school, and she'd be...

Jariah shuddered to think what she'd do if she still didn't have a job. Her car needed repairs, and Ava needed back-to-school clothes and supplies. If she didn't land an accounting position soon she'd have to stop doing all the things she loved—like taking Ava to the amusement park, sponsoring children in need and going for cocktails with her girlfriends.

"Jariah, wait up!"

Searching the parking lot for the face that matched that deep, husky voice, she slowed her pace and narrowed her eyes. And when her gaze landed on Nicco Morretti—looking all kinds of sexy in his fitted blue shirt and jeans, her feet froze to the ground.

Standing there with her heart pounding and her limbs shaking, Jariah decided that it should be a crime for a man to be *that* good-looking. A sin, actually, because all the thoughts that flooded her brain involved handcuffs, a blindfold and whip cream. The restaurateur oozed an intoxicating blend of masculinity and sensuality, and he moved like a tiger prowling the jungle.

"Good evening, Jariah. It's great to see you again."

Nicco stopped, just inches away from her face, and when Jariah got a whiff of his cologne her heart murmured inside her chest. The sexy CEO made her hyperventilate—his gaze was so powerful she felt vulnerable and exposed. Jariah hated the effect Nicco Morretti had on her, and wondered how she could be attracted to a guy who'd hit on anything with a pulse.

"I'm sorry I'm late." His voice was low, and he appeared apologetic. "Something important came up as I was leaving the office, and I couldn't get away."

Jariah didn't believe his story, not for a second, but she didn't question him. Why bother? He'd only lie, and besides, it didn't matter why he was late because she was leaving. Remembering their earlier conversation gave Jariah pause. She forced a sympathetic smile. "What did you want to discuss?"

"Not out here. Let's head back inside Dolce Vita."

"I was just leaving."

He cocked his head to the right. "I see that."

Jariah detected a hint of anger in his voice, and wondered what *that* was all about. *If anyone should be upset it should be me. You're thirty minutes late!* Confused by his reaction, she looked at him inquiringly.

"I invited you here so we could have a bite, and maybe get something—"

"I'm not hungry," she interrupted, annoyed by his blasé attitude. "I lost my appetite about *thirty* minutes ago."

"Then let me buy you a drink."

The feel of his hand along her bare shoulder weakened her resolve.

"I feel terrible for showing up late, but something came up that required my immediate attention," he explained. "I got here as soon as I could."

His explanation sounded plausible, reasonable even, but Jariah wasn't moved. Unsure of what to do, she vacillated between going home to her daughter and taking Nicco Morretti up on his offer. *This isn't a date,* she told herself, pushing her reservations to the back of her mind. *It's a business meeting and nothing more. I don't even like the guy.* But her tingling, inflamed body suggested otherwise. Her heartbeat roared in her ears, invisible beads of perspiration dotted her forehead and her sleeveless blouse stuck to her skin.

"Come back inside. I promise to make it worth your while."

To Jariah's utter disbelief and amazement, the word "yes" flew out of her mouth.

"Right this way." Nicco gestured to the restaurant with one hand and placed the other on the small of her back. "You look incredible tonight. Even more beautiful than I remember."

I do? The tips of her ears tingled, and her cheeks flushed with embarrassment. Commanding her legs to move and her hands to quit shaking, Jariah tried not to notice how dreamy Nicco Morretti looked or how delicious he smelled. Even though she was attracted to him, Jariah was determined not to be his next victim.

Tell that to your hot, lust-inflected body! her inner voice jeered. *You want Nicco Morretti so bad you can't even walk straight!*

Chapter 4

Nicco was having a hell of a time concentrating, and not just because Jariah Brooks was sitting across from him in his favorite corner booth at Dolce Vita looking like a million bucks. He found her worldly, sophisticated vibe appealing, and although the restaurant was loud and busy, he was having a kick-ass time in her company.

Boisterous conversation filled the restaurant, and all of the young, stylish diners were drinking, dancing and snapping pictures with their cell phones. From his seat, he had a bird's eye view of the lounge, and chuckled to himself when he spotted his head chef walking around greeting regulars, shaking hands and admonishing the tuxedo-clad waiters.

Like last night, the star power was definitely in abundance at Dolce Vita but to his surprise Jariah didn't get flustered or giddy when his celebrity friends dropped by their booth. She shook hands with each new arrival, but she seemed far more interested in her meal than chatting up A-list stars.

As Nicco surveyed the crowd, he wondered if he was being watched. Were the jerks who'd vandalized Dolce

Vita here tonight? Were they sitting at a table plotting their next move? Or at the bar keeping close tabs on him?

Anger burned inside him, and Nicco gripped his tumbler so hard he feared the glass would shatter into a hundred pieces. The police had given up searching for suspects, so it was up to him to find out who had trashed his restaurant. And he would. No matter the cost.

At the bar, Nicco spotted a slim, bald-headed man wearing dark sunglasses in deep conversation with one of the female bartenders, and he sat up taller, straighter. The stranger resembled his ex-friend and former business partner, Tye Caldwell. Nicco considered going into the lounge to find out for sure, but decided against it. Tye wouldn't be stupid enough to show his face at Dolce Vita after what happened last summer, would he? Nicco squinted, and peered inconspicuously around the young Asian couple sharing a steamy French kiss. The lights were low, and the lounge was packed, which made it impossible for him to get a good look at the well-dressed man. Thinking about, Tye—someone he'd once considered family—filled his heart with pain. Nicco felt a twinge of deep sadness. *First Tye screws me over, and then Gracie. Are there any honest, trustworthy people left in the world?* he wondered. *If my closest friend and confidant could betray me, then anyone can.*

"I'm glad I let you talk me into ordering the *vitello.* It's so moist and creamy…"

Nicco ditched his thoughts and turned his attention to his lovely dinner companion with the knock-out curves. He was a leg man, but couldn't resist admiring Jariah's other impressive physical assets. The twenty-seven-year-old beauty was glowing, radiating an inner light that literally lit up the whole restaurant. She smelled like cherry blossoms, spoke with confidence, and despite her youth, carried herself in a composed, mature way. Her ruffled, orange blouse was eye-catching and showed off her toned arms and a hint of cleavage.

"I'm glad that you're enjoying your meal," Nicco said, eying her over the rim of his glass. "If you'd like, I could order you another entrée."

"No, thank you. I've had more than enough food for one evening."

"Does that mean you're not having dessert?"

"I can't. I'm teaching a step-aerobics class in the morning, and if I pig out tonight I won't be able to keep up with my students."

Her beauty dazzled him, made him forget everyone else in the room. Nicco didn't know if it was the wine or the lively atmosphere in the lounge that helped loosen her up, but it was obvious Jariah was in great spirits. While waiting for their entrees to arrive, she'd asked smart, insightful questions about his company, and impressed him with her vast knowledge of the stock market. Jariah spoke with enthusiasm and passion about her volunteering work, and chatted excitedly about the new projects she'd developed at the Miami Food Bank.

"I'd love to discuss your business proposition now," Jariah said, setting aside her plate.

Clasping her hands together, she looked him straight in the eye, her gaze unwavering and intense. It held him in its powerful grip, refused to let him go, and for the second time that night Nicco hoped he didn't look as stupid as he felt. "I'd rather hear more about your hobbies and interests," he said, artfully dodging the question. "What do you do when you're not teaching fitness classes at Premier Fitness?"

"Not much. Now, back to your business proposition—"

"Come l'aragosta era? Fido di che sia stato anche il suo amare, Sig. Morretti."

Chef Gambro, an overweight man of fifty, bounded over

to the booth and clapped Nicco vigorously on the back. Speaking in Italian, his voice stern, but his manner playful, he explained that he was on a date and didn't want to be interrupted. Nicco saw Jariah tense, then raise a perfectly arched eyebrow, and wondered if she'd understood what he'd said.

Gambro turned to Jariah and took her hand. Lifting it to his mouth, he reverently kissed her palm. Gazing at her adoringly, he complimented her effusively in his native tongue, but before Nicco could answer on Jariah's behalf she responded—in Italian. Her tone was refreshingly light, but she spoke in a voice as lively and as animated as Chef Gambro's. Dumbfounded, Nicco leaned forward in his seat, unable to believe his ears.

"Grazie per un pasto meraviglioso, Chef Gambro voi. Tutto era spettacolare, e il vitello era il migliore che abbia mai avuto…"

Nicco listened, enraptured, and realized that Jariah Brooks was as gracious as she was kind. She thanked Chef Gambro for a delicious meal and promised to return soon for more of his spectacular Italian cooking. The chef beamed, and when he swaggered back to the kitchen seconds later, his chest puffed up with pride.

"You speak Italian?" Nicco asked, regaining the use of his tongue.

"Yes, and Spanish, as well."

"That's impressive."

"I had no choice. My parents forced me to take foreign language classes for years."

"That must have been a total drag."

"It was. My parents had very high expectations for me, and…" Jariah winced, as if she had a toothache, and her expression turned somber. "I owe all of my success to them."

Silence settled at the table like an unwelcomed guest.

"Tell me more about you background, Jariah."

The corners of her mouth tightened. "What do you want to know that we haven't already discussed tonight?"

Everything! he thought, draping an arm over the back of the booth. *Do you feel the chemistry between us? Have you ever had a summer fling? Would you like to?*

To keep from reaching across the table, and caressing her skin, Nicco picked up his glass tumbler and downed the rest of his cognac. He started to ask Jariah about her career aspirations, but she interrupted him and repeated the same question she'd posed earlier—the one he'd conveniently forgot. Nicco was enjoying their conversation, and wasn't ready to discuss his business proposition just yet. He wanted to hear more about her family, what she liked doing in her free time, and the kind of guys she dated. Not because he was interested in her, but because he planned to hire her, and felt it was important to know as much about her as possible, he had convinced himself.

"Did I get the account manager position?"

Nicco heard the vulnerability in her voice, saw the twinkle in her eyes and felt the impulse to lie. But he knew there'd be hell to pay if he upset Mrs. Reddick, and the HR Director was dead-set against hiring Jariah. Besides, he had something better in mind for her, and couldn't wait to see the look on her face when he shared the good news. "No, Jariah, I'm sorry, you didn't."

Her smile faded. "Why not? My interview went so well."

"You're right, it did," he conceded, troubled by the pained expression on her face. "But we decided to hire someone with more experience."

Jariah swallowed hard. "I understand."

Driven by compassion, Nicco reached across the table and touched her hand. Jariah jerked away, as if he'd zapped her with a stun gun, and pressed herself flat against the booth.

"You invited me down here to tell me I didn't get the job?"

He heard the accusation in her voice and rushed to explain. "No, of course not. I need an executive assistant, and thought you might be interested in the position."

Her eyes tapered, and a scowl stained her lush, red lips. "I'm not."

"Don't you want to hear the job description before you turn it down?"

"No, Mr. Morretti, I don't."

"Please, call me, Nicco."

"No offense, *Mr. Morretti,* but I have no desire to be a glorified receptionist."

He paused to organize his thoughts. Jariah's reaction was unsettling, and he didn't understand why she was glaring at him. "I don't need a receptionist. I already have one," he explained. "I need someone to manage my schedule, accompany me to various meetings, liaise with clients and respond to my correspondence in a timely and professional manner."

"Thanks, but no thanks."

"Let me finish, there's more," he said calmly, though his temperature raised a notch. "My older brother and I oversee the day-to-day operations of Morretti Incorporated, but my real passion is the restaurant business. I love acquiring struggling establishments and turning them around, and I need someone with passion and conviction to help me."

The waiter arrived, refilled their wineglasses and cleared the table of their dinner plates. He departed seconds later, but Nicco didn't speak. He thought of telling a joke to lighten the mood, but decided against it when he saw her sneak a glance at her silver watch. Jariah looked bored, wouldn't meet his gaze, and the tension hovering above their table was suffocating.

"I travel considerably for business, and have trips to

Los Angeles, Chicago and Washington planned this year. Also," he paused, to allow sufficient time for his words to sink in, "Morretti Inc. has numerous opportunities for employee advancement, and the next time there's a vacancy in the accounting department I would personally recommend you."

"Sorry, but I'm still not interested." Jariah stood, purse in hand, and eyed him coolly. "Thanks for dinner. Good night."

Determined to prolong their time together, Nicco slid out of the booth and boldly stepped in front of her, getting so close he could smell her strawberry-flavored lip gloss. "Let's discuss the position further over a round of drinks," he proposed, gesturing across the room. Every stool at the bar was taken, but he'd find a seat for her. Hell, he'd clear the entire bar if he had to. It was obvious Jariah was disappointed and upset, but Nicco didn't understand why. She should be jumping up and down for joy, not tapping her foot impatiently on the ground and shooting evil daggers at him. "Hear me out. You won't be sorry."

"I can't support my daughter on minimum wage."

Nicco gave her arm a light squeeze. Her skin was soft, and her spicy, floral perfume aroused his senses. And his erection. "I'd never pay someone with your qualifications seven dollars an hour," he said honestly. "Your salary would be sixty-thousand dollars, plus benefits, and three weeks paid vacation."

Nicco studied her reaction, and tried to surmise what she was thinking. Her face was blank, impossible to read, but he knew she was impressed. Had to be. He was offering her a great job package, and the opportunity to work at a successful, world-renowned company. "Take some time to think it over."

"There's nothing to think about."

"I think there is. I spoke to your references this morning, and—"

Her eyes doubled in size. "You did?"

"Yes, and your old boss at First National Trust Bank gave you a glowing recommendation," he said, nodding his head. "He said you were the best accountant he'd ever had, and one of the smartest, too. And now that I know you speak Italian, I'm even more convinced that you're the right person for the executive assistant position."

Too choked up to speak, Jariah stared down at the floor, wishing it would open up and swallow her into the ground. The weight of her disappointment was crushing, so heavy she couldn't look Nicco in the eye. Convinced she'd landed the account manager's job, she'd imagined herself signing the contracts at Dolce Vita, and toasting her success over a glass of rose champagne. But it wasn't to be.

Could this evening get any worse? What's he going to do next? Ask me to do his laundry? Jariah shook off her thoughts and her feelings of utter despair. This wouldn't be the first time a man had ruined her night, and it probably wouldn't be the last time. Agreeing to meet Nicco was a mistake, and as Jariah blinked back the tears that formed in her eyes, she regretted ever coming to the restaurant to meet with him.

"Are you sure you can't join me at the bar for a glass of merlot?"

Scared her emotions would break free if she spoke, Jariah shook her head and opened her purse in search of her keys.

"I'll walk you to your car."

"No, thank you. I can manage."

Nicco leaned in close and grazed his fingers across her bare shoulder. A thousand volts of electricity rushed through her body. For a moment, Jariah lost herself in the depths of his deep brown eyes. She feared he was going to kiss her right then and there in the middle of the dining room, and didn't know whether to run or hide.

Clapping and spirited singing rang out behind her, and just like that, their spell was broken. Turning on her heels, Jariah blew out of the dining room at lightning-fast speed. Anxious to put as much distance as possible between herself and Nicco Morretti, she marched briskly through the restaurant, and out the front doors into the starry, summer night.

Minutes later, Jariah was sitting inside of her Dodge Plymouth with her face buried in her hands. Her thoughts were on dinner and the time she'd spent getting to know Nicco Morretti. From the moment they'd been seated in the restaurant, he'd been warm and complimentary, and even agreed that she'd nailed her job interview on Monday. But instead of offering her the account manager position, he'd insulted her.

"What a jerk," Jariah grumbled, putting on her seat belt. "He must do recreational drugs because his business proposition is the most ludicrous thing I've ever heard!

Jariah jammed the key in the ignition and turned the lock. The engine coughed and sputtered but didn't start. "Oh, no, not again." Taking a deep breath, she closed her eyes and counted to ten. Feeling calmer, she tried the key again. And again. On the third try, the engine roared to life, and Jariah sighed in relief.

As she drove out of the restaurant parking lot, she spotted Nicco Morretti standing in front of Dolce Vita, lighting a cigar. Smoke billowed around him, adding to his mysterious, bad-boy allure. Pretending she didn't see him, she returned her attention to the road and stepped on the gas pedal. His words played in her mind, wounding her afresh.

You showed a lot of poise and professionalism during your interview, but we decided to hire someone with more experience in the accounting field.

Tears spilled down her cheeks, but Jariah furiously slapped them away. She didn't have time to cry; she had a daughter to take care of and a full-time job to find. Jariah told herself that she was stressing over nothing, that she'd be gainfully employed in no time, but her doubts and frustrations remained.

Sweat drenched her skin, and the fear of losing everything she held dear—her independence, her home and custody of her daughter—burned inside the walls of her chest. *What am I doing wrong?* Jariah wondered, drumming her fingers on the steering wheel. *How many more interviews do I have to go on before someone hires me?* Jariah didn't know what she was going to do when the money in her emergency fund ran out, but there was one thing she knew for sure: the next time she saw Nicco Morretti she was running the other way.

Chapter 5

Laughter, pop music and the heady scent of fresh straw-berries drifted out the kitchen window in Jariah's town-home. Despite the cheerful atmosphere inside and the mouth-watering aromas sweetening the night air, she dragged herself up the stone walkway. Not because she was tired, but because she didn't want to answer Sadie's incessant questions about her business meeting with Nicco Morretti.

At the front door, Jariah shook off her melancholy mood and fussed with her hair. She didn't want Sadie to know that she'd been crying, so as she unlocked the door she arched her bent shoulders and plastered a smile on her face.

Inside the kitchen, fixing themselves a snack were Sadie and Jariah's cousin, Felicia. The thirty-year-old divorcee had a flamboyant personality, and was such a social butter-fly, she had no trouble making friends. Or meeting hand-some, successful men, either. Her silky hair was touched with honey-blonde streaks, and her zebra-print body suit was so tight, Jariah wondered if she could breathe.

"Hey, you guys, what's up?" Jariah dumped her things on the end table and joined her friends at the breakfast bar. It was covered with junk food, movies and fashion magazines.

"We're just making a late-night snack." Felicia opened the tub of ice-cream and dunked her spoon inside. "Do you want a chocolate sundae with caramel syrup?"

"No thanks. I just ate." Jariah sat down on a stool and plucked a strawberry out of the fruit bowl. The oversized glass dish was a gift from her mom for her birthday. Every time she looked at it her heart ached. "Felicia, I'm surprised you're here. I thought you had a date."

"I did, but the guy turned out to be a dud, so I faked a migraine and came home."

"Wow, that's harsh."

"Not to me," she chirped. "If the chemistry isn't there, I leave. No exceptions."

Sadie piped up. "I agree. I don't have time to waste with Mr. Wrong or Mr. Maybe. My biological clock is ticking so loud my mother can hear it all the way in Tennessee!"

The cousins hooted and laughed.

"How was Ava?" Jariah glanced up at the staircase to the second floor, where Ava's bedroom was, and imagined her adorable daughter curled up in her Dora the Explorer bed sleeping soundly. "I hope she didn't give you any trouble."

"Not at all. She fell asleep twenty minutes after you left." Sadie ripped open a bag of Doritos chips and popped one into her mouth. "Since Ava was already in her pj's, I carried her to her room and tucked her in."

"Thank you, girl. You always take such great care of my baby."

"It's my pleasure. I love Ava. She's smart and saucy just like me!" When Sadie laughed, her short, thick curls tumbled around her pretty oval face. "How did things go tonight?"

"Yes, do tell." Felicia faked a swoon. "I love Italian

men, and when Sadie told me you had a date with Nicco Morretti, I almost creamed my panties!"

"It wasn't a date. He wanted to discuss a business proposition with me."

"Did you get the account manager job?" Sadie asked.

"No. They gave it to someone with more experience."

Felicia put her bowl down on the breakfast bar. "I don't understand. The guy invited you to his restaurant just to tell you that you didn't get the job? Wow, that's cold!"

"He wants me to be his assistant," Jariah explained, still unable to believe it herself.

"I bet that's not all he wants," Felicia drawled, eyebrows raised.

"Ignore her, girl. Congratulations. When do you start?"

"I don't. I told him thanks, but no thanks."

Sadie wore a confused face. "Why? Working for Nicco Morretti would be a huge coup."

"I didn't bust my butt in college just to end up being a glorified secretary."

"What's wrong with being a secretary?" Felicia asked, cocking an eyebrow.

"Nothing, but it's not the right career for me."

"Why not?"

"Because I went to school for accounting, not to fetch coffee and answer phones."

"I was a receptionist back in Chattanooga," Felicia said, pointing at her chest. "I made decent money, and I was employee of the month twice."

"I wasn't trying to imply that I'm better than you—"

Felicia sucked her teeth. "Sure you weren't."

Jariah felt trapped, like a rabbit cornered by a coyote in the woods. She feared if she didn't apologize to Felicia, their relationship would be irretrievably damaged, but before she could even think about what to say, Sadie spoke up.

"Tell us more about the executive assistant position." Leaning forward on her stool, her expression curious, she propped a hand under her chin and waited expectantly. "What's the job description? Is there a signing bonus? Do you have to work evenings and weekends?"

Reluctantly, Jariah recounted her conversation with Nicco Morretti. The night was a blur, clouded by intense gazes, blinding chemistry and disappointments. The only thing she remembered clearly was the moment Nicco had touched her. His hands were warm, strong and they set her body ablaze. "After he told me I didn't get the account manager position, I kinda zoned out, so I don't remember the specifics of the EA position besides the sixty-thousand-dollar salary."

"Sixty-thousand dollars is great money."

"Amen to that," Felicia quipped. "Shoot, if you won't take the job, I will!"

"I'm surprised you didn't jump at the offer, especially in light of the rent increase."

Jariah frowned and shot Sadie a questioning look. "What are you talking about?"

"Didn't you get a letter from the condominium board yesterday?"

"No, why? What did it say?"

"On September 1st, our rent and condo fees are increasing by eight percent."

Felicia threw her hands up in the air. "Oh, great, there goes my mani-pedi money."

It's been so long, I can't even remember the last time I went to the salon, Jariah thought sadly. *I wish I could get my hair done, and update my wardrobe, too, but I just can't afford it.*

Her gaze fell across the calendar and zeroed in on the date. Jariah had a full day ahead of her tomorrow, but she wasn't excited about any of her upcoming interviews. Job hunting was stressful, but throwing in the towel wasn't an option. She was going to find a full-time job—no if, ands or buts about it. And when she did she was buying herself a new car, because she was sick of hearing her Dodge cough and sputter.

"I think you should take the EA job. It's the smart thing to do," Sadie said emphatically. "Take the position, and if something better comes along, just quit."

"Mr. Morretti's going to want me to sign a one-year contract."

"So what? People break contracts every day." Felicia flipped her hair over her shoulders, and gave a nonchalant shrug. "It's no big deal. What's he going to do? Sue you?"

Jariah gave serious consideration to what her girlfriends said, but still wasn't convinced. "I don't think I can…" She broke off speaking, and shook her head. "Forget it."

"What is it?" Sadie asked, resting a hand on her shoulder. "What's bothering you?"

"I'm scared of what people will say when they find out I'm a receptionist."

And by people, I mean my parents. I've disappointed them so many times, and I don't want them to hear how much of a failure I am. Jariah stared at the framed photograph on the wall. It had been taken the day of her high school graduation, long before college, wild frat parties, and Wesley Covington came along. Back then, her parents had had complete control of her life, and Jariah had been so anxious to break free she'd applied to dozens of out-of-state universities. The day she'd received her acceptance letter to Miami University she'd danced around the kitchen, feeling like the luckiest girl alive. To this day, it still amazed her how young and naive she'd been. If she hadn't been so trusting, and head over heels in love with Wesley—the first guy she'd ever kissed—she never would have gotten pregnant her senior year.

The thought froze in Jariah's brain. Scared of where her emotions would take her, she shook her head to ward off the memories that threatened to break free. Thinking about the day she broke the news of her pregnancy to her parents always brought feelings of guilt, shame and regret. Jariah had enough on her plate to deal with without adding the mistakes of her past to the mix. Her rent was going up, she had no job prospects, and her car was on its last leg. *What more could possibly go wrong this week? Am I ever going to catch a break?*

"Who cares what people say?" Sadie gave Jariah a one-armed hug. "You'll be making an honest living, and that's all that matters."

"I couldn't agree more." Felicia peeked inside Jariah's purse, took out her cell phone and offered it to her. "Go on. Call him."

"Who?" Jariah asked, playing dumb.

"That Italian heartthrob with the bedroom eyes, of course!"

"I need to sleep on it."

"Tomorrow might be too late," Felicia said, her tone grave.

Jariah folded her arms. "Why are you pressuring me? What's in this for you?"

"I'm just being a good friend."

"Right, and you're a natural blonde!" Sadie quipped, her tone full of attitude and sarcasm. "You're up to something. I just know it."

Felicia batted her fake eyelashes. "Who, me?"

"Yes, you. Come clean. Why do you want Jariah to work for Morretti Inc. so bad?"

"Because Nicco's older brother, Rafael, is exactly my type!"

Giggling, the cousins exchanged high-fives.

"How do you know so much about the Morretti family?" Jariah asked.

Felicia waved her BlackBerry in the air. "Google, of course!"

"I almost forgot. I got our tickets to the Kings of R & B concert this morning." Sadie unzipped her handbag, took out her wallet and handed a ticket to Jariah. "Don't worry about paying me back until you get a job. I know you're good for it."

"This ticket's a hundred and fifty bucks!" she complained. "I can't afford that."

"You could if you took the executive assistant job," Felicia pointed out.

"It's not about the position or even the pay," Jariah confessed. "Nicco Morretti thinks he's God's gift to women and I honestly couldn't imagine working for him."

"No one says you have to love the guy. Just do your job and collect your paycheck!"

"It's a good thing you have Wesley's child support payments to help keep you afloat—"

Jariah cut Sadie off, annoyed at what she was implying. "I can't use Ava's money to pay my living expenses. That wouldn't be right."

The women exchanged curious glances.

"But you've been out of work for months," Felicia said. "How are you getting by?"

"I'm using my emergency fund, and when that runs out I'll just sell my car."

"Girl, please, you couldn't *give* that old hoopty away, let alone sell it!"

The women cracked up.

"I'm going to go check on, Ava." Jariah finished her orange juice and stood. "Thanks again for watching her you guys. I really appreciate it."

Sadie picked up one of the DVDs on the counter and

held it up in the air. "We were about to watch *Think Like A Man,* but if you're turning in we'll skedaddle."

For effect, Jariah licked her lips and fanned a hand to her face. "And miss my chance to see my future husband, Michael Ealy, on the big screen? No way! I'll be right back."

Jariah climbed the staircase, thinking about the advice her girlfriends had given her. An hour ago, she'd stormed out of Dolce Vita, vowing never to speak to Nicco Morretti again, but now she wondered if she'd acted in haste.

Dismissing the thought, she decided rejecting the CEO's business proposition was the right thing to do. *I'll have a new job by the end of the week,* Jariah pledged, more determined than ever to find a position in her field. *And it damn sure won't be a lowly receptionist position.*

Chapter 6

The first thing Jariah did when she returned home from picking up Ava from day camp on Thursday afternoon was check her answering machine for missed calls. It had been a week since her last interview, and Jariah was running out of options *and* money. There were no new messages, no lucrative job offers, and as she sank into her favorite chair in the bright and airy living room, she became overcome with feelings of hopelessness. Her body felt weighed down with stress and fatigue—Jariah knew it would be a struggle to stand up.

"Mom, can I play outside?"

Her vision was blurred by the unshed tears in her eyes, but Jariah nodded and said, "Sure, sweetie, but stay in front of the house. No wandering off, okay?"

"Okay, Mom. I won't."

Jariah heard the front door open and close. Shrieks of laughter gushed through the window, and the hot, blustery wind ruffled the curtains.

Thinking about her situation caused a tear to skid down her cheek. Being at home, day-in and day-out, while her friends were at their respective jobs was discouraging, but Jariah wasn't sure of what else she could do to fix her situation.

To take her mind off her troubles, she turned to the stack of mail she'd dumped on the side table. Scooping it up, she dumped the letters in her lap and propped her legs up on the coffee table. As Jariah scanned the electricity bill, she realized that she'd been a fool to turn down Nicco Morretti's business proposition. Despite applying to dozens of companies, the executive assistant position was all she had, her one and only offer. And now that Jariah had realized the error of her ways she wasn't going to let the opportunity slip through her grasp.

Sitting up, Jariah took her cell phone out of her purse, found Nicco Morretti's number in the call history, and after hitting Send, she waited for him to pick up. Her heart threatened to explode from her chest, but she carefully rehearsed what she wanted to say.

"Daddy!"

Frowning, Jariah stood and strode over to the window. She pulled back the curtains just in time to see Ava race down the walkway and leap into Wesley's open arms. Jariah was annoyed that her ex had showed up unannounced, but she decided not to give him a hard time. He'd come to spend time with his daughter, and seeing them together warmed her heart. Ava was beaming, fiercely clutching her dad's hand, and proudly showing him off to the neighborhood kids, as if he was a new toy.

The phone beeped in her ear, cuing her to leave a message, but Jariah hung up. She'd call Nicco later, once Wesley was gone. Deciding to get started on dinner, she went into the kitchen and put her cell phone down on the counter. Jariah opened the fridge and took out everything she needed to make chili. Within seconds, the vegetables were chopped and the stew was bubbling.

Just because I don't have a job doesn't mean I should

mope around feeling sorry for myself, Jariah decided, mincing a clove of garlic. *Especially when Wesley's around. The last thing I need is him getting on my case.* Back when they were living together, he constantly teased her about being a stay-at-home mom, and joked that she sat around all day watching TV and eating bon-bons while he slaved away at work. That irritated Jariah, but not as much as his disrespect and total disregard for her feelings.

The front door slammed shut, and footsteps pounded on the hardwood floor.

"Good afternoon, Jariah. How have you been?"

"I'm fine thanks, and you?"

"Great, now that I'm with my number one girl." Wesley scooped Ava up in his arms and spun her around in the air. "I finished work early, so I decided to stop by. If you girls aren't busy, I'd love to take you out for dinner. How about we go to our favorite spot?"

"Ava, Daddy's going to take you to Groovy's Pizza. Isn't that wonderful?"

"Yahoo! Let's go!"

"Why don't you go change into one of the pretty new party dresses Grandma Stella bought you for your birthday?" Jariah suggested, cupping her daughter's shoulder and steering her out of the kitchen. "And don't forget to wash up."

"Stay right there, Dad. I'll be right back."

Jariah waited until Ava raced out of the kitchen before she spoke to Wesley.

"Next time you're in the mood to drop by, please call first."

"I'll keep that in mind." He looked her up and down. "I see that you've stopped going to the gym."

"I'm a certified fitness instructor, thank you very much."

His eyebrows drew together and formed a long, crooked

line. "I find that hard to believe. You've definitely put on weight since the last time I saw you."

And you're a lousy lover, but you don't see me warning the female masses via Twitter, do you? "It's a lovely day," she said, gesturing to the door he'd just arrogantly swaggered through. "Why don't you wait for Ava outside?"

He chuckled, as if she'd just told him a knock-knock joke, then leaned casually against the breakfast bar. "Have you found a new job?"

"No, but I've had several promising offers this week."

And by several, I mean one, but whose counting?

"I'm happy for you," he said tightly, his jaw clenched. "We'll celebrate at dinner."

Jariah held her tongue. She hated when Wesley showed up unannounced and expected her to drop everything. But instead of cursing him out in every language she knew, she picked up the wooden spoon and stirred the pot of chili. "I'm not going with you guys. I have housework to do." It was a lie, and Jariah knew Wesley wouldn't believe her, but she didn't care what her ex thought. They weren't a couple anymore, and if not for Ava, she'd have nothing to do with him or his bougie parents.

"Is something wrong with your cell?" Wesley swiped her BlackBerry off the counter and examined it. "My mom said every time she calls you your phone goes straight to voice mail."

Raising an eyebrow as if confused, Jariah said, "Is Stella calling about something specific, or to cram her new-age parenting philosophies down my throat?"

"She wants to take Ava to Orlando in August. Is that cool with you?"

"I'll check my schedule and get back to you."

"I have your child support check for this month." Wearing a broad grin, Wesley reached into his back pocket, took out an envelope and offered it to her. "Don't blow it all at Macy's."

Jariah dropped the spoon on the counter. "I've never, *ever,* used Ava's money on myself. I pay for her extracurricular activities, and put the rest away in her savings account."

"Sure you do." Wesley dropped the envelope on the breakfast bar. "You've been out of work for months, and I know your parents aren't helping you, so you must be using Ava's child support checks to help stay afloat."

"I'm telling you the truth," she argued, struggling to control her temper. "I have no reason to lie, *and* I have the bank account statements to prove it."

"You know," he began, lowering his voice a notch, "I'm not dating anyone."

Jariah rolled her eyes. "Good for you."

"I want you and Ava to come back home. We're a family, and we should be together."

"I want to be a wife, and I'd love to have two or three more children. Don't you?"

Wesley coughed and raked a hand over his short, brown hair. He looked uncomfortable, and was restlessly shuffling his feet.

"That's what I thought."

"Jariah, we've been over this a million times. I'm just not ready," he said sternly, as if he was admonishing an errant child. "We'll get married one day. I promise."

"One day isn't good enough, Wesley. We've been arguing back and forth about this for years, and I'm tired of it."

"You've been tripping ever since you started reading Dr. Rashondra Brown's stupid self-help books," he argued, scowling. "You should be thanking your lucky stars that I'm a good man because I know a lot of single moms who don't have it as good as you."

Jariah propped a hand on her hip. "Is that so?"

"It sure is. Their exes are all trifling, dead-beat dads who don't give them diddly squat."

"And you should be thanking your lucky stars that I was a patient, understanding girlfriend because I don't know anyone who'd put up with you *or* your mother for five years."

"You're never going to find anyone better than me."

"Why?" she replied, snorting a laugh. "Because you're *such* a great catch?"

"No, because I can afford to buy you anything you want. Clothes, jewelry, purses—"

"I want a commitment, Wesley, not another Hermès bag."

Muttering in response, he thrust his hands into the pockets of his dark, tailored slacks. His gaze bounced around the room, looking everywhere but at her face.

"I'm ready." Entering the kitchen, Ava curtseyed, and then did a twirl around the breakfast bar. "Daddy, do you like my dress?"

Wesley's smile returned. "I love it, sweetheart. You look like a princess."

"Be a good girl," Jariah admonished, adjusting the straps on Ava's pink floral sundress. "Have fun with Daddy, and don't give him any trouble."

"I won't, Mom. I'll be on my best behavior."

Jariah kissed Ava on the cheek and gave her a hug. "See you later, alligator."

"In a while, crocodile!"

She stood in the doorway, waving at Ava, but the second Wesley's Range Rover turned out of the condominium complex, she snatched up her cell phone and hit Redial. Time was of the essence, and Jariah feared if she waited until tomorrow to contact Nicco, it would be too late. She needed that executive assistant position now, and was willing to humble herself to get it. Jariah hated the thought of doing the CEO's bidding, but she'd rather work at Morretti Inc. than spend another day at home waiting for the telephone to ring.

"This is Nicco Morretti."

His voice filled the line, warming her all over. Her heart rate spiked, but Jariah cautioned herself to remain focused. She was attracted to Nicco, but he wasn't her type, definitely not the kind of guy she'd ever fall for, and flirting with him would only bring trouble. "Yes, hello, this is… ah…ah…" Jariah drew a blank, and wanted to slap herself for forgetting her own name.

"It's great to hear from you, Jariah. I hope you and your daughter are doing well."

Staring down at the phone, her mouth agape, Jariah was convinced she'd misheard him. *He recognizes my voice? But we've only spoken on the phone once!*

"I, um, feel terrible about the way I acted last week at Dolce Vita, and I want to apologize." Jariah cringed at the memory of that night, but pushed past her shame and spoke from the heart. "I was disappointed because I didn't get the account manager job, and I let my emotions get the best of me. I'm sorry."

"I understand, Jariah. It happens to the best of us," he said sympathetically. "Even me."

"Really?"

"Absolutely."

He chuckled, and the knot in her chest loosened, abated.

"Remind me to tell you about the time I lost my cool and slugged a retired navy SEAL."

"No way. You didn't."

"I did, and I have his medical bills to prove it!"

Jariah laughed. She didn't know if Nicco was serious or just tying to make her feel better, but to her surprise, he did.

"I hope you're calling about the executive assistant position, because I could really use someone with your skill and expertise in my office."

Jariah swallowed a laugh. Making coffee didn't require any skill or expertise, but she was smart enough not to argue with him. "The position is still available?"

"It's yours if you want it."

"That's great. Thanks so much. When would you like me to start?"

"How does tomorrow sound?"

"But tomorrow is Friday."

"I know. Is that a problem?"

"No, not at all," Jariah rushed to say, again feeling foolish for letting her nerves get the best of her. "What time would you like me to be at the office?"

"Nine o'clock sharp."

"Nine o'clock it is."

"I'm excited about you joining the Morretti Inc. family," he said after a beat. "I think we're going to make a dynamic team."

"I agree, and I'm really looking forward to seeing you tomorrow morning." Stunned by her loose, wayward tongue, Jariah cupped a hand over her mouth. *I can't believe I just said that! What was I thinking?*

"Get a good night's sleep, Jariah." His tone was filled with an intoxicating blend of heat and sensuality. "Tomorrow's going to be an exciting day. One you won't ever forget."

Chapter 7

Morretti Incorporated was housed inside a ten-story building located in the heart of downtown Miami on a street lined with billboards, palm trees and colorful flowers. It was surrounded by soaring skyscrapers, trendy art galleries and high-end restaurants and cafés frequented by local celebrities and gossip-hungry socialites.

Locking her car doors, Jariah swung her purse over her shoulder and strode briskly across the parking lot. Her palms were drenched with sweat, and her legs were wobbling, but she managed to march confidently through the sliding glass doors and identify herself to the impeccably dressed redhead manning the front desk.

In the reception area, Jariah drank a cup of coffee and read the *Miami Herald*—twice. Thirty minutes passed, but she remained upbeat, happy to be at Morretti Incorporated, instead of at home perusing the classifieds. But after an hour of waiting for her new boss and watching other employees come and go, Jariah's good mood fizzled. *Is he ever on time?* she wondered, peering outside the front window in search of him. *Doesn't he know how rude it is to keep people waiting? Does he even care?*

"Ms. Brooks, good morning."

Jariah spotted the HR director traipsing across the lobby and stood. "Good morning, Mrs. Reddick," she said brightly. "How are you?"

"I understand that you're coming on board."

"Yes, I am, and I'm very excited to be here. I look forward to working with you and the rest of the Morretti Incorporated team."

"I must confess, Ms. Brooks, I was quite surprised when Mr. Morretti told me the news." A sneer curled her peach lips. "Don't you think being an assistant is beneath you?"

Jariah choked on her tongue. Taken aback by the question and Ms. Reddick's curt tone, she schooled her features to remain impassive, unperturbed. She didn't know if it was a rhetorical question, and didn't know how to respond. What was she supposed to say? *I don't want to be an executive assistant, and I think Nicco is going to be a handful, but I've been out of work for months, and I have no other job prospects. But don't worry, Mrs. Reddick, as soon as I find an accountant manager position, I'm out of here!*

"I need to review the orientation packet with you, so be at my office at one o'clock."

"That sounds great. I really appreciate you making the time to meet with me."

"Don't forget to bring a voided check and two pieces of ID for your personnel file."

Jariah nodded her head in understanding.

"Very well. I will see you this afternoon."

"Is there anything you need me to do?"

Lines of confusion wrinkled Mrs. Reddick's face. "Excuse me?"

"Nicco isn't..." Jariah saw the HR director's eyebrows shoot up, and broke off speaking. Adopting a professional tone, she said, "Mr. Morretti isn't here yet, so I was hoping I could help out in your department until he arrives."

"No, thank you. I'm busy training new employees, and you'd just be in the way."

"Can you point me in the direction of the accounting department then?" Jariah was disappointed that Mrs. Reddick was being brisk with her, but she remaining upbeat, determined not to let anything ruin her day. "It's the end of the month. I bet they could use a hand."

"I think not." Turning her nose up in the air, she flapped her hands like a bald eagle taking flight. "Have a seat in the waiting area. Mr. Morretti will be here any minute."

Before Jariah could respond, Mrs. Reddick walked off. Releasing a deep sigh, she returned to the couch and sat down. Jariah was bored and growing impatient, but she had no choice but to wait for Nicco to arrive. She retrieved her cell phone from her purse and punched in her password. Jariah had a new text message from her supervisor at Premier Fitness, informing her that her Saturday morning aerobics class was canceled, but it was the message from Wesley's mother that set her teeth on edge.

"Please have my granddaughter dressed and ready to go at five o'clock sharp. We are having dinner at the country club tonight, so ensure that her attire is semiformal."

Jariah's first thought was to call Mrs. Covington and ask her if she was out of her damn mind, but decided against it. On her lunch break, she'd call Stella and explain why Ava was not available tonight. She'd promised her daughter they could go back-to-school shopping, and then grab a bite at Chuck E. Cheese's. And if Jariah canceled her and Ava's plans, her daughter would throw a divalike tantrum.

"Good morning, Jariah. Sorry to keep you waiting."

Feeling guilty for getting caught on her phone, she hurled her BlackBerry into her leather handbag and surged to her feet. She parted her lips to greet her new boss, but when her eyes fell across Nicco's face the word got stuck in her throat. His hair was a mass of loose curls, he smelled like baby powder, and his gaze was so crippling, Jariah couldn't move. In his navy open-collar dress shirt, and tailored white slacks, he would be a shoo-in for a role on the television show *Hawaii Five-O*.

"Are you okay? You look upset."

Nicco gave her arm a light squeeze. His touch made her hot in places that made her blush, and sent her hormones into overdrive. "Me, upset? No, I'm fine. Great actually."

Jariah vigorously nodded her head, pretended everything was A-OK, but it wasn't. Not by a long shot. Nicco had impeccable swag, a unique style all his own, and she was hopelessly attracted to him. Damn it. And her body was sending mixed signals to her brain. She was breathing hard, and her heartbeat was pounding in her ears. Nicco had a strong presence, and confidence to spare, and his tender caress filled her with a deep, aching longing. *He's just a man. You can do this. Keep it together.*

"I love the cut of your dress, and the color looks incredible on you."

Incredible? Really? Pleased, Jariah touched the pearl necklace she'd paired with her turquoise wrap-style dress.

"How about we kick off the day with a tour?"

"That would be great." Jariah opened her purse, and took out a pen and notebook. "Lead the way. I'm right behind you."

Nicco frowned. "What's with the Sherlock kit?"

"I'm horrible with names, and I don't want to offend anyone, so I figured I'd take notes of all the key players in each department."

"Ingenious. I'm already impressed."

Taking her by the arm, he led her through the lobby and into the waiting elevator.

For the next hour, Nicco escorted Jariah to each department and introduced her to his staff. At the end of the tour and the impromptu meet-and-greet, they returned to his tenth-floor office. Larger than a high-school gymnasium, it was filled with books, collectible airplanes and more electronic gadgets than the Apple Store. Framed photographs of Nicco at various sporting events with his celebrity friends and at famous monuments covered the walls. The chocolate-brown decor was striking, and the leather furniture, modern lights and vintage movie posters created a laid-back feel. The windows were open, infusing the office with sunshine, and warmth, but the air held the faint scent of tobacco.

"What's your impression of my company?" Nicco leaned against his white, lacquer desk and crossed his legs at the ankles. "Do you think you'll be happy working here?"

"Absolutely," Jariah said, unable to hide her excitement. Her first day was off to a great start, and she couldn't wait to go home and tell her girlfriends about all of the amazing employee perks at the multi-million dollar company. "Everyone's been incredibly kind, and your staff room is so cozy that I may never go home!"

"Fine by me. I often work late into the night, and I could use the company."

His words and the grin that shaped his mouth were filled with sexual innuendo. To stop herself from making googly eyes at him, Jariah flipped open her notebook and scanned her notes. "I was hoping to meet your vice president, Tye Caldwell. Is he here today?"

Nicco crossed his arms. "What do you know about Tye?"

There was a bitter edge in his tone that surprised her.

"I was doing some research on Morretti Inc. last night, and found the article you did for *Eminence* magazine back in 2001," she explained. "Is it true that you met Mr. Caldwell during a stint in juvy when you were both sixteen?"

"Yes, unfortunately it is. Tye grew up on the wrong side of the tracks, and I was a spoiled rich kid with a chip on my shoulder, but the moment we met we clicked," he said with a fond look in his eyes. "We partied, chased girls and ripped and ran the streets together for years."

"It sounds like you two have a tight bond."

Sadness flickered in his eyes, but he straightened to his full height and tapped his wristwatch. "How about some lunch? I'm hungry and I bet you are, too."

"Lunch? But I haven't done anything yet."

"You've done plenty," he insisted. "I like the way you handled yourself with the department heads. They're great guys, but they can be rude and curt sometimes. Don't let them get away with it."

"Duly noted." Jariah dropped her notebook in her purse and zipped it up. "If it's okay with you, I'd like to see my office and get settled in before I take my coffee break."

"Your office?" He extended his hands to his sides. "You're standing in it."

Completely floored, all Jariah could do was stare wide-eyed at her new boss. She struggled with her words, and foolishly said the first thing that came to mind. "Are you serious?"

Nicco grinned.

"You expect me to work here, with you, all day long?"

"Absolutely. After all, you *are my* executive assistant."

He gestured across the room, and Jariah reluctantly followed the route of his gaze. An L-shaped desk and matching swivel chair was positioned beside the far wall. Next to the computer was a vintage lamp, an iPad, a leather-bound agenda and a glass vase overflowing with long-stemmed yellow roses. "I thought I'd be out front in reception."

"Why? You're a vital part of this company, and I need you close at hand at all times."

"I can't work in here," she blurted out. Jariah could

feel the tension in the air, and saw the challenge in Nicco's eyes. "You smoke, and the smell of tobacco makes me queasy. How can I do my job effectively if I'm nauseous every day?"

"I'm not a smoker." Nicco thought for a moment, then shrugged and said, "Sometimes, when I'm stressed, I like to fire up a cigar, but now that I know it bothers you I'll stop."

"You will? Just like that? Cold turkey?"

"You have my word. This is your office, too, and I want you to feel comfortable."

Nicco's words blindsided her. He was reputed to be one of the most charming bachelors in Miami, and now Jariah could see why. He made her feel special, made her think he cared. But still, her doubts persisted and grew with each second that ticked off the wall clock, so Jariah asked the question circling her brain. "What are you going to do the next time you're stressed out?"

His eyes zeroed in on her face. "Sit back and enjoy the view."

"You're right. This is an amazing view of the Miami skyline," Jariah said, moving toward the window. It was another clear, summer day, and seeing the deep blue sky had a calming effect on her. "Okay, I'm ready to get started. What would you like me to tackle first?"

"Lunch!" Nicco patted his stomach. "I'm starving, woman!"

Jariah laughed. "Would you like me to order something from one of the nearby cafés?"

"My restaurant provides lunch for all Morretti Inc. employees, but since today is your first day I've arranged something extra special for you."

"You have?"

"I made reservations for us at Casa Tua. Do you like it there?"

Like it there? Hell, I've never even heard of the place!

"Maybe if we're lucky we'll run into the cast of *Dating in the City*," he continued. "They're in town filming their season finale, and they paid a visit to Dolce Vita last night."

"You don't have to take me out for lunch. It's really not necessary—"

"I think it is," Nicco said firmly. "You joined the Morretti Inc. family, and that's definitely worth celebrating. Let's go enjoy a great meal and get to know each other better."

His sensual tone made her temperature soar. Jariah was experiencing emotions that were foreign to her, desires she had no business feeling. Not about her new boss, anyway. "I'm not hungry," she lied, ignoring her hunger pangs. "I'll just grab something from the vending machine later."

"First, you ditch me at my restaurant, and now you're giving me a hard time about taking you out for lunch. Do you have a problem being seen with me in public?"

Jariah dropped her gaze to the floor. "No, of course not, but I have a one o'clock meeting with Mrs. Reddick, and I'm worried we won't be back in time."

"Trust me, Mrs. Reddick won't mind if you're a few minutes late."

"Maybe not, but it's important to me to me to be punctual and prepared. My dad always said it's better to be an hour early than a minute late, and it's a motto I live by."

His scowl faded. "Your father sounds like a wise man. I look forward to meeting him."

Confused, she looked at him inquiringly. *Come again?*

"I'll call Mrs. Reddick from the car and give her a heads up. Sound good?"

"I guess that would be okay."

"Of course it's okay. I'm the boss, remember?"

Gesturing to the door, Nicco scooped his keys off his desk and hustled Jariah back through his office. In the reception area, he stopped to give instructions to his secretary and checked the day's mail. Jariah felt uncomfortable with the hand Nicco had on her back, but what made her break out into a cold sweat were the murderous glares she received from the other female employees in the lobby.

Chapter 8

Jariah popped a breath mint into her mouth, slapped a smile on her face and knocked on the open door at the end of the hallway on the ninth floor. The office was spotless, and furnished with oil paintings and scrumptious furniture.

"Good afternoon, Mrs. Reddick. I'm here for my employee orientation. Is now a good time or would you like me to come back?"

"You're late," she said coolly, not bothering to look up from the document she was reading. "I was expecting you an hour ago."

"Mr. Morretti pushed back our meeting. Didn't you get the message?"

Mrs. Reddick whipped off her eyeglasses and dropped them on her desk. "I don't appreciate the last-minute notice, or having to rearrange my schedule for you, either."

Then take it up with the boss, not me, Jariah thought, but didn't dare say.

"Come in and close the door behind you."

Her tone was sharp, but Jariah didn't take offense. She was in a great mood, feeling as light and carefree as a ballerina gliding across the stage. And for the first time in months she was hopeful about her future. She'd had a long, relaxing lunch with Nicco, and learned some surprising information about her new, Italian-born boss. He spoke three languages, had traveled to more than fifty countries and was a die-hard sports fan. The biggest shock of all? He coached Little League Soccer, and mentored at-risk youth. Nicco Morretti was a walking, talking contradiction, and when they finally left Casa Tua two hours later, Jariah realized that there was more to the CEO than met the eye. And that intrigued her.

"I said come in and sit down."

Startled, Jariah blinked, and snapped out of her thoughts. Commanding her legs to move, she strode inside the office and took a seat at one of the brown arm chairs in front of the desk.

"I need to ask you a few questions." Mrs. Reddick sat up taller and clasped her hands together. "Why did you take the executive assistant job?"

"Because Morretti Incorporated is a successful, innovative company with countless opportunities for personal and professional growth."

"And," she pressed, leaning forward in her leather, swivel chair.

"And because I know I have what it takes to be a topnotch executive assistant."

"You expect me to believe that your attraction to Mr. Morretti had nothing to do with it?"

Jariah felt her eyes pop and her mouth sag open.

"The only reason you took the job is to get close to Nicco, isn't it?"

"Excuse me?"

Mrs. Reddick leveled a finger at her. "Don't play dumb with me, Ms. Brooks. I see the way you look at him, and more importantly how he looks at you."

Her words shocked Jariah, causing adrenaline and desire to flare inside the walls of her chest. So what? She was attracted to Nicco. Big deal. It didn't mean she was going to sleep with him or do anything to jeopardize her new job. That's why instead of coming clean, Jariah furrowed her eyebrows and wore a confused face. "I'm afraid I don't know what you're talking about."

"I think you do," she shot back. "I'm onto you, Ms. Brooks. I know what you're after."

Perspiration drenched Jariah's skin, and a cold shiver ripped through her body. She couldn't think and the room was spinning on its head. The walls were closing in, and the office suddenly felt smaller than an airplane bathroom. Jariah struggled to kept her composure. Lashing out would get her nowhere, and she had no intention of losing her job on the first day.

"I don't believe in beating around the bush, so I'm going to get straight to the point."

The HR director's icy tone put her on edge. Jariah wanted to storm out of the office and slam the door so hard the windows shattered, but she didn't want Mrs. Reddick to know she'd gotten under her skin.

"Mr. Morretti hired you for one reason, and one reason only, and that's to get you into bed."

Jariah swallowed a gasp. Her heartbeat pounded in her ears like a jackhammer. At the thought of making love to Nicco—a man she shared amazing chemistry with—blood rushed straight to her core. Her breasts swelled, and her nipples hardened under her dress.

Flustered, Jariah wet her lips with her tongue, and breathed deeply through her nose. Her thoughts cleared, but her burning desire for her new boss remained.

"It's obvious you're taken with Mr. Morretti, and he with you, so I thought it was important to have an honest talk with you."

"I'm not taken with anyone, Mrs. Reddick."

Her oval-shaped eyes were pools of blue, and filled with skepticism. "As I was saying, I hired you to assist Mr. Morretti in his day-to-day affairs, not to seduce him, and I won't tolerate any hanky-panky at this company."

Hanky panky? You've got *to be kidding me!* Jariah bit the inside of her cheek to keep from laughing out loud. Her legs stopped shaking, and for the first time since arriving at Mrs. Reddick's office Jariah felt herself relax and her confidence return.

"Mr. Morretti is a smooth talker who loves female attention," she explained with the air and expertise of a trained psychologist. "He flirts with everyone, so don't think you're special. You're simply one of many. Furthermore, he's never been a one-woman man and is dead-set against ever getting married."

Annoyed, Jariah struggled to control her temper. *Does she warn every new female employee about Nicco? Or did she tailor-make this speech just for me?*

"I know a lot of people in the financial sector, and if I find out in the future you had an inappropriate relationship with Mr. Morretti, you'll never work in this town again."

Jariah gripped the arms of her chair. She didn't want to get into a screaming match with Mrs. Reddick, but she had to make it clear where she stood on office romances. "I have years of work experience under my belt, and a résumé I'm incredibly proud of," she began, though her tone was free of pride. "I have never been inappropriate with a colleague, and I have no intention of having an affair with anyone at this company."

Mrs. Reddick raised her eyebrows in a questioning slant, but didn't speak. The phone rang, but she ignored it and continued staring Jariah down as if she were a common criminal.

"Mr. Morretti and I will have an employer-employee

relationship and nothing more. I'm not here to find a husband, Mrs. Reddick. I'm here to advance my career."

"I won't let you or anyone else bring shame to this fine company again, and if…"

Again? The word rattled around Jariah's head, rousing her curiosity. *What had Nicco done?* she wondered. *And more importantly, what the hell have I gotten myself into?*

"Don't indulge Mr. Morretti," Mrs. Reddick continued, raising her voice above the noise and animated conversations streaming through the office walls. "Do your work and remain professional at all times. Have I made myself clear?"

"Like crystal," Jariah said tightly, her jaw stiff and her teeth clenched.

"I'll be watching you." Mrs. Reddick opened her bottom drawer, pulled out a large manila envelope and slammed the drawer shut. "Read through the employee handbook and don't forget to date and sign your contract. Make yourself a copy and put the original in my mailbox."

"What about my employee orientation?"

Mrs. Reddick pushed the envelope across the desk. "We just had it."

"But I have questions about the benefits package and the upcoming training sessions."

"Then read the employee handbook. It covers everything, but if you still have—"

A female voice floated over the intercom, causing the HR director to trail off.

"Sorry to interrupt but Mr. Morretti Sr. is on line one," she said in an urgent tone. "I told him you were in a meeting, but he demanded I put his call through."

Sweat glistened on Mrs. Reddick's forehead, and panic filled her eyes. "That's all for now." She made a shooing motion with one hand and snatched up the phone receiver with the other. "Please close the door on your way out."

Standing, Jariah scooped up the envelope and thanked Mrs. Reddick for her time. As she exited the office, she overhead the HR director say, "You have nothing to worry about, Arturo. I just spoke to Ms. Brooks. Trust me, she isn't going to be a problem…"

Outside in the hallway, Jariah slumped against the wall. She needed a moment to make sense of what just happened. The HR director was a know-it-all, the type of woman who liked throwing her weight around, in essence, a bully in a Chanel suit. Jariah wondered what Nicco would think about the disparaging things Mrs. Reddick had said about him. Her brain was hazy, but she remembered every detail of her conversation with Mrs. Reddick.

I see the way you look at him, and more importantly how he looks at you… Mr. Morretti hired you for one reason, and one reason only and that's to get you into bed.

Jariah banished the thought from her mind, straightened and strode purposefully down the wide, bright corridor. No one was going to intimidate her, or push her around. She was going to prove her ingenuity, and by the time she found an account manager job and quit Morretti Incorporated, Nicco would be singing her praises. And not because she'd slept with him but because she'd worked her ass off.

Sleeping with him to advance her career was a ludicrous notion, one she would never consider. It wasn't going to happen. Ever. No way.

Jariah spotted Nicco exiting the staff room surrounded by a bevy of young, wide-eyed interns, and felt her gaze slide down his broad, sinfully sexy physique. Their eyes met, and her world stopped. His face brightened, and a devilish grin curled his full, juicy lips.

Jariah clutched the envelope tightly to her chest. To her surprise, he turned away from his adoring group and headed straight toward her. Her heart fluttered with nervous anticipation. His footsteps pounded on the floor, and his expensive cologne wafted through the air, seizing every woman's attention on the ninth floor.

Butterflies swarmed her belly, danced and fluttered earnestly. In her mind, she imagined herself kissing and caressing Nicco's lean, chiseled face, and quickly deleted the thought. Advancing her career was all that mattered. Tonight she was going to educate herself about the company, and come Monday morning she'd be up to speed.

"How did your employee orientation go?"

Trust me, you don't want to know. "It was great," she lied, glancing over her shoulder to ensure Mrs. Reddick wasn't spying on them. Jariah wouldn't put anything past the HR director, and as she followed him to the elevators, she made a mental note to keep Nicco's office door open at all times. Being alone with him was too risky; there was too much temptation. The last thing Jariah wanted was to give her colleagues—especially the female staff—the wrong impression. "Mrs. Reddick is a wealth of useful information, and I learned a lot from her."

"I'm glad to hear it."

Inside the elevator, they discussed his schedule, his upcoming business trip to Los Angeles, and the anniversary party he was throwing for his parents next month. He spoke about his parents with love and affection, and Jariah found herself overcome with sadness and longing. She wanted to make things right with her mom and dad, but didn't know how. They'd been estranged for months, and she missed them dearly.

When they reached tenth floor, Jariah noticed it was dead quiet and that all of the offices were empty. "Where is everyone?" she asked as they approached the reception area. "This place looks like a ghost town."

"On Fridays, employees only work half days," he explained, cocking an eyebrow. "Didn't Mrs. Reddick mention that during your employee orientation?"

"I, um, must have forgotten."

"No worries, Jariah. It's you're first day, and you've been bombarded with information."

He pulled back the sleeve of his dress shirt and checked his gold wristwatch. "It's already three o'clock. You better get going or you'll get stuck in rush hour on your way home."

"Are you sure? I don't mind sticking around a little longer."

"There's no point. I'll be heading out shortly, and everyone else is gone for the day."

"You must have a hot date tonight." Jariah heard the question spring out of her loose lips, and wished she could stuff them back inside her big, fat mouth. *What is the matter with you? Do you want Mrs. Reddick to march in here and bitch slap you?*

"What I meant to say was, you must have a busy weekend planned with your friends."

"Yeah, tonight I'm hanging out with my godson, and on Sunday my boys and I will be at Gulfstream Park." Nicco wore a curious expression. "Do you like thoroughbred racing?"

"The sport of kings is a little too rich for my blood. I'm more of a fly-fishing girl."

Amusement lit his eyes. "Fly-fishing, huh?"

"My dad taught me everything there is to know about the sport."

"I've always wanted to learn. Maybe you can teach me one day."

And earn Mrs. Reddick's wrath? No way!

"Why don't you bring some of your girlfriends and join me in my luxury box?" Nicco proposed. "The food is outstanding, the view is spectacular, and the park will be crawling with celebs. It's a guaranteed good time."

"Thanks for the invitation, but I have plans with my

daughter." *Eating junk food and watching Disney movies is hardly exciting, but I'm a homebody at heart, and I love the idea of spending quality time with my baby girl.*

Rap music filled the air. "That's my personal cell," Nicco said, glancing inside his office. "Have a good weekend, Jariah. See you on, Monday."

"Thanks, you, too. Good luck on the race track."

Jariah scooped up her handbag and walked down the hallway, feeling better than she had in weeks. Finally, things were going her way, and if she kept her attraction to Nicco quiet and found a way to avoid Mrs. Reddick, life would be perfect.

Chapter 9

Noise, laughter and squeals of delight filled the Chuck E. Cheese's on Biscayne Boulevard, and as Jariah entered the family-friendly restaurant with Ava, she noticed every booth in the seating area was occupied. The center was crowded, and children raced around bumping into each other and everything that got in their way.

The scent of corn dogs and cheese pizza stirred Jariah's hunger, making her mouth water and her stomach grumble. Walking around Aventura mall for hours, trying on shoes and clothes with a temperamental six-year-old was exhausting, and all Jariah wanted now was a cold drink and a place to rest her aching feet. Inside her tote bag was the employee package, the Morretti Incorporated summer report and a copy of Nicco's August schedule. Her plan was to read while Ava played, and when Jariah spotted a family of three vacate their booth, she rushed across the room and dumped her things on the table.

"Mom, can I go to the kid's zone?" Ava asked.

"You have an hour to play, and that's it." Jariah helped her daughter out of her purple raincoat and chucked it on the seat. "And no running. I don't want you to get hurt."

Ava stuck out her hand and wiggled her fingers. "Mom, I need some money for tokens."

Jariah reached inside her tote bag and gave Ava five dollars.

"That's it? Dad usually gives me twenty bucks."

"Is that before or after you throw a hissy fit?"

"I need more money."

Reluctantly, Jariah opened her wallet. Ava snatched a ten-dollar bill, and took off like a rocket into the games and arcade section.

Jariah sat down in the booth, and got down to work. What she read in the employee package fascinated her. Morretti Incorporated was one of the leading players in the shipping industry, but it was their investment division, which was headed up by Nicco, that was growing in leaps and bounds. Since opening Dolce Vita in 2004, the charismatic CEO had used his charm and connections to shoot up the celebrity stratosphere. In ten short years, he'd built a multi-million-dollar empire comprised of five-star restaurants, trendy cafés and endorsement and sponsorship deals. But what impressed Jariah most of all about the family-owned company was their commitment to charity work and their employee-friendly work environment.

"Are you ready to go down, chump?"

"Bring it on, Uncle Nicco. I'm not scared of you!"

Frowning with her yellow highlighter suspended in mid-air, Jariah glanced around in search of the familiar voice. And there, at the arcade basketball game was Nicco and a small boy with glasses. Amused, Jariah watched them play, and laughed when Nicco threw his hands up in victory. Nicco did the moonwalk around the pinball machine, and the kid—and everyone standing nearby— cracked up.

Unable to resist teasing her boss, Jariah slid out of the booth and joined the pair at the arcade basketball game. "No one likes a show-off," she said, shaking her head in disapproval. "I think you owe your opponent an apology *and* something from the concession stand."

"Jariah, what are you doing here?" Nicco folded his arms as if he was upset, but a grin was playing on his lips. "Are you stalking me?"

"You wish!" she quipped, her tone full of sass.

"Now, is that anyway to talk to the man who'll be signing your paychecks?"

Shame burned her cheeks. "You're right. I am so sorry. I wasn't thinking—"

"Relax, Jariah. I was only kidding."

His touch to her forearm was warm and gentle. "This handsome kid with the killer jump shot is my godson," he said, ruffling the kid's hair. "Richie, say hello to Ms. Brooks."

"You're pretty," the boy gushed, his eyes bright. "Do you have a man?"

Surprised by the question and the child's obvious confidence, Jariah gave Nicco a pointed look. "You put him up to that, didn't you?"

"I did no such thing." Nicco raised his hands in the air, like a fugitive surrendering to the police. "He's a smart kid. He knows a quality woman when he sees one."

"So, now you're his wingman?"

Nicco threw his head back and chuckled long and hard.

"Mom!" Ava ran over, her pigtails flapping in the air and her face covered with excitement. "I need more money. Can I have twenty bucks?"

"No, I just gave you ten dollars."

Nicco took out his wallet and handed Ava a fifty-dollar bill. "Here you go, Ava. Knock yourself out."

"Wow." Her mouth agape, Ava stared intently at the bill, as if her big, brown eyes were deceiving her. "Thank you, mister!"

Jariah shook her head. "Nicco, that's too much money. She's only six-years-old."

"Let her have some fun," he said with a wink.

Ava danced around in circles. "Yippee! Now, I can play 'Western Wrangler'!"

"You like that game?" Richie wiggled his eyebrows. "But you're a girl."

"So, what?" Ava sassed. "I'm good at it. I bet I can beat you."

"Bring it on!"

The children took off running and made a beeline for the "Western Wrangler" machine.

"Thanks a lot, Nicco. Now, I'll *never* see my daughter again!"

"Or you can look at it as an opportunity to schmooze with your new boss."

"I must admit," Jariah said, dodging his heated gaze, "I'm surprised to see you here."

"I don't know why." Mischief twinkled in his eyes and his mouth held a teasing smile. "I've been coming here since I was Richie's age, and the only thing I like more than arcade games is playing 'Dance Dance Revolution' on my Wii."

Jariah giggled. To her friends and family she was Ms. Independent—a serious, no-nonsense woman who didn't have time to play. But deep down she longed to be with someone fun, lively and energetic, and found herself wishing Nicco was anyone *but* her boss.

"Let's order some snacks," Nicco said, gesturing to the concession stand. "The kids will be starving once their tokens run out, and I don't want to feel your daughter's wrath."

"We can share a booth. There's more than enough room at mine."

"That's great. I'll go get the snacks and meet you there."

Ten minutes later, Nicco returned carrying two trays filled with junk food.

"How much do I owe you?" Jariah asked, reaching for her purse.

"Put your money away. It's my treat."

"I'd like to pay my share."

"Too bad," he said, settling into the booth. "Your money's no good here."

Dismissing his words, she took out a twenty-dollar bill out of her wallet and slid it across the table. "Thanks again for grabbing this stuff. Everything looks delicious."

"Are you always this difficult?"

Jariah didn't know what to say, so she smiled.

"Keep your cash. Or better yet, give it to Ava so she can buy more tokens." Nicco picked up the money, tucked it back inside Jariah's purse and gestured to the manila envelope. "You brought work with you to Chuck E. Cheese's? Why? You're supposed to be having fun with your daughter, not memorizing the employee handbook."

"I know, but next week is going to be extremely busy, and I want to be prepared. I have a lot to learn, and I don't want to embarrass myself during the Monday morning staff meeting."

He plucked a piece of cheesy bread out of the wicker basket and took a healthy bite. "I don't expect you to know everything about Morretti Incorporated overnight. It's going to take time for you to learn the ins and outs of the company. As long as you're driven and hardworking, we'll get along fine."

"Thank God." Releasing a sigh of relief, Jariah wiped imaginary sweat from her brow. "I was worried I'd get canned if I couldn't recite the company mission statement by Monday!"

The lively atmosphere inside Chuck E. Cheese's helped Jariah relax, and soon she was laughing at Nicco's jokes and cracking some of her own. As they ate, they chatted about their families, the upcoming Kings of R & B concert, and their mutual love of romantic comedies.

"What's your all-time favorite movie?"

"That's an easy one," Jariah said without missing a beat. *"Poetic Justice."*

"Back in the day you had a thing for Tupac Shakur, didn't you?"

"Everyone did!" she quipped, laughing. "I've seen it a million times, and I still love Tupac!"

A dimple appeared in his cheek when he chuckled. Leaning forward, he rested his elbows casually on the table. "Do you and your ex have a good relationship?"

"Yeah, for the most part." Jariah searched the arcade for Ava, and when she found her precocious daughter at the "Pac Man" machine she thought her heart would burst with love. "Ava means the world to us and at the end of the day that's all that matters."

"Are you guys done for good or trying to work things out for your daughter's sake?"

"That ship sailed and sank a long time ago. We're definitely over."

"And you're not dating anyone right now? I find that hard to believe."

He had a hungry, predatory look in his eyes, one that caused her body to tingle and vibrate in a hundred different places. It was times like this, when Nicco was flirting with her, that she forgot he was one of the most successful restaurateurs in the country—and her boss. "You ask a lot of personal questions."

"I don't mean anything by it. I just want to get to know you better. I figure learning more about you and your beautiful daughter is a great place to start.

"It's your turn," Nicco said, draping his hands casually along the back of their booth. "Go ahead. Ask me anything."

Reaching for her glass of lemonade, Jariah tried to recall everything she'd read online about Nicco. "Is it true you dated three *Sports Illustrated* models at the same time?"

Jariah expected him to laugh or flash a bad-boy grin, but he didn't. He looked embarrassed, not proud, and his eyes darkened with regret. "That was a long time ago, back when I had more money than sense. I was twenty-five, new to Miami and thought I was 'the man.'"

"And now?"

"And now I'm older, wiser and smarter about relationships," he replied quietly. "I recently met a woman I'm completely smitten with and I'm not afraid to pursue her."

Jariah sat perfectly still. She didn't want Nicco to know his words had excited her, or that she craved his touch. Just the thought of his strong, masculine hands caressing her flesh shot a fiery rush of desire down her spine.

"Cheese pizza! Yay, my favorite!"

Jariah blinked and gave her head a hard shake. It didn't help, but she turned away from Nicco and focused on her daughter. Patting the seat beside her, she smiled and kissed Ava on the forehead. "Hey, sweetie. Did you have fun playing in the arcade with Richie?"

"I beat him twice, Mom!"

"No, only once," Richie argued. "The second time I let you win."

Everyone at the table laughed.

"Are you my mom's new boyfriend?" Ava asked, facing Nicco. "My mom dumped my dad because he wouldn't marry her. Are you going to marry her and become my stepdad?"

Jariah was mortified, but waved a hand in the air, as if her daughter's question was no big deal. But it was. She didn't want Nicco to think—not even for a second—that she was interested in him. According to Mrs. Reddick, he liked to screw the help, and Jariah had no intention of becoming his office plaything.

"I'm your mom's new boss, Ava, and she's doing a fantastic job," Nicco said in a sincere tone. "You should be very proud of her."

"Way to go, Mom!" Ava cheered. "Can you give my mom a raise so she can take me to Disneyland for Christmas?"

Jariah cupped a hand over her daughter's mouth, and gestured to her half-eaten plate of food. "Ava, leave Mr. Morretti alone and finish eating your pizza."

"I love Disneyland." Richie licked barbecue sauce off his fingers. "Uncle Nicco takes me and my mom to California every year. Maybe you guys can come, too."

"I like the way you think. The more the merrier, right?"

"Right, Uncle Nicco, and we can take your RV!"

Jariah raised her eyebrows. "You have an RV?"

"I sure do." He wore a proud smile, as if he'd built the recreational vehicle with his bare hands. "I've racked up thousands of miles since buying my Platinum Plus RV last year, and I have plans to drive to Disneyland for Thanksgiving. Are you and Ava free?"

"We're free!" Ava chirped, eagerly clapping her hands. "Wait until I tell the kids at day camp I'm going to Disneyland. They're going to be *so* jealous!"

"Nicco, you can't be serious. We can't go with you to Anaheim."

"Why not? There's plenty of room, and I'm absorbing the costs."

"I started at Morretti Incorporated this morning," she pointed out, blown away by his outrageous offer. "I don't even know how you take your coffee."

He winked. "I don't. I prefer to start my day off with a banana and a glass of O.J."

"Uncle Nicco, can we play another round of hoops before we go?" Richie guzzled down his apple juice and jumped to his feet. "I'm feeling lucky, and I know I can win this time."

"Sure. What about you, Ava? Are you up for a game of one-on-one?"

Jariah spoke up. "Not tonight. We have to get going. It's almost nine o'clock."

"But I don't want to go," Ava whined, folding her arms. "I want to play basketball."

An awkward silence fell across the table.

"Ava, be a good girl for your mom, and next week you can come with us to Boomers."

Ava's frown disappeared. "All right. I'll behave." She stood and put on her raincoat. "I love Boomers. I'm great at miniature golf, but I'll let you guys win when we play, okay?"

"You're going down," Nicco vowed. "I'm the king of miniature golf. Tell her, Richie…"

A moment passed before Jariah realized Nicco had not only diffused the situation, but he'd also brightened her daughter's mood. She was chatting excitedly and laughing at Richie's jokes. He definitely had a way with kids, and although Jariah would never bribe Ava, she appreciated him making the effort to connect with her daughter.

"Thanks for everything, Nicco. I'll see you on Monday morning."

"You can bet on it," he said, standing. "Good night, ladies."

Quickly, Jariah collected her things, waved goodbye and hustled Ava back through the play center. Ten minutes later, they were on the I-95, listening to the radio. Her conversation with Nicco filled her mind. It turned out she'd pegged him all wrong. He loved the ladies—no doubt about it—but he was laugh-out-loud funny, had a weak spot for kids and was incredibly generous. *Shoot, if I can survive living with my ex, I can definitely handle a pretty-boy CEO who loves kids, junk food and arcade games!*

Chapter 10

August was a whirlwind of business meetings, visits to Dolce Vita and laughs shared between Nicco and Jariah during coffee breaks, long, relaxing lunches and after-work drinks. Although she'd been working at Morretti Incorporated for weeks, Jariah still couldn't believe she was being paid to attend industry events, to socialize with foreign clients and to schmooze with celebrities. As she unlocked Nicco's office door on Friday morning, she decided taking the executive assistant position had been one of the smartest decisions she'd ever made.

Opening the blinds, Jariah stood in front of the window, soaking in the early-morning sunshine. She stared at the sky and admired the peaceful, tranquil view of downtown Miami. The streets were surprisingly quiet; traffic flowed smoothly in and out of the core, and casually dressed people wearing shades and clutching coffee cups strolled through the business district.

Remembering she had a full day ahead of her, Jariah hung her jacket on the coat rack and got down to business. At her desk, she flipped through the mail she'd collected from the administration office, anxious to find her first paycheck. It was on the bottom of the pile, and when Jariah ripped open the envelope her eyes froze on the check. Several seconds passed, but her mouth remained wide-open. Someone in accounting had made a mistake, and although Jariah could use the extra nine hundred dollars she knew keeping the money would be wrong.

Jariah dialed the extension for the financial administrator, and when prompted left a detailed message. The moment she put down the receiver her cell phone buzzed. It was Nicco texting her to find out what she wanted to eat for breakfast. Every day, he arrived at the office with the most delicious foods, and although Jariah would never admit it, their morning talks were the highlight of her day. Jariah read the text, and her heart swooned.

Beautiful, I have a surprise for you. See you in a few minutes.

Excitement radiated throughout Jariah's body, but she warned herself to relax. Just because Nicco showered her with compliments and did sweet, thoughtful things for her every day didn't mean they were soul mates. They weren't. She had Ava, and he had a harem of lovers, and no matter how much she desired him, they could never be more than colleagues.

Mrs. Reddick's words came back in a rush, flooding her mind.

Mr. Morretti is a smooth talker who flirts with everyone, so don't think you're special. Furthermore, he's dead-set against ever getting married...

Jariah shook off her thoughts, but the HR director's voice echoed in her head like a bullhorn. *You're simply one of many...* A scowl curled her lips. Funny, but in the past few weeks, she hadn't seen Nicco put the moves on anyone. Not a hostess, not a waitress, not even the attractive soap star who'd pounced on him yesterday at Dolce Vita.

Hearing her desk phone buzz, she picked it up and hit

line one. "Good morning. This is Ms. Brooks, executive assistant to Nicco Morretti. How many I help you?"

"I'm sorry," a woman with a low, throaty voice said. "But I didn't catch your name."

"It's Jariah. Who may I ask is calling?"

"It's Vivica Morretti, Nicco's mother. Is my son around?"

"No, not yet, but I'm expecting him any minute now."

Mrs. Morretti released a long, deep sigh. "That boy is never going to change. He arrived two weeks *after* my due date, and has been late ever since!"

Jariah swallowed a laugh.

"You sound awfully young, Ms. Brooks. Just how old are you?"

"I'm twenty-seven."

"Of course you are." Mrs. Morretti sounded exasperated, like a customer waiting in a slow-moving line at the bank. "Are you sleeping with my son? Is that why he hired you?"

A cold shiver tore through her. *Why do people keep interrogating me about Nicco? Why is our relationship suddenly on everyone's mind?* Last night at dinner, Sadie and Felicia had questioned her relentlessly, and now Mrs. Morretti—a woman she'd never met—was in her business. Jariah actually considered disconnecting the phone, but instead spoke in a firm, strong voice. "No, Mrs. Morretti, I'm not. I don't believe in mixing business with pleasure, and furthermore I'm here to serve the needs of the Morretti Incorporated, not your son."

"And that's the truth?"

"Absolutely. I want to advance my career, not ruin my reputation."

"Good answer," she said, her tone warmer, brighter. "I look forward to meeting you, Ms. Brooks. Will you be at my anniversary bash?"

For the second time in minutes, Jariah's eyes widened.

"You know about the surprise party? How? Nicco has gone to great lengths to ensure you don't find out."

"I know, isn't that cute? My sons and my husband think I'm completely in the dark about the surprise party, but I knew about the anniversary bash before *they* did!" Mrs. Morretti's loud, feverish laughter floated over the line. "I raised three troublesome boys and helped my husband get his business off the ground. Nothing *ever* gets past me."

"Nicco's going to be crushed when he finds out you know about the surprise party."

"That's why we're not going to tell him, right, Ms. Brooks?"

"Right," she said with a nod of her head. "I won't say a word."

"I have to run. I have a ten o'clock appointment at Le Chic. I haven't found a gown yet, and the anniversary bash is just weeks away."

"Good luck finding the perfect dress."

"I don't need luck," Mrs. Morretti quipped. "I have my husband's platinum card *and* Oprah's stylist along for the ride!"

Laughing, Jariah hung up the phone and turned on her computer.

She was hard at work, answering emails and proof-reading documents, but the moment she heard Nicco out in reception, she grabbed the mirror from inside her bottom drawer and assessed her look. This morning she'd made the time to do her makeup, and loved how her scarlet-red lipstick made her eyes pop and brightened her entire face.

"Sorry I'm late." Nicco stalked over to the sitting area, put the brown paper bag on the glass table and took off his sunglasses. "I stopped to grab us breakfast from Javali-cious and the line was ridiculously slow. Ready to eat?"

Jariah sucked in a deep breath at the sight of Nicco dressed in a white, short-sleeve shirt, khaki slacks and leather sandals. Desire rushed through her veins. He was standing on the opposite side of the office, a good ten feet away, but shivers of electricity crackled between them. He looked like an all-American boy but his dark locks and scrumptious grin made him irresistible. That's why, despite the warning from Mrs. Reddick weeks earlier, her gaze crawled all over his toned physique. She wanted to touch him, could almost feel her hands playing in his hair as she stroked his body with her own.

"Nicco, you didn't have to bring me breakfast," she said, wiping her damp palms along the side of her chair. Goose bumps broke out across her skin. Her attraction to Nicco was spiraling out of control, literally turning her into a sex fiend, and Jariah feared what would happen if she acted on her feelings. There was nothing cute about getting axed, and she had no intention of being unemployed again. "I'm not hungry. I had a protein bar on the way here."

"Then consider this a mid-morning snack."

Nicco pulled out one of the padded leather chairs. "Come eat. The food is getting cold."

The air was filled with a yummy, lip-smacking aroma, but Jariah didn't move. Her body was a raging inferno, and she couldn't stop staring at Nicco's mouth. All hell would break loose if he touched her, and Jariah didn't want to put herself in harm's way.

"You go ahead. I'll join you once I finish my to-do list." To prove how busy she was, Jariah swept her hands over the paperwork cluttering her desk. "I have to finish the PowerPoint presentation for your Tuesday-morning meeting, and I have to process your monthly travel and expense reports before I leave at noon."

"Work can wait." He spoke in a stern, authoritative tone. "Now, get over here and sit down before I take you over my knee for insubordination."

His words and his sinfully sexy grin made Jariah weak.

The shaking in her body was uncontrollable, fast and over-whelming, and Nicco hadn't even touched her.

"I'm not going to ask you again."

"Okay, okay, I'm coming." She stood, scooped up her iPad and marched her quivering, horny body over to the sitting area. "While we eat, we can discuss your September schedule."

He released a deep sigh, one that spoke of his frustration. "I hate discussing business when we're eating. You know that."

"But you have a meeting with representatives from the Miami Convention Center next week, and I'm dying to know what it's all about."

His smile was back, shining in full force. "I want Dolce Vita to be the official sponsor of the 2016 Miami Auto Show, so I'm meeting with representatives to get the ball rolling."

"Nicco, that's wonderful! They're going to love you and Dolce Vita." Jariah sat down and rested her iPad on the table. "I've been going to that car show since I was a little girl, and every year it gets bigger and better."

"What do *you* know about exotic sports cars? You drive a death trap," he teased, unloading the food containers from the brown paper bag. "I swear, the next time that monstrosity stalls in the employee parking lot, I'm dous-ing it in gasoline and striking a match!"

Jariah laughed, feeling the stress and tension in her body recede some.

"La colazione è servita, bello. Scavare in!"

His words, though spoken in jest, made her heart swell with pride. *Breakfast is served, beautiful. Dig in.* Jariah loved when Nicco spoke to her in Italian, and every time he paid her a compliment, a big fat smile exploded across her face. *I'd be fine if he wasn't so dreamy,* she thought, draping a napkin over her lap. *Nicco is one of the funni-*

est, most charming men I've ever met. He'd brought her breakfast from her favorite café, and each scrumptious bite Jariah took of her veggie omelet made her moan inwardly. "This is so good," she gushed, closing her eyes in silent appreciation for chefs everywhere. "You should have Chef Gambro add something like this to the menu for Monday's meeting."

"Menu? There is no menu. I'm having a short, informal meeting with representatives at the convention center," he explained. "And besides, Dolce Vita is a classy, high-end restaurant, not a cheap breakfast joint with two-for-one specials."

"Push back the meeting to noon, invite the representatives to your restaurant and have Chef Gambro prepare some of his famous award-winning entrées." Growing excited, she put down her fork and scooted forward in her chair. "Nicco, give them the whole five-star, fine-dining experience. Spare no expense. Go all-out."

"Jariah, you're an accountant," he reminded her. "You're supposed to be helping me save money, not pressuring me to spend more!"

"Sometimes to make money you have to spend money."

Raising his coffee cup in the air, he gave a slow nod. "Touché, Ms. Brooks. Touché."

"Once Dolce Vita becomes the official sponsor of the 2016 Miami Car Show, and people are lined up down the block at your restaurant, you'll be singing my praises. Just wait and see."

"Too late. I already am."

Jariah held her breath. His words left her speechless, rattled her, and when he reached across the table and took her hand, desire scorched her skin. He stroked her fingers ever so gently, as if she was a fragile piece of glass. His sweet caress kindled her body's fire, and every inch of her flesh was sensitive to his soothing touch.

"I think your idea's brilliant," he announced, his voice a thick, sensual whisper. The huskiness of his tone aroused her, and so did the boyish grin that shaped his lips. "But I'm not surprised. You're one of the most creative, insightful people I've ever met, and I feel fortunate to have you working at Morretti Inc."

It was hard to think, to concentrate when Nicco was stroking her skin, sliding his fingers upward, ever so gently. Jariah blinked, convinced herself she was imagining it. Fantasy or not, she recognized the only way to survive the sensual onslaught was by changing the subject. "While you're at The Wine Cellar, I figured I'd make the necessary arrangements for your upcoming trip to L.A.," she said, ignoring the tremor in her voice and her erratic heartbeat. "Do you want me to book a suite for you at the Hilton or The St. Regis?"

"Jariah, you're coming with me to my eleven o'clock appointment."

"Why? I know nothing about wine."

"I want to find some fresh, new brands to add to Dolce Vita's menu and I'd love if you could help me at the sample tasting." His fingers played along the inside of her wrist, turning her on in the worst possible way. "And while we're there we can select the wine for my parents' anniversary bash."

"I almost forgot. Your mother called about an hour ago."

"I figured she would," he said, shrugging his shoulders. "I talked her ear off about you last night, and now she's anxious to meet you."

"You did? What did you say?"

He leaned forward, moving so close his scent wrapped itself around her like a bear hug. "I told her that you're doing an awesome job keeping me in line, and that you're a strong, independent woman with a great head on her shoulders."

His gaze zoomed in on her face, sliding from her eyes to her lips and way down south.

A telephone buzzed, breaking the silence and their steamy connection.

Jariah surged to her feet and dashed across the room. Her hands were slick with sweat, but she snatched up the receiver and put it to her ear. She thanked the financial administrator for returning her call, promised to be at her office in ten minutes, and hung up the phone.

"Is everything okay?" Standing, a frown marring his features, he regarded her closely. "Don't tell me the accounting department screwed up your first paycheck."

"I'm afraid they did. They paid me for three weeks instead of two."

"So, what's the problem?"

"I was paid for days I didn't work."

"And?" he asked, raising an eyebrow.

"And, it's money I didn't earn. I can't keep it. That would be wrong."

Nicco felt his jaw hit the ground. He knew he was standing there, gawking at Jariah, but he couldn't help it. He wouldn't have been more shocked if a spaceship had landed on his desk, and a Martian had popped out singing Broadway show tunes.

"I'm going down to the accounting department to straighten things out." Jariah grabbed her purse off her desk. "I'll meet you in the lobby in fifteen minutes."

Nicco watched Jariah glide through his office door, looking fly and fabulous in her fitted, short-sleeve dress, and tried not to stare. Tried, and failed, of course. *Who knew perfection came in a curvy, five-foot-nine-inch package?* he thought as his eyes trailed her down the hallway. Her legs went on for miles, and then some, and her wicked shape made his nature rise. Nicco didn't know how long he stood there ogling her, but it felt like an eternity. His thoughts were all over the map, and he still couldn't make sense of what Jariah had said moments earlier.

I was paid for days I didn't work... I can't keep the money... It would be wrong.

Jariah was a beauty, a stone-cold fox that made his blood pressure soar, but he admired her honesty more than anything. He'd been enamored with her from the moment he spotted her at Javalicious, and working side-by-side with her for the past three weeks had only increased his interest. Jariah had a hold on him he just couldn't explain. Amazingly, she wasn't impressed by his wealth, and was so fiercely independent, she balked whenever he spent money on her.

For the first time in his life, Nicco found himself thinking about settling down. He could actually envision himself being in a serious, committed relationship with Jariah, but he didn't have the courage to tell her how he felt about her. What if she rejected him? What would he do if she didn't share his feelings?

Releasing a deep sigh, he dragged a hand down the length of his face. He'd never felt so indecisive, so unsure of himself before. He was one of the most successful restaurateurs in the country, and entrepreneurs paid top dollar to hear him speak at various business conventions and workshops. He'd never flubbed a speech, never once let his nerves get the best of him, so why did the thought of having a heart-to-heart talk with Jariah make him break out in a cold sweat? He wanted to take her out on a date—tonight, tomorrow, hell, any day of the week—but how was he supposed to wine her and dine her when their relationship was strictly business?

An idea came to him in a flash. If he wanted to get Jariah alone, after dark, he'd have to trick her. Lying to her didn't sit well with him, but he had no choice. At least that's what he told himself. Nicco wanted Jariah in his bed, *and* on his arm, and he was going to pull out all the stops to make it happen.

Nicco checked his watch, scooped up the phone and dialed the head of his security division. When the call went to voice mail, he left a message and hung up. Gerald and two other guards were escorting a Portuguese businessman to a high-profile function at noon, and although he trusted his team to get the job done, he wanted to ensure everything ran smoothly. Pocketing his cell, he slipped on his sunglasses and exited his office.

In reception, he gave instructions to his personal secretary. "I'm going to The Wine Cellar. Please forward all calls to my cell phone," he said without breaking his stride. "And have the cleaners tidy my office while I'm out."

Minutes later, Nicco strode through the lobby, searching for Jariah. He spotted her in the waiting area, yakking it up with a short, well-dressed man holding a brown leather briefcase. The muscles in his jaw clenched, and his hands curled into fists. What the hell? Who was Jariah talking to? And why was she laughing at the guy's jokes?

Anxious to reach her, Nicco broke into a jog. By the time he got to the waiting area, the stranger was gone, and Jariah was typing furiously on her cell phone. "Who's the suit?" he asked, keeping his tone calm, casual. "What did he want?"

Jariah wore a girlish smile, one Nicco had never seen cross her face before. He loved the way it lit up her eyes and warmed her skin. *Damn, I have it bad,* he thought. He didn't understand his feelings and told himself to get a grip. He wanted to impress her, not drive her away by acting like a jealous control freak.

"He asked me out for dinner."

Nicco cocked an eyebrow. "And what did you say?"

"I said yes. He's a single dad with a son Ava's age, and he seems like a nice guy."

"He seems like a nice guy?" he repeated. "You only talked to him for a few minutes. He could be an ex-con or a serial killer for all you know."

"You need to stop watching *CSI: Miami*. It's making you suspicious of everyone!"

"I'm not kidding, Jariah. This is serious. There are a lot of sick wackos out there who like to prey on lonely women."

"I'm not lonely." She laughed. "I'm a hopeless romantic. There's a *big* difference."

The sound of her amusement grated on his nerves. Not because it was annoying, but because he didn't appreciate her making light of his warning. "I know what I'm talking about. If you're not careful you could get hurt, or worse, assaulted—"

"That's not going to happen. I teach self-defense classes at Premier Fitness." Squaring her shoulders, she lifted her chin and met his gaze head-on. "Last year, a teenager tried to snatch my purse outside of the mall, and I brought him down so hard he burst into tears!"

Nicco believed her story, but he didn't share her laughter. Spotting the white business card in her hand, he took it from her and inspected it. "'Edison Wayne, Attorney at Law'?" he read, wrinkling his nose. "The guy sounds like a square."

"I'm not looking for Mr. Excitement. I'm looking for an honest, sincere man who loves children and wants to be in a serious, committed relationship."

"You don't want much."

Jariah scoffed and wore a sad face. "Tell that to the guys on my online dating app. Apparently, my standards are too high."

"Online dating is a terrible idea. Do you know how

many psychos troll the internet looking for single, vulnerable women like you?" Nicco recognized that he was shouting, and that his eyelids were twitching manically, but he couldn't control his temper. The thought of Jariah going out with other men—perfect strangers at that—made his blood boil and his head throb.

"I don't need you or anyone else to look out for me. I can take care of myself."

Her cold, terse tone told Nicco he'd struck a nerve; no doubt he'd pissed her off. He'd put his size-twelve foot in his mouth, and would need the Jaws of Life to extract it. But instead of apologizing for hurting her feelings, he said, "I just don't want you putting yourself in harm's way."

"What I do in my spare time and who I go out with is none of your business."

"This isn't your free time," Nicco shot back. He felt a burning sensation in his chest, and didn't know if it was a rush of anger or desire. "In the future, please refrain from picking up men during company time."

Her eyes narrowed with righteous indignation.

Nicco knew he was being unreasonable, and that he had no right to give Jariah a hard time for talking to the attorney, but he couldn't control his feelings—at least not where she was concerned. "Now, if you're finished flirting with everyone inside the lobby, I'd like to go. I have a schedule to keep."

Without another word, Nicco took Jariah by the arm and led her through the sliding glass doors. Outside, he opened the passenger door of his Lamborghini parked at the curb, and watched as Jariah put on her seat belt. His hands were itching to touch her, to hold her in his arms, but he knew now was not the time to put the moves on her.

The air inside the car was thick, consumed with tension, but Nicco pretended not to notice. Behind the wheel, cruising through downtown Miami, he decided he'd waited long enough. He had to tell Jariah the truth before some slick-talking clown stole her away.

Nicco glanced at her, and almost lost control of the car when she crossed her legs. His testosterone level spiked, and his erection grew inside his boxer briefs. Jariah was the kind of woman men fantasized about making love to, and Nicco was no different. He wanted her more than he'd ever wanted anyone before. There was a toughness about her that he found incredibly sexy—even when they argued, and got on each other's nerves. That's why he was going to lay all his cards on the table and hope to God that Jariah didn't laugh in his face.

Chapter 11

The Wine Cellar, a by-appointment-only wine boutique, was known for its swank location, esteemed clientele, and ridiculously expensive liquor. And when Jariah entered the store and saw the Vincent van Gogh paintings, the cushy furniture and the cutting-edge decor she understood why. An elegant establishment, rich in style, substance and class, it was no surprise that the staff was comprised of young, attractive blondes, or that all of the patrons were dripping in bling.

Bottles were on display library-style, and the vaulted ceilings and brass chandeliers gave the wine boutique a cathedral feel. Classical music was playing, and the air smelled like pastries. The low, muted lights were relaxing—which was exactly what Jariah needed. She was angry that Nicco had snapped at her back at the office, and had no intention of speaking to him during the appointment. Hell, if he could be immature, so could she.

"Welcome to The Wine Cellar, Mr. Morretti. We're so glad to have you here with us again." A female wine steward dressed in a slinky red dress appeared, wearing a smile that showcased every tooth. "I've set you up in one of our private tasting rooms at the rear of the boutique."

"Thank you, Christi. Please lead the way."

"Yes, of course. It would be my pleasure." The wide-eyed steward was so busy gazing at Nicco, she backed into a wine barrel and stumbled. Righting herself, she regained her composure and spun on her heels. "I selected some exquisite brands for you to sample…"

"Are you coming?"

Nicco offered his hand, but Jariah stepped past him and followed the loquacious steward through the boutique. He was her boss, not her father, and she wasn't putting up with any of his macho, tough-guy crap today. The man had a serious attitude problem, and an ego that could rival a rap star, and if he thought he could push her around he was sadly mistaken.

Much like the rest of the boutique, the private tasting room was decked out in dark, gleaming wood. Leather-bound books and magazines covered the end tables, plush chairs were situated around the room, and flat-screen TVs were mounted on the sable-brown walls. Bread baskets, wine bottles, miniature glasses and silver trays overflowing with hors d'oeuvres covered the table.

"Mr. Morretti, please feel free to peruse our vast collection of wines," the steward said, gesturing to the shelves behind her. "With more than a hundred samples to enjoy, I'm confident you'll find that perfect gem to add to your restaurant's menu."

"I'm ready to get started. How about you?" Nicco picked up one of the trays and swept his free hand across it with more flair than a British butler. "The stuffed mushrooms taste amazing with full-bodied wines, and…"

Jariah's stomach rumbled in hungry anticipation. *It wouldn't hurt to sample one or two, would it?* She was still mad at Nicco for insulting her, but she took a healthy bite of the stuffed mushroom. It tasted delicious, moist and flavorful, and within seconds she had devoured three.

"Try the baked brie," he encouraged. "It's one of my personal favorites."

Happy to oblige, she sampled the appetizer. "I better stop or I'll split my dress!"

Laughing, they stood side-by-side, reading the information cards for each wine sample.

"Let's just jump right in. It's more fun that way." Winking lasciviously, Nicco picked up two miniature glasses and handed one to Jariah. "*Per un rapporto di lunga e prospera.* Cheers!"

To a long and prosperous relationship? His toast threw her, made her wonder exactly what he was referring to, but she dismissed the thought from her mind. Of course he was talking about work. She was his assistant, and it didn't matter that she secretly lusted after him.

As they tasted the wine samples, Nicco questioned her about the flavors and brands she liked the best, and even fed her caviar. Enjoying herself immensely, she listened to the female steward relay relevant information about each brand and vineyard.

"We need a moment to discuss in private," Nicco announced.

"Of course, no problem, I'll get out of your hair." Christi hustled around the table, snatching up the empty food trays. "If you need anything, just press zero on the phone and I'll be back before you can say Cabernet Sauvignon!"

The steward left and closed the door behind her.

"Are you still mad at me?"

Nicco's question caught Jariah off guard, but instead of lying to make him feel better about acting like a jerk, she told him the truth. "I didn't appreciate what you said, but I'm not the kind of person to hold a grudge. I can move past it, but the next time you disrespect me you'll be looking for *another* executive assistant."

"Don't hold back. Tell me how you really feel," Nicco joked, returning his empty glass to the table. His attempt to lighten the mood earned him a frosty glare. Undeterred, he moved closer until they were face-to-face. "Do you feel better now that you've given me hell?"

"Yes, as a matter of fact, I do."

His gaze held her hostage, refused to let her go.

"You're like a steel magnolia. Soft on the outside, and hard as metal on the inside."

"I don't know if I should be flattered or offended."

"You're not just any girl, Jariah, you're special and I hate the idea of you hooking up with guys online. If you want to go to a show, or a movie or out for dinner, I'm your man."

"You're not my man, Nicco. You're my boss."

"I love when we're together," he confessed, brushing his knuckles against her cheek. "You make me feel things I've never felt before."

"I—I—I do," she stammered, taken aback by his confession.

"Yes, you do."

Jariah stopped breathing. Her hands were shaking hard and fast, and she was so nervous she couldn't stand still. *This can't be happening. I* must *be dreaming.*

"When you're around I can't think straight." He sounded conflicted, as if he was struggling with a moral dilemma. "I think about you all the time, and when we're apart I wonder what you're doing and if by some stroke of good luck you're thinking about me, too."

Her internal alarm blared inside her head. Nicco was playing mind games with her— just like Mrs. Reddick said he would—and his pitiful attempt to lure her into bed was sickening. Disgust must have clouded her face because he cupped her chin and forced her to meet his gaze. "I'm not bullshitting you. I'm for real."

"No, you're not. You're a player who gets off on screwing your staff," she shot back, determined to speak her mind. "How many of your subordinates have you slept with over the years? Five? Ten? Twenty?"

His face fell, and his eyes darkened with contempt.

Guilt troubled her conscience. She'd gone too far, said too much, and when Nicco dropped his head and raked a hand through his dark, lush hair, Jariah wished she had bitten her tongue. "You have a reputation, and—"

"I know, but instead of believing the hype, why not get to know me for yourself and form your own opinion? I haven't been a Boy Scout, but I'm not the man whore people make me out to be on social media."

He took another step closer and lowered his hands from her cheek to her waist. Swallowing hard, Jariah pretended she wasn't affected by his touch, but she was—in every way—and her aching breasts and moist clit proved just how much she desired him.

Something Mrs. Reddick said weeks earlier came back to her. "What happened to your previous assistant?" she asked. "Why is she no longer working for you?"

"She found a better gig, I guess."

Jariah heard Nicco's cell phone ring, and welcomed the interruption. Their conversation was getting heated, and she needed a moment to clear her head. She expected Nicco to slip out of the room to take the call, but he didn't. Instead, he took out his iPhone, switched it off and placed it on the table. "Now, where were we?"

"*We* weren't anywhere." Jariah pressed herself flat against the wall and propped a hand on her hip to prove she meant business. It didn't matter that she yearned for his kiss, or that her body was on fire—they could never be lovers, and nothing he said or did would ever change that. "I won't sleep with you. Not today, not tomorrow, not next week."

"That's not what I'm about. This isn't about sex or about me trying to play you, either. This is about me wanting to spend time with you after hours, *outside* of the office."

His words gave her pause.

"Mi sono rettilinei. Voglio a corte, Jariah."

"Court me?" she repeated, amused by his words and the boyish expression on his face. "What is this? The Elizabethan era?"

Nicco chuckled. "I want to get to know you better and I think going out on dates a few nights a week is definitely the way to go, don't you?"

He flashed a broad grin, one that made Jariah's heart flutter and dance. Fidgeting with her hands, she dropped her gaze to the plush beige carpet. Not because she was embarrassed, but because she didn't want Nicco to read her like a book. She wanted to get to know him better, too, behind closed doors, and feared he'd take one look at her and see the truth in her eyes.

"No one has to know we're seeing each other. It'll be our little secret…"

Fear and excitement filled her. Their conversation was getting more outrageous by the second, but damn it, if flirting with him wasn't turning her on. *Why does the thought of sneaking around with Nicco excite me?* Jariah wondered, confused by her feelings. *What is it about him that makes me nervous and giddy at the same time?*

"Let's do dinner and a movie tomorrow night," he proposed. "I know you have to drop Ava off at her grandparent's house, so I'm cool with meeting you at the theater."

"Aren't your brothers flying in tonight?"

"No, they'll be here tomorrow night. If you're not busy, I'd love if you could join us for dinner," he said. "They're going to love you, I just know it."

Jariah's body was humming with excitement at the prospect of going on an honest-to-goodness date with Nicco, but she played it cool and pretended as if she wasn't completely sold on the idea. "I'll think about it and get back to you."

"What's there to think about? I'm not inviting you to Vegas for a weekend of booze and debauchery, I'm inviting you to dinner and a movie."

Laughter fell from Jariah's lips. "The last time we made plans to meet *you* were late, so forgive me for being leery about taking you up on your offer."

Nicco wore an innocent face. "You must have me confused with someone else, because only an ass would make a beautiful woman like you wait."

"I wholeheartedly agree!"

"Mi piace il tuo intelligente, bocca fresca, e che splendido corpo di vostro."

You think I'm hot? Seriously? No way! But I'm a size eight, not a size two and you have a thing for thin women with big, fake boobs!

"I'll be at Paragon Theaters at six o'clock sharp, and if I'm late I'll owe you a massage."

His breath tickled her ear, and when he trailed a finger down the length of her cheek, Jariah swallowed a gasp. His touch made her wet and desperate for more.

"Would you like that?" he asked, leaning into her, his smoldering gaze probing and intense. "Would you like to feel my hands all over your body?"

You have no idea.

Electricity crackled between them, causing the air in the room to swelter. Nicco seized Jariah around the waist and drew her right up to his chest. Then, the unthinkable happened—he kissed her. He brushed his lips against her mouth, gently at first, but the kiss quickly evolved into a passionate, desperate plea. Nicco kissed her with urgency, with a passionate, ferocious heat.

They'd crossed the line, jumped headfirst over it, and now there was no turning back.

Burying her hands in his hair, Jariah grabbed a fistful of curls and stirred her fingers around his dark, lush locks. Playing in his hair increased her sexual hunger. Finally, after weeks of stolen glances and lascivious smiles, she knew just how delicious his mouth tasted. And it was better than she'd imagined. Beyond her wildest dreams. His lips were flavored with wine, carried a hint of spice, and the intoxicating blend made her delirious with need.

For a split second, Jariah considered fleeing the private tasting room, but she was helpless to resist his kiss, and his sweet, sensuous caress. Her ear throbbed. Tremors erupted inside her body, and she could feel the blood rushing to her tingling sex.

Devouring his lips, she inclined her head toward him and boldly gave him everything she had. A wild, primal hunger took over her body. Hot with lust, she locked her arms around his neck and pressed herself flat against his solid, toned physique.

Standing chest-to-chest, their lips, mouths and hands greedily explored each other's flesh. The kiss was long overdue, and not only well worth the wait, but the best thing Jariah had ever experienced. His lips were pure ecstasy, and more addictive than Godiva chocolate. She felt alive, energized, and the more they kissed and stroked each other, the harder it was to keep her head. Her lust veered out of control, had her saying and doing things out of character. Nicco was the world's greatest kisser, a pro when it came to pleasing a woman with his lips, and Jariah craved him in ways he couldn't imagine.

"You knew from day one this was bound to happen, right?" His voice was a husky growl, but he stroked her cheeks with loving tenderness. "From the moment we met, I knew it was just a matter of time before we surrendered to our desires."

The truth got stuck in her throat. Yes, deep down, Jariah always knew this day would come but she never imagined it would be so soon. Her mind and her body were in turmoil, and the cravings of her flesh warred against her morals.

"I want you so bad it hurts," Nicco groaned, between each passionate kiss. "I want to rip off your dress, bend you over the table and love you until I'm spent."

At the thought, a fierce, powerful contraction erupted between Jariah's legs. She should have been offended, appalled by his crude, raunchy talk, but she was so turned on by his words her body was a raging inferno. Every breath was a fight. In public, Nicco played the role of the wounded, misunderstood bad-boy to the hilt, but behind closed doors he bore a different persona. He had a softer, gentler side, one she was wholly attracted to, and Jariah couldn't imagine anything better than making sweet love to him.

The more she rubbed herself against him, the more urgent his kiss. They were connected, finally experiencing the joy of each other's mouths, hands and bodies. She felt wanton, naughty, and couldn't rein in her hot, weak flesh.

Caught up, Jariah couldn't bring herself to stop kissing him, to quit rubbing her full, aching breasts against his chest. His touch was out of this world, like no other. Jariah felt a hint of his tongue, just the tip, and all but lost her mind. She clung to him desperately, held him tight.

"From the moment I saw you, I knew you were 'the one.'" Nicco took her hand and placed it over his heart. "I felt it in here, deep in my soul, and over the past few weeks my feelings for you have only gotten stronger. You're all I

think about, Jariah, and every night when I close my eyes
I see your beautiful face."

Stunned, Jariah felt her mouth gape open. His confession and the strength of his gaze blew her away. There was
no way, after working together for a month that his feelings
could be so deep, so intense. He was playing. Had to be.

Why is it so shocking? her conscience asked. *You feel
the same way and the only reason you're not sexing him
on the couch is because your unmentionables don't match!*

"I'll never, ever do anything to hurt you, Jariah. You
have my word."

Jariah didn't speak, couldn't vocalize her feelings. His
words penetrated the thick walls around her heart, and the
kiss he dropped on her lips brought a girlish smile to her
mouth. Her throat was dry, her legs were shaking something fierce and her sex was throbbing so hard she ached
to feel him deep inside her.

Pulling herself together, she surfaced from her sexual
miasma and pushed all thoughts of making love to Nicco
out of her mind. "We're getting way ahead of ourselves,"
she said, determined to be the voice of reason. "It was just
a kiss. It didn't mean anything."

"You're wrong. It meant everything to me."

Me, too, but I'm terrified you're going to hurt me.

Taking her hands in his, he tenderly kissed each palm.

"Nicco, you're a great guy, but—"

Wincing as if in physical pain, he pressed a finger to
her mouth, and nodded solemnly. "I know. You don't have
to say it. If someone found out about us it would ruin your
reputation."

"That's not it," Jariah said, smiling sadly. "I'm a single mom."

A frown marred his features. "What does that have to
do with anything?"

"Isn't it obvious? Ava and I are a package deal, and that will never change."

"I know, and that's a plus, not a minus."

"Nicco, I'm not interested in having an office romance or a tawdry summer fling. I want to get married and have more children."

His smile was pure sin. "Sounds good to me. Want to start practicing right now?"

"I'm serious," she said, struggling to keep a straight face.

"So, am I."

"You're ready to be in a committed relationship?"

"Three months ago, I couldn't fathom settling down, but since meeting you, it's all I can think about. Crazy, huh?"

"Insane," she breathed, her head spinning faster than the ceiling fan above them.

"Think you could get used to me being around 24/7?"

Are you kidding? In a heartbeat! But instead of speaking her mind, she asked the most logical question. "What now, Nicco? Where do we go from here?"

"We're going to kiss and make out some more." Nicco dropped his gaze to her cleavage and slowly licked his lips. "Is that okay with you?"

Jariah heard the word, "Absolutely," fall from her lips, and raised her mouth to meet his kiss. As they came together, a young, breathy voice filled the air.

"I'm sorry to bother you, but I've been knocking on the door with no success."

Over his shoulder, Jariah peeped at the female steward, standing inside the doorway. Her face gave nothing away, but she sensed the woman's displeasure.

Despite the pep talk, Jariah felt a stab of guilt and was embarrassed about getting caught fooling around with Nicco. She tried to move out of his arms, but he tightened his hold around her waist and gave her a peck on the lips.

"What is it?" he asked, tossing a glance over his shoulder at the steward. "I'm in the middle of something."

"I know, sir, and I apologize for the interruption, but you have a phone call."

"Take a message."

"I think this is a call you'll want to take," the steward said. "Someone's been shot."

Chapter 12

"Shot!" The word exploded like a bullet out of Nicco's mouth. He snatched the phone out of the steward's hand, put it to his ear and stalked over to the window. Curious and concerned, Jariah stared at Nicco, hoping that everything would be all right. She knew from past conversations that he was a proud mama's boy, ridiculously close to his brothers Demetri and Rafael, and that he was concerned about the break-in at Dolce Vita. Had there now been a shooting at the restaurant? Was someone he loved fatally hurt?

Hearing a noise behind her, Jariah glanced over her shoulder. The steward cut her eyes, and pursed her lips in disdain. Tossing her hair over her shoulders, she turned and stomped out of the room.

What was that *all about?* Jariah stared down at her clothes, realizing her boobs were on display, lace push-up bra and all, and cringed. By now, the entire store would know she'd made out with Nicco, and that made her feel cheap, dirty. *I should have exercised more self-control.*

More? Her conscience mocked. *When it comes to, Nicco, you have no self-control!*

A sudden thought occurred to her, increasing her anxiety. Was this a setup? Had Nicco brought her to the wine boutique to help him select wines or to put the moves on her? His words flooded her mind.

You knew from day one this was bound to happen, right? From the moment we met, I knew it was just a matter of time before we surrendered to our desires.

Jariah knew then without a doubt that Nicco had planned this little jaunt to the wine boutique for one reason and one reason only: to put the moves on her. Feelings of guilt and shame engulfed her, and her head throbbed in pain. Was Mrs. Reddick right? Was getting her into bed nothing more than a game to him? One she would inevitably lose?

"Son of a bitch! How could you be so stupid?"

Nicco's harsh, biting tone made Jariah flinch. Pacing the room like a caged animal, he yelled into the phone with such ferocity the windows shook.

"Gerald, don't give me that crap. I pay you very well to ensure things like this don't happen," he roared. "Was Mr. Sarmento badly injured?"

Listening to Nicco berate the head of his security division was not only upsetting, it was infuriating. The ex-navy SEAL was a quiet, soft-spoken man with a genial demeanor. Available day and night, he worked tirelessly for Morretti Incorporated and seemed to genuinely love his job.

"Meet me back at the office in an hour. We'll drive to Jackson Memorial together."

Nicco ended the call. "Grab your things. We have to go."

Quickly, Jariah retrieved her purse. "What's going on?"

"It's a long story. I'll tell you in the car."

At the entrance of the boutique, Nicco apologized to the owner for his hasty departure and promised to return next week to place his order.

Inside the car, as they sped up the block, Nicco explained what happened that morning when his security team and the Portuguese businessman were leaving the Beach Bentley Hotel.

"An armed gunman surprised them as they were boarding the private elevator, and during the scuffle, Mr. Sarmento was shot."

"Oh, my goodness, that's terrible. Is Gerald okay? Did he get hurt?"

"Who the hell cares?" Nicco spat, his eyes blazing with fire. "If Gerald had done his job, Mr. Sarmento wouldn't be lying in a hospital bed with a gunshot wound to the chest. I have half a mind to fire him, and the two idiots working with him, too."

"Nicco, you're being unreasonable. You don't even know what happened."

"I never asked your opinion."

Instead of lashing back, Jariah crossed her arms and stared out the windshield.

"Stay out of this," Nicco warned, his voice a harsh, grating tone. Stepping on the gas, he shot onto the freeway and switched lanes with the skill of a championship-winning race-car driver. "Gerald's a big boy. He can take it."

"That still doesn't make it right. He's dealing with a lot right now and you're—"

"How the hell do *you* know? Do you have the hots for the guy? Is that why you're sticking up for him?" Jaw clenched and nostrils flaring, he tightened his grip on the steering wheel. "Just so you know, Gerald's married, and his wife is pregnant."

"I know. She was hospitalized last week, and he's worried sick."

"What?" Nicco shot her a puzzled look. "Who told you that?"

"No one. I overheard him talking to Mrs. Reddick in the staff room a couple days ago."

"Why didn't you tell me?"

"Because it's none of my business," Jariah said, suddenly feeling like a hypocrite.

Exhaling a deep breath, Nicco sank back in his seat. They drove in silence for several minutes, and when he finally spoke, his voice was hollow and his eyes were filled with regret. "I had no idea Gerald's wife was in the hospital. Now I feel like an ass for going off on him."

As you should, she thought, but wisely held her tongue. Making Nicco feel worse than he already did wasn't going to help matters. To lighten the mood, she said, "Don't worry. There'll be plenty of time for you to apologize to Gerald later."

"Why do I have a feeling you're going to hold me to that?" he asked, raising a brow.

"Because if you don't, I'll tell your brothers you play 'Dance Dance Revolution' on your Wii!"

"I know you're in a rush to pick up Ava from day camp, but if it's not too much trouble can you cancel all of my afternoon meetings before you take off?" Nicco asked, marching briskly through the reception area. "I'd do it myself, but I'm anxious to get to the hospital."

"Don't worry. I'll handle it," Jariah promised.

"And make sure you speak directly to Claudia Jeffries-Medina. Tell her there's been an emergency and that I'm sorry for canceling at the last minute."

"Will do, and to be on the safe side, I'll also notify your contacts by email."

"Thanks, babe, I really appreciate it."

"Nicco, don't call me that," she hissed. "Not here."

He wore an amused face. "You know I own the company, right?"

"Nothing's changed. I'm still your employee and you're still my boss."

"And?"

"And when we're at the office it's business as usual."

Nicco grabbed her around the waist and kissed her cheek. "That sounds boring."

"It wouldn't look good if a potential client or staff member walked in and saw us like this," Jariah said, breaking free of his grasp and smoothing a hand over her dress. The tenth floor was deserted, but she glanced around, convinced Mrs. Reddick was going to burst out of the washroom, screaming at her. "Let's get down to work. Gerald's going to be here any minute, and I don't want him to catch us slacking off."

Chuckling, Nicco pushed open his office door and strode inside.

"I've been a *really* bad girl this week, and I want you to spank me."

Frowning, Jariah peered over Nicco's shoulder in search of the female with the sultry voice. A half-naked beauty was sitting on the middle of his desk, holding a black leather paddle, purring like a Siamese kitten. She had silky hair, hot pink lips and a body that could tempt a man of the cloth. Jariah stared at the light-skinned temptress, stunned by the woman's audacity. *Doesn't she see me standing here? Isn't she embarrassed about me—a perfect stranger—seeing her in her bra and G-string?*

"Estelle, what are you doing here?" Nicco asked. "You're supposed to be in St. Lucia."

"I know how much you love surprises, so after my *Penthouse* shoot wrapped up, I decided to come pay you a visit." The woman spoke with a heavy Caribbean accent, and crossed her legs with more flair than an exotic dancer. "Do you like my new paddle?"

Licking her lips, she leaped off the desk and sashayed

provocatively across the room. "I'm anxious to try it out, so get rid of that girl and let's get down and dirty…"

Jariah swiveled her neck and propped a hand on her waist.

"Get going." The woman flapped her hands in the air as if she was swatting a pesky fly. "You're messing up our groove."

Her dismissal was like a slap in the face.

"Are you hard of hearing or just stupid?"

"Estelle, don't talk to my girl like that."

"Your girl?" Raising her eyebrows sky-high, she wrinkled her nose. "You're kidding, right?"

Shame and embarrassment burned Jariah's skin. Despite standing eye-to-eye with the leggy model, she couldn't help feeling small and insignificant. Trembling, her eyes burning with tears, she turned and fled the office.

"Jariah, don't go! I can explain. It's not as bad as it looks…."

You're right, Nicco. It's worse!

As Jariah rushed through the reception area, she heard the elevator ping. The doors slid open, and Gerald stepped off, looking haggard and spent. "Hello, Ms. Brooks."

Too choked up to speak, Jariah hurled herself inside the small metal box and frantically jabbed the down button. The doors closed, sealing her inside the elevator with her hurt and frustration. She was angry at herself for running out of Nicco's office like a scared little girl, and furious at Nicco for trying to play her like a fool.

Slumping against the wall, she closed her eyes and dropped her face in her hands. Fighting back tears, she inwardly chastised herself for the way she'd acted back at the wine boutique. *How could I have been so foolish? How could I actually believe that Nicco could be interested in me when he has* Penthouse *models throwing themselves at him? And why in the world did I let him kiss me?*

Her cell phone rang from inside her purse. Jariah decided to let her voice mail take the call then remembered she was still technically on the clock and whipped her BlackBerry out of her purse.

The phone had stopped ringing, but started up again seconds later.

"Yes?" she snapped, reluctantly putting her cell to her ear. "What do you want?"

"Come back. I got rid of her."

"Was that before or *after* you broke in her new paddle?"

"Jariah, I haven't looked at another woman since the day we met."

"Right," she said sourly.

"Estelle's gone, and she's not coming back."

"How long have you guys been lovers?"

Nicco paused, and then released a heavy sigh. "It's not important."

"It is to me."

"We used to hook up whenever she came to town, but now we're over. I told her that you're my girl, and she left."

"Just like that."

"Just like that. Please come back. We need to talk."

He couldn't see her, but she shook her head, refusing to entertain the idea. "You have to go to Jackson Memorial, and I have calls to make," she said, checking the time on her watch. "If it's okay with you, I'll work from home for the rest of the day."

Silence descended on the line.

"Hello? Nicco? Are you still there?"

"Yeah, I'm here."

"Did you hear what I said?"

"Yes, but I really wish you'd come back so we can talk about us."

There is no us. "Nicco, I'm fine."

"That you are," he said smoothly, his voice regaining

its warmth, its cheer. "Fine, I'll cool my heels for now, but tomorrow you're mine, all mine, no excuses."

Jariah wanted to argue, but she didn't have the energy. She was emotionally spent, so drained she had no fight left in her. It was all too much—Nicco's heartfelt confession, the kiss, his old flame popping up in his office—and the only place Jariah wanted to be tomorrow night was at home in bed. She'd had enough excitement today to last her a lifetime, and decided instead of beating around the bush, to be straight-up with Nicco. "I don't think we should date. It's a bad idea, and there could be serious repercussions for both of us."

"I'm sorry about what just went down, but nothing's changed. I still want to spend time with you this weekend, and I won't let you blow me off."

"I have to go. I, ah, have another call coming through, and it could be Ava. Bye."

Click. Nicco dropped the phone back in the cradle and slumped in his chair, thinking about the mess he'd gotten himself into. He only had himself to blame—he should have cut ties with Estelle weeks ago. If he had, he wouldn't be beating himself up now.

Why hadn't Estelle just stayed in St. Lucia? Why did she have to show up today of all days? Finally, after weeks of sweating Jariah, she was opening up to him, even letting her guard down, but in the space of an hour, all of his hard work had gone up in smoke. Now her wall was back up, firmly erected around her heart, and that sucked, because he had plans for her. Big plans that would prove how much he cared for her.

Needing something to calm his nerves, Nicco opened his bottom drawer in search of his Cuban cigars. He reached for the yellow box bearing the Romeo Y Julieta logo, but he quickly remembered his promise to Jariah and slammed the drawer shut. He hadn't had a cigar in weeks but he refused to go back on his word. He didn't want to disappoint her. Not now. Not when they were on the verge of something special.

Shaking his head, he wore a rueful smile. His parents were going to love Jariah and not just because she was a spirited young woman who freely spoke her mind. She'd succeeded in getting him to quit smoking, and once his mom found out, she'd probably propose to Jariah on his behalf. The thought should have terrified Nicco, but it didn't. In fact, the idea of sleeping with Jariah nestled in his arms every night filled his heart with joy.

"I'm here, boss. Sorry it took me so long. Traffic was crazy on the 1-95."

Gerald stood in the doorway, his expression grim. Nicco wondered if the ex-navy SEAL looked pitiful because he felt guilty about what happened at the Beach Bentley Hotel, or because he was worried about his pregnant wife. Nicco remembered what Jariah had said in the car, and knew, deep down, that she was right—he shouldn't have berated Gerald—but he couldn't bring himself to apologize. Later, when Mr. Sarmento was discharged from the hospital and the police found the crook behind the brazen early-morning attack, he'd make things right with Gerald. And Jariah, too, because after the drama Estelle had just caused he owed her big-time.

Up on his feet, he pushed back his chair and scooped up his car keys. Thoughts of Jariah filled his mind as he drove to Jackson Memorial Hospital. Smoothing things over with Gerald would be easy, but Nicco suspected it was going to take a hell of a lot more than a steak entrée and a round of beers to convince Jariah to give him another chance.

Chapter 13

Teeming with mansions and luxury vehicles with personalized license plates, Coconut Grove had long been home to Miami's richest, most esteemed residents. But no couple was more revered than Lee and Stella Covington. The plastic surgeon and his socialite wife proudly flaunted their wealth and routinely entertained celebrities and politicians in their mansion. "We're here." Jariah drove through the wrought-iron gates and parked in front of the bronze Zeus fountain. She turned around to remind Ava to be on her best behavior, but before she could get a word out, her daughter threw open the back door and took off running up the driveway. "Ava Faith Covington, get back here."

"Bye, Mom!" she yelled, with a quick wave over her shoulder. "I love you!"

By the time Jariah grabbed her daughter's overnight bag and made the trek up the winding cobblestone walkway, Ms. Covington was standing on her doorstep.

"Hello, Stella. How are you?

"Ava, why don't you go around back and say hello to Grandpa Lee?" Mrs. Covington kissed her granddaughter on the top of her head, then steered her toward the backyard. "He is playing with the poodles, but if you ask nicely he might take you for a ride on his golf cart."

"Yippee!" Ava cheered. "Maybe he'll even let me drive."

Before she could take off again, Jariah gave her daughter a hug. "Call me before you go to bed, and be a good girl for Grandma and Grandpa."

"Don't worry, Mom, I will. See you on Sunday!"

Once Ava left, the smile slid off Mrs. Covington's face. "Do you *have* to buy my granddaughter bargain basement clothes?" she asked, folding her long, bony arms across her chest. "A couple washes and that pink Dora dress will be a tattered, frizzy mess."

"There's nothing wrong with the clothes at. J. C. Penney. They're cute and affordable."

"And cheap."

"It doesn't make sense buying expensive designer outfits for Ava when she's just going to ruin them playing outside with her friends."

"It's no wonder! What do you expect when you shop at thrift stores?"

"The clothes at Target are every bit as good as the clothes in Nordstrom."

"And I suppose you think Jack in the Box is a fine dining establishment," she scoffed. "But you would. You *were* raised in Overtown."

Jariah warned herself to keep a cool head. Every time she did something Mrs. Covington didn't like, she insulted her old neighborhood. Overtown was an impoverished community, overrun with crime, drugs and poverty, but Jariah wouldn't trade her humble beginnings for anything in the world. At a very early age, her parents had taught her the value of self-respect and hard work, and all of the struggles and hardships she'd witnessed in their housing project had made her the woman she was today. And for that reason alone, she refused to take any of Stella Covington's crap. "I'm proud of where I come from."

"Of course you are, dear," she said, her tone dripping with sarcasm. "It must be *very* exciting to see your old neighborhood featured on the evening news every single night."

Her words hit a nerve. Thankfully, Jariah didn't see Mrs. Covington often, because whenever she did, the witch of the south made a point of insulting her. But Jariah wasn't ashamed that she'd been raised in the inner city, or that her parents had factory jobs.

"You should thank your lucky stars you won that scholarship to the University of Miami, or you never would have met my sweet Wesley."

Sweet? Ha! "I didn't win anything," Jariah said, feeling her temperature rise. "I had the highest GPA in my high school, and I worked damn hard to earn that academic scholarship."

"I have to give it to you, Jariah. You're much smarter than you look," Mrs. Covington continued. "You met my son, got knocked up and moved into his apartment all in one semester. If that isn't ingenuity, I don't know what is…"

Jariah wore a blank face, but inside she was on fire. She imagined herself snatching the curly wig off Mrs. Covington's head and flinging it into the infinity pond, but took a deep breath instead. Any other day, she would've fired back with a zinger of her own, but she wasn't trading insults with the crotchety housewife today. She had a two o'clock appointment at Glamour Girlz Salon. If she was late her beautician would give her slot to someone else, and she wanted to look extraspecial for her date with Nicco.

At the thought of him, her frown morphed into a smile. Jariah could hardly wait for six o'clock to roll around. Nicco had called that morning while she was making breakfast, and the moment she heard his voice her spirits soared. They'd talked and laughed for over an hour, but as Jariah listened to Nicco describe the plans he'd made for their date, her fears returned with a vengeance.

"I still think this is a bad idea," she'd said, unable to shake free of her doubts, or images of Mrs. Reddick chasing her around the offices of Morretti Incorporated with a letter opener. "What if we run into someone we know during dinner?"

"You worry too much. Loosen up. We're going to have a great time tonight."

"I'll loosen up as soon as you do."

"Me?" he'd scoffed. "Woman, please, I'm so loose I could teach your hot yoga class!"

Hours later, the joke still made Jariah crack up. Nicco was taking her out tonight, and although she wouldn't admit it to anyone—not even herself—she was looking forward to spending time with him. The kiss they'd shared yesterday at The Wine Cellar was all Jariah could think about, and she was hungry for more—

"Ava is a Covington, and I expect her to look and act like such at all times."

The sound of Stella's loud, shrill voice yanked Jariah out of her reverie. "She's only six years old. You can't expect her to be perfect."

"Yes, I can," she shot back, her self-righteous tone as haughty as ever. "Wesley was a model child, and he never gave me any trouble whatsoever." She paused. "If I wasn't so busy with my charity work, I'd take Ava in and raise her as my own."

Over my dead body.

"Since it's obvious you can't handle, Ava, you should relinquish custody to my son."

"Which son? Do you have another child I don't know about?"

"Wesley is a terrific father, and a noble young man with great morals."

You are so delusional, Jariah thought, rolling her eyes behind the safety of her sunglasses. *Wesley grumbles about paying child support and routinely breaks plans with Ava.*

"It's also obvious that you're still bitter."

"Bitter?" Jariah repeated, incredulous. "I'm the one who called off our engagement."

"That's because deep down you know you're not good enough for my son, and it was killing you inside."

Jariah tossed her head back and laughed out loud. "That was a good one. Thanks, Stella. I really needed that."

"Go ahead, yuck it up, but you will never, *ever* be a Covington!"

I know. Talk about a stroke of good luck! Jariah knew she was adding fuel to the fire, but she couldn't resist saying, "Thank God for that," as she turned and walked back to her car.

"Honey chile, where are you going? You look hella hot!"

Jariah wheeled around, saw Felicia double-parked behind her car and waved. "Hey, girl. What's up? Where are you rushing off to?"

"You first." Displaying a coy smirk on her lips, she leaned out the window of her red SUV. "Don't tell me. You and that fine-ass boss of yours are meeting up at one of those ritzy downtown hotels to get your freak on!"

Ever since Nicco and Richie had come over for dinner last month, Felicia had been questioning her incessantly about their relationship. Her neighbor was convinced they were lovers, and although Jariah fervently denied the accusation, her friend believed otherwise.

"You're hot for that gorgeous Italian millionaire, and he's hot for you. Just admit it."

"No, I'm not," she said, avoiding Felicia's gaze. Jariah

didn't want anyone to know about her plans with Nicco—especially the neighborhood gossip—so she did the only thing she could and she lied. "If you must know, I'm meeting my old college roommate for coffee."

"In that sexy getup? Yous a damn lie!" Her demeanor turned serious, and her tone was filled with concern. "Be careful, Jariah. Your boss has a reputation for being a heartbreaker, and I'd hate for you or Ava to get hurt."

Me, too, Felicia. That's why I'm going to take things slow.

"Men love the thrill of the chase, and rich guys are the biggest dogs of all," she continued, her tone no-nonsense. "I'm not saying Nicco's going to play you, but it would be crazy for you to think you're the only girl he's kicking it with…"

Jariah nodded as if she was listening intently, but she wasn't. Reading bestselling books on relationships had turned her friend into an amateur shrink. And since Jariah didn't have the time to listen to Felicia's unsolicited advice, she changed the subject. "You look great, and I love your new haircut. Where are you going?"

"For coffee with my old college roommate." Felicia winked, slid her sunglasses on and cranked up her car stereo. "See you later, girlfriend. Have fun with boss man!"

Seconds later, Jariah got inside her car and put on her seat belt. She slid the key into the ignition and turned the lock, but it didn't start. It didn't even make its usual noises. Sweat trickled down her forehead, and the car sweltered with heat, but she continued furiously pumping the gas. Jariah didn't know how long she sat there, willing her temperamental Dodge to start, and when her cell phone rang from deep inside her purse she ignored it.

It rang incessantly, until Jariah couldn't take it anymore. Taking her cell out of her purse, she saw that it was six forty-five, and that she had four missed calls from

Nicco. *No wonder he's blowing up my phone. He thinks I stood him up!*

Taking a deep breath, she put the phone to her ear. "Hello."

"Is everything okay? I've been worried sick about you."

Jariah felt a swell of emotion inside her chest. His voice was filled with concern. Jariah didn't know if it was the heat finally getting to her, or how sweet he sounded, but she fell apart. Her eyes welled up with water, and tears gushed down her cheeks. "I'm still at home. My stupid car won't start."

"Sit tight. I'm on my way."

"Nicco, I'll be fine. I can handle it." Embarrassed that she'd lost her composure, Jariah grabbed a Kleenex from her purse and wiped her face. "I'll just call a tow truck."

"Go inside and relax. I'll take care of everything."

"Are you sure? I feel terrible for inconveniencing you."

"It's no inconvenience at all, and like I told you this morning, nothing is more important to me than seeing you. Now get off the phone and go inside," he ordered.

Twenty minutes later, Jariah spotted a sleek black Jaguar turn in to her complex and knew that Nicco was behind the wheel. He collected luxury vehicles the way most women collected shoes, and drove a different car every day of the week.

Stepping out onto the porch, Jariah waved and walked down the steps. She wanted to run—straight into Nicco's arms—but cautioned herself to not to act like a forlorn teen. But seeing him looking all kinds of sexy in his all-black attire made her heart soar. Diamond earrings twinkled in each ear, and tattoos covered his left arm.

"Hey, you." Nicco hugged her, and every muscle in her body tensed. "What's the matter? Are you still upset because your car died? I told you it's no big deal. It happens."

"That's not it." Jariah glanced nervously around the complex. "Someone could see us."

"And?" he challenged. "You're my lady, and I don't care who knows."

Jariah felt like jumping up and down, but remembered she was a grown woman, not a toddler, and told herself to relax. Inside, Jariah was dancing, but on the surface she played it cool. They weren't a couple, and although she loved the idea of dating Nicco, she knew their attraction wasn't enough to forge a long-term relationship. "I'm not your girl—"

"Not yet, but you will be. Mark my words."

"My, my, aren't we overconfident."

"Not overconfident. Determined."

He stroked her neck softly, nuzzling his chin against her cheek.

"I don't stop until I get what I want," he confessed, his gaze as strong as the sun's blinding rays. "I'm going to make you mine. Just wait and see."

Be still, heart! she warned, aroused by his bold declaration.

Suddenly a loud rumbling noise polluted the air. A blue tow truck was chugging up the block, blaring rock music. Mechanic Motors was embossed on the hood of the truck, and the bearded driver nodded in greeting as he pulled up behind her Dodge.

"Leave everything to me." Nicco took Jariah's car keys out of her hand and dropped a kiss on her cheek. "Wait here. I'll be right back."

Nicco jogged over to the tow truck and spoke to the driver. Seconds later, he was back at Jariah's side, hustling her around the front of his Jaguar.

"Shouldn't we wait for the tow truck driver to remove my car?"

"There's no need. Luciano's a pro. He's got this."

"Do you think he'll have a chance to look at my Dodge tonight?" Jariah asked. "I have to pick up Ava from her grandparents' house on Sunday afternoon, and taking a cab to Coconut Grove would cost me an arm and a leg."

"I'll take you."

"I can't let you do that."

"I want to." Closing the space between them, he cupped her chin in his hands and forced her eyes to meet his. "I want to help, so let me."

His words filled her heart with joy, and the urge to kiss him was so overwhelming she couldn't think straight. Common sense kicked in, but her need for the Italian heart-throb still remained. "I appreciate the offer, but trust me, you do not want to meet Ava's grandmother. She'd take one look at your tattoos and diamond earrings and go into attack mode."

"I guess you haven't noticed, but I have a way with the ladies."

"Not this one," Jariah quipped. "She's so mean she could scare the devil!"

Chapter 14

Dinner was an indulgent, five-course meal at the most expensive restaurant in town. By the time Nicco escorted Jariah out of The Greek Isles, the sun was making its descent, and the sky was bathed in a brilliant yellow-orange hue. Laughter and boisterous conversation carried on the summer breeze, decorative lamps showered the streets with light and a Hispanic teenager dressed in army fatigues recited poetry with the conviction of a Civil Rights Leader.

"What did you think of The Greek Isles?"

"Isn't it obvious? I finished my entrée *and* yours!" Jariah said with a laugh. "The service was outstanding, and you were right about the honey lemon cake. It *was* to die for."

"I hate to say I told you so, but well, I did!"

Nicco chuckled, and the hearty, good-natured sound brought a smile to Jariah's lips.

"Tell me more about Italy," she said, curious to know more about his native country. During dinner, he'd talked much about his relatives in Venice, and the five-room villa he owned in his beloved hometown. "Do you go there every summer?"

"Of course. Sometimes three of four times a year if my schedule permits. My family didn't immigrate to the States until I was twelve, so in my heart Italy will always be home."

"I've always wanted to go, but I've never been. What's it like?"

"Loud, energetic and very much like New York City. There's always something to see and do, and Italians are the most gregarious people in the world. They love to entertain and socialize and nothing matters more to them than their family. Sunday dinners at my grandmother's house were always non-negotiable," he said, his eyes bright and his tone warm.

"I've always dreamed of seeing the Colosseum and Vatican City."

"Then I'll take you. Let's go for New Year's, because no one knows how to party like my Uncle Guido. And he's seventy-five!"

"My ex would never agree to keep Ava."

"He doesn't need to. We'll take her with us."

His voice was firm and final, as if the matter was decided. Shock prevented Jariah from speaking, and her heart was beating so loud she couldn't hear herself think. *Is he for real? Is it possible he cares for me and my daughter or is he just saying what he thinks I want to hear?*

"I'm having a great time with you, Jariah. I only wish we had done this sooner."

Nicco took her hand in his, held it tight, causing her to feel mushy inside. She couldn't remember ever having this much fun on a first date, and wasn't ready for the night to end. There didn't seem to be anything the restaurateur didn't know, and every day he taught her something new. Yesterday, it was how to select the perfect wine, and tonight it was how to order her entrée in Greek. It was awesome being alone with Nicco, laughing, joking and flirting.

Jariah wondered what else the Italian-born businessman
had up his sleeve.

As they strolled down Grand Avenue, hand-in-hand,
they discussed his brothers' upcoming visit to Miami, and
his parents' anniversary bash on Labor Day weekend.

"How did your parents meet?" Jariah asked.

"At Mardi Gras. They spent the weekend together, and
when my dad returned to Italy, he sent mom a ticket to
come visit. They've been inseparable ever since."

Awed, Jariah shook her head. "Wow, that's some story."

"Pops said it was love at first sight, and the moment I
saw you, I knew how he felt."

He angled his head toward her, as if he was going to
kiss her, but didn't. Jariah felt a twinge of disappointment.
Tonight was about getting to know Nicco better, not jumping his bones.

"What color is your dress?"

"My dress?" Jariah repeated, puzzled. "For what?"

"My parents' anniversary bash of course."

"I'm not going."

Nicco slowed his pace. "Why not? All Morretti Incorporated employees are invited."

"I know, but I haven't been with the company long, and
I don't know a lot of people."

*And I can't handle Mrs. Reddick giving me the evil eye
all night!*

"You have to come," he said, grasping her hand tighter.
"I want to introduce you to my friends and family, and my
mom is dying to meet you."

"She is?" Jariah questioned, baffled by his words.
"Why?"

"Because I told her I finally met the woman of my
dreams."

Eyes wide, her heart began to beat in double time, and
she swallowed hard. "You didn't..."

"I did, and there's more. You're going to be my date for my parents' anniversary bash."

"Nicco, I can't." Jariah tried not to notice his sweet, endearing smile, or the puppy-dog expression on his face. "Being your date would be career suicide."

"Baby, what are you talking about?"

Baby? Oh, God, I love the way that sounds!

Chiding herself to remain focused, she searched for the right words to make Nicco understand why she couldn't be his date for his parents' anniversary bash. Deep down, she was tickled pink that he'd invited her, but she knew attending the party with her boss would be a mistake. "If we go to the party together everyone will think that we're lovers."

"What's wrong with people knowing we're a couple? Are you ashamed of me?"

The wounded expression on his face pierced her heart. "No, of course not. You're great, and fun to be around, but I don't want our coworkers to think we're sleeping together. I want to advance my career, not ruin my reputation—"

"I would never fire you. You know that."

You won't, but Mrs. Reddick will, and I need this job!

"Why don't you ask Estelle to be your date?" Jariah said casually, though the thought of Nicco with the provocative, sex-crazed model made her burn with jealousy. "You guys make an attractive twosome, and besides, she'd look much better on your arm than I would."

Nicco stopped walking. Releasing her hand, he studied her closely as if he was seeing her for the first time. "Who's the real Jariah Brooks?" he asked, his quiet tone belying the significance of his question. "Is she the strong, tell-it-like-it-is woman I met a few months back, or is she the insecure woman standing before me who doesn't recognize her own self-worth?"

His question literally knocked the wind out of her sails. Feeling exposed, as if she was standing on the street buck naked, she lowered her eyes to the ground. Jariah had never allowed herself to be vulnerable with anyone, and although she had feelings for Nicco, she wasn't about to reveal her deepest fears to him. Not after one date. Likely, not ever. Unfortunately, he reminded her of Wesley, and Jariah knew if push ever came to shove he'd choose his family over her in a heartbeat. Guys with trust funds always did.

"I didn't mean to hurt your feelings."

"You didn't." It was a lie—his words stung, but Jariah put up a brave front. "And I'm not insecure. I just don't like people talking behind my back, and that's *exactly* what's going to happen if I accompany you to your parents' anniversary party."

Their gazes locked, zeroing in on each other like laser beams.

"Don't belittle yourself. I don't like it. You're better than that."

"Okay, so I have issues. Sue me!"

"Now, there's the strong, feisty woman I know and love."

Love? The word echoed around her head in surround sound. At the thought of spending forever with Nicco, her heart skipped a beat and danced inside her chest.

"Next Saturday is a special night for me, and the only woman I want by my side is you." He cupped her face in his hands and kissed the tip of her nose. "Got it, Ms. Brooks?"

Stunned by his bold declaration, all Jariah could do was offer a meek nod. Outwardly, she pretended as if his announcement was no big deal, as if it didn't cause her senses to go berserk. But his words floored her. *Did Nicco just say what I think he said? He'd rather go to his parents' anniversary bash with me than that gorgeous sex fiend who snuck into his office yesterday?*

"Next Friday, I'm giving you the day off."

"But we have a meeting with the Miami Capitals basketball team about a catering contract."

"I know, and I won't screw it up. I promise."

Ordering her legs to move, Jariah fell into step beside him. Keeping her wits about her was paramount. Nicco was doing what he did best—charm, seduce and entice. But she knew the Italian heartthrob had no interest in ever settling down or starting a family.

Besides, they had little in common. Jariah was a creature of habit who lived by a schedule, while Nicco liked to wing it and craved spontaneity. He loved going out, partying with his friends, but she preferred relaxing at home watching movies and reading romance novels. It was his way or the highway, and they butted heads at least once a day. Add to that his collection of freaky ex-lovers who were on call and ready to satisfy his needs faster than a New York minute. It was just a matter of time before their differences tore them apart, and she didn't want Ava to get hurt. Her daughter adored Nicco and if he walked out of her life six months down the road she'd be devastated.

"On Friday, you have a ten o'clock dress fitting at Chanel," he explained. "After lunch, you're going to Destination Wellness for some serious pampering. Think you can handle that *very* difficult assignment?"

"Nicco, I can't blow my check on spa treatments."

"I know, but I can." He flashed a sly wink. "Consider it an early birthday present."

"My birthday is six months away."

"You don't say?"

Jariah sighed. There was no use arguing with him. Stubborn and headstrong, he'd find a way to convince her and in the end she'd cave. But she wasn't sticking him with an exorbitant shopping bill. She'd pay for her outfit for the party. It was only fair. *I hope the Chanel boutique has a clearance section.*

"I feel like eating buttery popcorn." Nicco gestured at the movie theater. "You game?"

Jariah scanned the lit marquee board. "I'm not interested in seeing any of the movies playing. They're either action flicks or animations."

"I figured as much, so I planned something extraspecial for you."

"You did? What is it?"

"You'll have to wait and see."

His grin was irresistible. And when he wrapped his arms around her waist, pulling her right up to his chest, a dreamy sigh escaped her lips.

"God, you're beautiful," he praised.

The kiss came out of nowhere. At the feel of his mouth pressed firmly against hers, her body trembled, quivered and shook. Desire built, consuming her body whole. Nicco was arrogant and flamboyant, everything Jariah *didn't* want in a man, but he made her feel things she'd never experienced before—a passion so intense it paralyzed her. And his touch was divine, the best thing to ever happen to her.

They kissed in the middle of the street without a care in the world for what felt like hours. Nipping at her bottom lip, he captured it between his teeth, and gave it a flick with his tongue. "We better head inside," he said smoothly. "Our movie is about to start."

Paragon Theaters was crowded, packed to the brim with eager moviegoers, and the scent of cinnamon pretzels and nacho cheese was heavy in the air. After a trip to the concession area, Jariah had more candy than a trick-or-treater, and when Nicco ribbed her for spending all of his hard-earned money on junk food, she laughed and gave him a shot in the ribs.

Theater twelve was empty, but Nicco suggested they sit in the last row. During the previews, they chatted about dinner and fed each other Skittles. When the lights dimmed, they switched off their cell phones and made themselves comfortable.

The moment Jariah read the words that appeared on the screen, she immediately recognized the movie as *Poetic Justice.* "I can't believe they're showing this movie," Jariah said excitedly. "If I had known it was playing, I would've told my girlfriends! They love Tupac, too!"

"Baby, this is a private screening."

"A private screening?" Realization dawned, and her eyes widened. "You rented out the theater so I could watch my favorite movie?"

"Of course I did. You know I'll do anything to make you happy."

Electricity crackled in the air, and something came over Jariah. Something that made her feel feverish, wanton and sexy. Touched by his thoughtfulness and his kind, heart-felt words, Jariah leaned over and kissed his lips. A slow, lingering kiss that took Nicco by surprise. For a moment, Jariah forgot everything—the movie, her doubts, her fears about the future—and focused on pleasing the man holding her in his arms. She didn't care that they were in a movie theater or that an usher could walk in any moment and catch them making out. Jariah was going to have Nicco tonight, and nothing was going to stop her.

The spicy cologne stimulated her senses, energizing and invigorating her. Her body caught fire, and her heart beat quickened. His kisses were her weakness, his caresses her downfall. The moment his hands touched her skin, her willpower evaporated, her insides turned to mush and her nipples hardened inside her bra. Her mind and body were at war, duking it out like two heavyweight boxers in a Las Vegas ring.

And though her thoughts confused her, in the end her flesh won out. Jariah wanted a quickie—hot, fast, exhilarating sex—and Nicco was just the man to give it to her. She needed this, and if his sex was like the way he kissed, she was going to have the most explosive orgasm ever.

The lights from the movie illuminated the expression on Nicco's face. Want shone in his eyes, and his grin hinted at things to come. Reclaiming her lips, he crushed his mouth to hers. Overcome, Jariah lost count of how many times they kissed. She felt crazed, like a sex addict locked away in rehab, and yearned to feel him inside her. His kisses tasted that good, that sweet. Using the tip of his tongue, he tickled her earlobe, drew circles across her neck and licked her collarbone. Jariah felt his hand under her shirt stroking her warm, quivering skin. He cupped her breasts, and they spilled out over the top of her bra.

He fondled and caressed her breasts as if he were worshipping them, but he never took his eyes off her face. "You have beautiful breasts," he said, his expression one of awe and wonder. "They're full and luscious and perfect."

Playfully, he pinched and tweaked her nipples. Heat rushed to Jariah's core. And when Nicco trailed a finger up from her thigh to her sex and massaged her throbbing clit through her panties, she wanted to climb into his lap and ride him until he said *her* name.

Thrusting her hips against his hand, she willed him to put her out of her misery, to touch and stroke her wetness. Nicco slid a finger inside her, and then another. Moans exploded from Jariah's lips. She griped the armrest and rotated her hips. In and out, in a slow, erotic pace, his long, deft fingers worked their magic.

Exhilarated, Jariah tossed her head back and screamed her pleasure. Not once, not twice, but three ear-splitting times. It wasn't one of her finest moments, but she couldn't control her mouth or stop the tremors racking her inflamed body. The tingling sensation in her clit walloped her, pushed her to the brink. Jariah couldn't believe it, and was convinced this was nothing more than an erotic dream. But then her orgasm hit, and her body spiraled out of control, proving that her secret fantasies about her suave, sexy boss had finally come true.

Deep, savage groans fell from Jariah's lips, and several minutes passed before her legs quit trembling and the room stopped spinning around her. A heady, euphoric sensation washed over her. It made her feel light-headed, and left her unable to speak. Her mouth was dry, her lips were stuck together and her skin felt clammy and hot. Her limbs felt heavy with fatigue, but Jariah was so anxious for more she climbed onto Nicco's lap and clamped her thick thighs around his waist. "I need to feel you inside me. Here. Now," she panted, her words a desperate plea.

Straddling him, she pressed her body flat against his and massaged his broad, muscled shoulders. She stroked his chest, marveling at his chiseled upper body, and drooled over his rock-hard pecs and abs.

She buried her hands in his hair and cradled him to her chest like a mother nursing her child. He mashed her breasts together, and then slowly sucked each dark chocolate bud into his mouth. Nicco licked her nipples, kissing and nipping each one. It was a sensual, erotic game, and each flick of his tongue made Jariah moan louder and longer. Her clit was throbbing, dripping wet, and her body quivered in eager anticipation.

Pleasure built and rose to impossible heights.

"Do you have a condom in your wallet?"

"I do." The sound of his voice yanked Jariah out of her sexual haze.

Jariah dropped her gaze to his lap and licked her lips lasciviously. She unbuckled his pants, and eagerly worked her fingers over the tip of his shaft, impressed by its staggering width and length. He then pulled a condom from his wallet, removing the wrapper and sliding it down his long, thick erection.

Nicco drew his hands along her thighs, hiked up her flouncy, floral skirt and pushed aside her panties. As Jariah lowered herself onto his erection, she felt strong and sexy. Clamping her legs around him, she slowly rocked her hips back and forth.

"Damn, baby, you feel amazing. So tight and wet, I could love you like this all night."

Love me all night? Please do!

Clutching her hips in a viselike grip, he gave quick, fast thrusts. He ground himself against her clit and used his mouth and tongue to lick her earlobes. On and on it went, until Jariah was a shivering, bumbling mess. She cursed and screamed, bucked and cooed. Nicco wore a devilish grin, but never let up, only plunged deeper inside her. He alternated between slow circles and powerful thrusts that took her breath away. And just when Jariah was sure she'd had enough, he'd start the wicked, delicious pattern all over again.

His touch was divine ecstasy, as addictive as French wine. Nicco was an amazing lover, a man who knew how to arouse and please a woman, and Jariah knew that no one else would ever be able to compare to him.

Their lovemaking was wild, frenzied, but Nicco spoke in a soft, tender voice. *"Ti amo, e io sono al cento per cento pronti a impegnarsi per voi..."*

Her temperature spiked, and her body burned out of control. An insane rush of pleasure gripped her. Jariah couldn't think straight, couldn't make sense of what Nicco was saying. It couldn't possibly be true. Not after just one date, could it? He'd had too much to drink at dinner. He was tipsy, talking crazy, that had to be it. Why else would he say the words, "I love you, and I'm a hundred percent ready to commit to you," over and over again?

A shiver skidded down her spine. Jariah closed her eyes, and fought the tremors raking her damp, sweaty body. She was floating, weightless, soaring high above the clouds. Quivering, she gripped his shoulders and furiously pumped her legs like a horse jockey.

Jariah jerked and shuddered. She felt his erection growing inside her, filling her. Surrendering to her orgasm, she climaxed and collapsed like a ton of bricks against his chest. Shaken, she clung to him, panting each breath.

"Non ho mai saputo che eri un hellcat."

Raising her eyes to his face, she curled her lips in an angry pout. "I'm not a hellcat, Nicco, and just so you know, I've never, ever had sex on a first date."

"I know, baby, I'm just teasing. And just so *you* know, I loved every minute of it."

His fingers caressed her face with loving tenderness, and Jariah covered his hands with her own. It was in that moment—with their eyes locked and their bodies intertwined—that she knew, deep in her soul, that her life would never ever be the same again.

"Spend the night with me," he whispered, pressing his lips against hers. "I want to wake up tomorrow morning with you by my side."

Staring at him longingly, she felt an inaudible moan escape her lips. Jariah was anxious to get to Nicco's house, but she didn't let her excitement show on her face. Standing, she straightened her clothes, grabbed her handbag, and sashayed past him with a seductive swish of her hips. "I'm ready when you are."

Chapter 15

Yanked out of her sleep by a shrill, deafening noise, Jariah awoke and shot straight up in bed. Disorientated, she clutched the black satin sheet to her chest and glanced around at her surroundings. Her body was aching, her thoughts were cloudy and her head was pounding.

Next time, I'll drink less wine and more water.

Sunshine poured into the master bedroom through the open balcony doors, filling the space with warmth, light and fresh air. The scent of orange juice made Jariah's mouth water, and the sound of R & B music—a raunchy, explicit Robin Thicke number—made her wonder if she was, in fact, still dreaming. But then her gaze fell across the empty box of Magnum condoms on the bedside table, and she remembered her all-night sexcapade with her insatiable boss. It all came flooding back—her tryst with Nicco in the movie theater, their romantic stroll along the beach and returning to his estate in the wee hours of the morning. *Where is Nicco?*

Yawning, she swung her tired legs over the side of the bed and stretched her hands high above her head. A massage would hit the spot, and at the thought of Nicco knead-

ing and stroking her body goose bumps erupted across her
skin. It was amazing the effect he had on her, how desperate she was for him after only one night of lovemaking.

As Jariah stood, she spotted a piece of white paper lying
where Nicco should have been.

I went for a run. Be back in time to make you breakfast.

Excitement and joy bubbled inside her. Only Nicco
could make her feel this good, this happy. Last night, after
making love for the third spellbinding time, they'd snuggled in each other's arms and talked for hours. No subject
was off-limits and the crazy, outrageous stories Nicco told
her about his teenage years made Jariah giggle.

Voices filled the air, drawing her gaze to the open doors.
Hoping to catch sight of Nicco jogging around his estate,
Jariah pushed aside the curtains, and stepped out onto the
balcony. "Wow, talk about gorgeous," she gushed, shaking her head in awe.

Shielding her eyes from the sun, she marveled at the
size of Nicco's opulent bachelor pad. Groundskeepers
rushed about watering the lawn, trimming the shrubs and
planting flowers.

Jariah heard her cell phone ring from somewhere in the
master bedroom, but didn't know the first place to look.
Returning inside, she frantically searched under the bed,
the sitting area and the master bathroom. She couldn't find
it anywhere. As she wandered around the room, trying to
remember the last time she had her cell phone, Jariah noticed the outfit she wore yesterday hanging up in front of
the closet door. Desperate to make love to Nicco last night,
she'd tossed her sleeveless blouse and floral skirt on the
floor, but to her surprise her clothes didn't look wrinkled
or dirty. In fact, they looked clean, spotless.

Curious, she closed her eyes, and buried her nose in her
Kate Spade blouse. It smelled like lavender fabric softener
and had been ironed. *What a sweetheart!* she thought, and

a girlish smile warmed her lips. Jariah wondered when Nicco had found the time to wash her clothes, and as she dressed made a mental note to thank him.

For the second time in minutes, her cell phone rang. Moving to the bed, Jariah dropped to the floor and searched around on her hands and knees. Bingo! Mrs. Covington's number appeared on the screen, but Jariah didn't panic. She knew it was Ava calling to check in, and greeted her daughter warmly. "Good morning, sweetie. How are you? Are you having a good time with Grandma and Grandpa?"

"No. I want to go home." Her voice wobbled with emotion. "I want to eat pancakes and bacon for breakfast, but Grandma said, 'no.'"

"Ava, that's no reason to cry."

"It's not my fault I'm a big-boned girl, is it, Mama? Big-boned girls are pretty, too, right?"

Jariah stared down at the phone, confused and bewildered by her daughter's words. "Honey, what are you talking about? Who said you were a big-boned girl?"

"Grandma Stella. She said big-boned people like me have no business eating bacon, and gave me a bowl of yucky oatmeal instead. Gross! I hate oatmeal."

Fighting mad, Jariah struggled to control her temper. Where did Wesley's mother get off insulting her baby? Had the woman lost her ever-loving mind? Jariah wasn't going to wait to find out. She was going to pick up Ava, and if Stella didn't like it, that was just too bad. Maybe next time she'd keep her big mouth shut and her offensive comments to herself. "Don't worry, baby girl. Everything will be fine."

"The other kids are calling me Big-Boned Ava."

"Where is Grandma Stella now?" Jariah asked through clenched teeth.

"Sitting in the sun room with her friends. They're eating brownies, but they won't let me have any," she complained.

"Ava, politely ask Grandma Stella to come to the phone."

"Are you going to come get me, Mom? I promise to be a good girl," she said. "I'll clean my room and vacuum the house…"

Jariah's heart split in two as she heard her daughter beg and plead. "I'll be there soon, I promise, but first let me talk to Grandma Stella."

"Okay. Hold on."

Jariah heard a rustling sound, boisterous female laughter, and then an eerie silence.

"Yes," Mrs. Covington drawled, sounding annoyed. "What would you like?"

"I'm coming to get Ava. Please have her ready to go in an hour."

"I will do no such thing. She is having a lovely time playing with my friends' grandkids, and is on her way to join the others in the pool."

Jariah repeated herself, speaking louder this time. "I said, I'm coming to pick up my daughter. What part of that don't you understand?"

"You can drive all the way out here if you want to but security won't let you pass through the gates. And think of how embarrassed Ava would be if you came down here and caused a scene. Is that what you want, Jariah? To embarrass your only daughter?"

Jariah wished she could reach through the phone and wring Mrs. Covington's bony neck. She thought of calling Wesley and raising hell, but knew her ex would never stand up to his mother. In his eyes, she could do no wrong. Jariah didn't care if she had to walk to the Covington estate, she was going to pick up her daughter and no one was going to stop her. "What time will your friends be leaving?"

"My book club members are staying for lunch."

"I understand." Jariah thought hard. And then she

smiled to herself as an idea came to mind. One that was guaranteed to work. "I was really hoping to take Ava to the Miami Art Museum this afternoon. The Pioneers of African-American History exhibit opens today, and I'm anxious to see it."

Stella's tone brightened. "I think that is a grand idea. Lee and I donated a million dollars to the project, and we attended the charity fundraiser, as well. Imagine how excited Ava will be when she sees our names on the gold sponsor plaque at the entrance of the exhibit."

"I was thinking the same thing," Jariah lied, rolling her eyes to the ceiling. "That's why I want to pick up Ava now. I want us to have plenty of time to explore the exhibit."

"Yes, wonderful idea, I will prepare Ava for your impending arrival."

Lady, get off it. This is not the Victorian Age, and you are no Queen Elizabeth!

"I will have her dressed and ready to go at one o'clock. Don't be late."

"Great, thank you, Mrs. Convington. See you soon."

"Park across the street when you arrive," she said, her tone losing its warmth. "Your car is an eyesore and I don't want my book club members to see it anywhere near my property."

Click.

Annoyed by the dig, Jariah swore in Italian. She stuffed her feet into her high heels, scooped up her handbag and tore out of the master bedroom. The sooner she called a cab, the sooner she could pick up Ava. Jariah wanted to see Nicco, and felt bad about leaving despite making plans to spend the day with him, but she couldn't sit around waiting for him to return from his jog. She was worried about Ava and wanted to pick her up before Wesley's mother completely shattered her self-esteem.

As Jariah descended the winding staircase, she admired

the striking decor on the main floor. In the morning light, Nicco's Coral Gables estate was even more stunning. The mansion had a modest brick exterior, but the inside was fit for a king. Oversized picture windows offered an abundance of natural sunshine and panoramic views of the Miami skyline. Decorated in rich beige and brown tones, the estate was decked out in designer furnishings and the best artwork money could buy. Brass chandeliers hung from what seemed to be every ceiling on the main floor, and a collection of Egyptian masks lined the walls. It was a dream house, one Jariah wished she could afford, and as she glanced out the window she imagined herself playing with Ava on the trampoline.

Jariah smelled the tantalizing aroma of bacon and freshly baked pastries, too, but ignored her hunger pains. Determined to make a clean getaway without running into Gerald or one of the groundskeepers, she tiptoed past the formal dining room and rushed through the grand foyer. *Almost there,* she thought, as her gaze fixed on the front door.

Her heart slammed violently against her rib cage, and her cold, clammy hands were shaking uncontrollably. As she sped passed the kitchen, someone reached out and grabbed her. Jariah shrieked, and her purse fell to the floor like a sack of potatoes.

Chuckling, Nicco wrapped her up in his arms and dropped a kiss on her cheek.

"Are you trying to kill me?" She touched a hand to her chest and breathed slowly through her nose. "You scared me half to death."

"That's what you get for trying to run off."

He turned her around to face him, and when their eyes met, Jariah felt suffocating rush of desire. Deep in her stomach, butterflies swarmed about. Her nipples hardened, strained against her bra, dying for release, and she just knew her panties were soaking wet. Nicco made her want to do wild and crazy things, and looked so damn sexy in his white T-shirt and blue running shorts, she wanted to have *him*—not Honey Nut Cheerios—for breakfast.

"Did you sleep well?" Nicco asked, blessing her with another kiss.

"Like a baby."

He laughed. "That's what I like to hear."

"How was your run?"

"Painful." His grin was sly, and his voice was undeniably erotic. "You worked me over real good last night, and I have aches and pains in places I haven't used since I was a teenager!"

His words aroused her and made her want to head back upstairs to the master bedroom for rounds four and five, but then she remembered her conversation with Ava minutes earlier, and her craving waned. "I know we made plans to have a picnic at Bayfront Park, but I have to leave," she explained, scooping her purse up off the floor. "Can you please call me a cab?"

His grin faded. "Don't go. Stay. I need you."

"You do?"

"Yeah, baby, I do." Nuzzling his face against her chin, he slipped a hand underneath her blouse and caressed the small of her back. "I'm starving. Let's go back to bed."

"Oh, so *that's* why you want me to stay." Eyeing him coolly, Jariah freed herself from his grasp. "I don't need you to walk me out. I can see myself to the door."

Nicco slid in front of her, cutting off her escape route. His features were touched with concern, and the hand he rested on her hip warmed her from the toes up.

"Baby, it's not like that," he argued, his tone as gentle as his caress. "I want you here because I love being with you. The fact that you're the best lover I've ever had is a bonus."

I'm the best lover you ever had? No way! she thought, resisting the urge to squeal.

"Sorry, Nicco, I didn't mean to snap at you." Embarrassed for overreacting, Jariah wore an apologetic smile. "I just got off the phone with Ava's grandmother, and that woman always brings the worst out in me."

"How is Ava doing? Is everything okay?"

"No, she's upset, so I'm going to pick her up early," Jariah explained, taking her cell phone out of her purse to check for missed calls. "That's why I need you to call me a cab."

"Let's go into the kitchen. You can bring me up to speed while we eat breakfast."

The glass table overlooking the deck was filled with an abundance of silver trays and juice jugs.

"Wow, your personal chef prepared quite the spread this morning."

Nicco filled a oversized plate with some of everything that was on the table. "I don't have a chef. I prefer to do all my own cooking."

"It must have taken you hours to make all of this food."

"It did, but you're worth it."

Sitting down at the table, Nicco seized Jariah around the waist and pulled her down on his lap. He picked up his fork, cut her blueberry waffle into small, tiny pieces and swirled it around in the maple syrup. "Open wide."

Jariah did and chewed slowly. Starving, she parted her lips for more. Between bites, Nicco stroked her neck, her shoulders and nibbled on her earlobes. *Who knew breakfast could be so sexy?* she thought, snuggling closer to him. He fed her until there was nothing left on her plate and dabbed her mouth with a napkin when she was finished eating.

"I could get used to this," he said, gazing up at her. "I like you being here."

I do, too. More than you know.

"I have something for you." Nicco reached into the pocket of his shorts and took out a gold key. "This is for you. I want you and Ava to come and go as you please."

"Thanks, but no thanks. I'd hate for us to bump into Estelle or one of your other exes."

"You won't."

"How can you be so sure?"

"Because you're the only woman I've ever given a key to."

Jariah felt her jaw drop, but couldn't close her gaping mouth.

"My past relationships were all superficial, short-term hookups, but I want more for us."

Fiddling with her watch strap, she avoided his searching gaze.

"What is it? Did I say something wrong?"

Silence, hung between them like a thick, dark curtain.

"Talk to me," he pleaded, taking her hands in his. "I want to know what's stopping you from trusting me. Is it my past and all of the reckless things you think I've done?"

"You come from a wealthy family, and I grew up in a low-income housing project in—"

"What does that have to do with anything?"

"I've been down this road before and I don't want to go down it again."

"I don't understand. You're talking in circles." Nicco frowned. "Is this about your ex?"

Bitter memories flooded her mind, and seconds passed before Jariah could speak.

"Ava's dad was my first love, my one and only boyfriend, and when I got pregnant three months before graduation he promised to take care of me. My parents were furious with me for having a baby out of wedlock, but I was too in love to care."

"You thought you were going to get married and live happily ever after, huh?"

"I was twenty-one, incredibly naive and believed everything would be okay as long as we loved each other."

"Sometimes love just isn't enough."

Knowing firsthand how true that was, Jariah nodded her head solemnly. "Things were going great, and I was thrilled when he asked me to move in but the minute his parents learned I was from Overtown, they started treating me differently."

"It sounds like his parents need to take a course on acceptance and sensitivity."

"I couldn't agree more. They act all high and mighty just because they have a private jet, and vacation in the Hamptons, but they are the most small-minded people I have ever met. In their eyes, I'm nothing but trash, and I'll never be good enough for their brilliant, successful son."

"Don't say things like that." His tone was one of suppressed anger, and his teeth were clenched. "You're not trash."

"Well, that's how Wesley's family made my parents feel," she confessed, her heart filled with a dull ache at the mention of her mom and dad. "Things got so bad between our families last year that my parents stopped talking to me. I got so frustrated with the situation, I sat down and wrote them a letter, but it was returned, unopened, a few weeks later."

"Keep trying. They'll come around. How could they not?" Nicco touched a hand to her cheek and kissed the corners of her lips. "You're smart and so beautiful."

"But I don't know what else to do. I've tried everything."

"Don't worry, baby, we'll think of something."

"We will?" she asked, stunned by the conviction in his voice.

"Absolutely. We're in this together, right?"

Jariah didn't speak. Tongue-tied, she didn't know what to say.

"Unless…" His face hardened like stone, and his shoulders grew stiff. "Unless you're still in love with you ex and are considering getting back together with him."

"It's not going to happen. I would never, ever take him back."

"Can I get that in writing?"

Jariah laughed. She thought Nicco was joking, but when he didn't flash his trademark grin and dodged her gaze, she realized he didn't believe her. *Why not? If anyone should be apprehensive about us dating it should be me.*

"I was willing to put up with my ex's parents, but I got sick of him giving me the runaround about our wedding," she confessed. "We were engaged for five long years, but every time I asked him to set a wedding date, he gave me one excuse after another. He had no intention of ever marrying me, so I broke things off and moved out nine months ago."

"Smart move. You deserve better."

"I think so, too."

Jariah glanced at the clock on the oven and saw that it was eleven o'clock, and she gasped. "I can't believe we've been sitting here talking for two hours," she said, standing to her feet. Quickly, she cleared the table of the dishes and put the leftovers in the fridge.

"What's the rush?" Nicco asked. He stood, picked up their empty glasses and joined her at the sink. "You have plenty of time to get to Coconut Grove."

"I know, but if I'm late, Ava's grandmother will call me a bad mother, and I'm not in the mood to hear her mouth today."

"You're an excellent mom. You know that. Don't let her get to you."

"That's easy for you to say. You've never had the misfortune of meeting her."

"True, but I have plenty of drama to deal with in my family and at the office."

"Can I ask you a personal question?"

Nicco nodded. Leaning against the counter, he folded his arms across his chest and crossed his legs at the ankles. "Ask away. I have nothing to hide."

Despite her misgivings, she asked the question that had been plaguing her thoughts from the first day she started working at Morretti Incorporated. "What happened between you and Tye Caldwell? There are rumors circulating around the office that he resigned because you slept with his wife."

He wore a dark gaze, but spoke in a calm, quiet tone. "It's not true."

"Which part? The part about Tye leaving the company or you sleeping with his wife?"

"I don't want to talk about it," he said through clenched teeth.

"I understand."

Annoyed, Jariah flung her dish towel on the counter and spun on her heels. Before she reached the breakfast bar, Nicco grabbed her waist and gathered her in his arms.

"Damn, that's not it." He hung his head and released a deep sigh. "I've never told anyone the truth about what happened with Tye."

"Why not?"

"Because it's embarrassing, and I want to forget what happened."

"Nothing you tell me will ever leave this room. I promise. You have my word."

Nicco paused, as if he was weighing the truth of her words. After a prolonged silence, he raised his head to meet her gaze, and dropped a bombshell. "Tye embezzled a million dollars from Morretti Incorporated and set me up to take the fall."

Chapter 16

Stunned, Jariah stared at Nicco with wide eyes, unable to believe his jaw-dropping confession. *His best friend had betrayed him? Why? How? When?* Dozens of questions filled her mind, but she couldn't get her thoughts in order or her lips to form a single word.

Instinctively, she moved closer to him. To comfort him, Jariah gently caressed his face. He stared off into space and when he finally spoke, the anguish in his voice brought tears to her eyes.

"I was so busy partying and enjoying the fruits of our labor that I didn't notice Tye was stealing from Dolce Vita right under my nose."

"Nicco, are you sure? Do you have proof that he was stealing from you?"

"One of the interns working in the accounting department noticed a discrepancy in the signature of a check Tye forged in my name and alerted his supervisor." Nicco laughed bitterly, and jabbed a finger at his chest. "Imagine that, a college freshman is smarter than I am!"

"Don't blame yourself. It's not your fault."

"It is," he insisted. "My family and the board of directors also think so."

"I don't care what they think," Jariah argued. "They're wrong. Tye was your best friend. You had every right to trust him."

Nicco hung his head and raked a hand through his hair. His shoulders were hunched in defeat and worry lines creased his forehead. "I knew something was up with Tye, but I didn't want to believe that my best friend would ever screw me over."

"Why did he do it? Was he in financial trouble?"

"No, he got greedy." His narrowed eyes appeared dark. "Tye was never satisfied, and spent money like it was growing on trees. He was always competing with me, but I didn't care. Business was booming, and at the time I felt I owed the success of Dolce Vita to him."

"Seeing your best friend locked up must have been hard on you."

"Tye's not in jail. Last I heard he was backpacking through Europe."

"Why didn't you go to the police and have him arrested?"

Anguish covered his face and seeped into his voice. "Because Tye was more than just a friend and a business partner. He was my brother."

"But he lied and betrayed your trust."

"Italians are incredibly loyal people, and nothing matters more to me than the happiness of my friends and family," he said, wearing a sad smile. "I couldn't let Tye go to jail, so I repaid the money he stole and forced him to resign. He caused a scene at the office, even threatened to kill me, but it was all for show. Tye wanted to save face, but we both know I did him a favor."

"Where's his family now? Are they in Europe, too?"

"No, they're here in Miami. The past twelve months

have been tough on Meredith and Richie, but they're hanging in there."

"Richie, your godson. Of course, now everything makes sense," Jariah said, as all the pieces of the puzzle fit together. "You're his surrogate dad now that Tye's gone."

"I'm trying, but I have a lot to learn. Meredith said if I don't toughen up, Richie's going to walk all over me. But it's hard to say no to such a cute, smooth-talking kid!"

As they chatted about Ava and Richie, they loaded the dishwasher and wiped down the counters. Once the kitchen looked spic and span, Jariah grabbed her purse and put on her jacket.

"I wish you didn't have to go. I love having you here," he said in a hushed whisper. Nicco tipped her head back and stared deep into her eyes. "I've fallen hard for you, Jariah. I hate when we're apart."

Something inside Jariah told her that he was telling the truth, but her doubts still plagued her troubled thoughts. One kiss was all it took to make her melt. Back in his arms, his hands linked around her waist, Jariah realized there was nowhere in the world she'd rather be. Nicco nibbled on her bottom lip. Her nipples hardened under her blouse, aching for his lips, his teeth and his nimble tongue.

"You can trust me with your heart. I won't ever hurt you or mistreat you…"

His words gave her reassurance. And when he cupped her face in his hands and kissed her passionately on the lips, Jariah knew deep in her heart that Nicco Morretti was the man she'd been waiting for her whole life.

"Baby, you have no idea what you do to me," he said, his voice hoarse. "I love you with all my heart, and I want a chance to prove that I'm the only man you need."

Jariah parted her lips and blurted out the question on the tip of her tongue. "You want to get married?"

"Are you proposing?"

"No, silly," she said, laughing. "I just want to know if marriage is on the table."

"Absolutely." Nicco dropped his gaze to her breasts and licked his lips. "I love the idea of you being my wife and coming home to you after a hard day's work. You are, without a doubt, the sweetest piece of chocolate I have ever tasted, and I'm hungry for you right now."

"But what if you change your mind about us? Or meet a gorgeous video girl when you're in L.A. at the end of the month? Where would that leave me?"

"Jariah, nothing is ever going to come between us. You're my heart, and I've found something in you that I've never found in anyone." Nicco gripped her hips, and rubbed his groin against her. The muscles bulging in his arms weren't the only thing rock hard. "And why would I want a skanky video girl when I have a little vixen like you waiting for me at home?"

"Why indeed?" Jariah quipped, batting her eyelashes.

Hungrily, he covered her mouth with his. His lips against hers was a heady feeling Jariah could never, ever tire from. "Nicco, stop," she panted, pressing her hands flat against his chest to keep him at bay. "What if one of the groundskeepers walks in on us?"

"Haven't you ever fantasized about having sex on the kitchen table?"

A soft moan escaped her lips. "Sex is like real estate, baby. It's all about location, and I'm going to do you right here, right now." His lips nipped at her earlobe, and his hands fondled her breasts. "And you don't have to worry about anyone interrupting us. Gerald is under strict orders not to let anyone inside the house while you're here."

His mouth covered hers, and her protest died on her lips. Weakened by his kiss, she sank against his chest and buried her hands in his hair. Jariah was turned on by his urgent caress and his deep, guttural groans.

Nicco pushed a hand under her skirt and slid two fingers inside her panties. Gently, he parted the swollen, fleshly lips between her legs. Breathless, she quivered. A shudder ripped through her, and her knees threatened to give way. Instinctively, she arched her body toward him, and returned his deep, sensuous kiss.

His tongue aroused her, and each flick of his fingers electrified her. To give him deeper access, she parted her legs, spreading them wide.

Quickening his pace, he flicked his wrist harder, pumping it vigorously inside her. His furious speed left her teetering on the edge of delirium. Cursing in Italian, she grabbed fistfuls of his hair and rocked her hips powerfully against his hands.

Her eyes fluttered closed, and an ear-splitting scream fell from her lips. Jariah couldn't get a handle on her emotions that were spiraling out of control, and felt the impulse to cry. His stroke was that intense.

Spasms stabbed her spine, racked her trembling, overheated body. Her legs buckled, and when he whipped off her blouse and closed his mouth around a nipple, Jariah threw her head back in ecstasy.

Their hands, and lips and bodies found sweet solace in each other, a passion she had never known. They staggered around the kitchen, stumbling into appliances and furniture as if they were in the dark. Nicco backed Jariah up against the kitchen table and turned her toward the window. She parted her legs, opened wide like a flower in bloom. He stroked and massaged her clit until delicious tremors rocked her body.

"Enough! I need you inside me now!"

"I love when you get mad. It's so primitive and sexy."

Tossing a coy grin over her shoulder, she swiveled her butt against his crotch.

"Don't start something you can't finish," he warned.

Nicco then slapped her lightly on the bottom, and when a moan fell from her lips, he did it again. They played and teased, kissed and laughed, and by the time he put on the condom he'd grabbed from his secret stash underneath the utensil drawer, and slid his erection inside of her, she'd had two explosive orgasms.

Nicco gave slow, calculated thrusts, as if it was her first time and he didn't want to hurt her. Love filled her heart and tears came to her eyes. Nothing had ever felt so right. Being loved by Nicco was everything Jariah had ever dreamed of and more. Completely in sync, they moved together as one, their bodies swaying to the inaudible beat of their hearts.

He trailed kisses down her neck, lovingly caressing and stroking her hips. Nicco was breathing heavily, but he moved in a slow, measured pace like he had all the time in the world. His stroke was divine, exquisite, and filled every inch of her.

"Kiss me." His words were an urgent command, and seeing the desire in his eyes made Jariah feel like the most beautiful woman in the world. Their lips touched, and their tongues lapped desperately against each other. Convulsing uncontrollably, she felt herself unraveling, and knew she was falling apart. Moaning and groaning at a deafening pitch, she feared if she screamed again the groundskeepers would run in.

"Don't fight it, baby. Let go...let go." Nicco plunged inside her deeper than ever before. Lust infected his body like a virus. He ran his hands down her shoulders, gliding them over her tight, perfectly round butt. *What a view!* Jariah had curves for days, and the most beautiful ass he'd ever seen. The sex was outstanding, without question the best he'd ever had, but that was not what he liked most about her. She was more than just a pretty face; she was honest and trustworthy. The more time they spent together the deeper he fell in love. He wanted a future with her and could picture her living with him in his Coral Gables mansion. He knew that one day soon she'd become Mrs. Nicco Morretti. But first, he had to tell her the truth about—

A door slammed, and footsteps pounded on the tile floor, which jarred Nicco from his thoughts. He heard laughter in the distance, and instantly recognized the voices of the intruders. *Son of a bitch!* His brothers were in his house, and if he didn't move fast they were going to see the woman he loved buck naked.

"Oh, my, goodness, someone's inside the foyer!" Jariah straightened, slipped her blouse back on and adjusted her skirt in record time. "This is so embarrassing. What if this gets back to the office?"

"It's not my staff. It's my brothers. I guess they caught an earlier flight."

The color drained from her face and fear flashed in her big, brown eyes.

"Baby, relax," he said, kissing her lips, "my brothers are going to love you."

Jariah frantically combed her hair with her fingertips. "Do I look okay?"

"You look sensational, and if I had my way you'd still be spread wide-open on my—"

Behind him, someone cleared their throat.

Nicco turned and saw his brothers standing at the entrance of the kitchen, and he smothered a groan. He was annoyed by their untimely arrival, but didn't show it. Casually dressed in T-shirts, khaki shorts and dark aviator sunglasses, they could easily pass for a couple of rich college students on summer vacation. "Hey, guys, it's good to see you. How was your flight?"

Demetri and Rafael exchanged worried glances, but didn't speak.

The silence in the air was suffocating.

"We've been calling and texting you for hours to update you about our flight schedule," Demetri said, taking off his sunglasses. "Did you lose your phone again?"

"I switched it off last night and forgot to turn it back on," he said, wearing a wry smile. "To be honest, I don't even know where it is!"

Rafael grunted. "Why doesn't that surprise me? It's obvious you've been *occupied.*"

Nicco heard the bitter edge in his brother's tone, but disregarded it. "This beautiful young woman is Jariah Brooks," he said, taking her hand in his and giving it a light squeeze. "Baby, these are my brothers, Rafael and Demetri."

"Jariah Brooks? You're new executive assistant?" Rafael folded his arms across his chest. The whites of his eyes doubled their size. "What the hell is going on here?"

"It's none of your business bro, stay out of it."

"I—I—I should go," Jaraiah stammered. "It's almost one o'clock."

Nicco could almost see the tension radiating off her body. To assure her that everything was fine, he shot her a playful wink. But it didn't work. She bit her bottom lip and nervously shuffled her feet.

"It's a pleasure to meet you both." Jariah slipped on her high heels and collected her things from the breakfast bar. "I have to go pick up Ava. I'll talk to you later."

"I'll drive you to Coconut Grove. It's not far from here."

"No, don't, stay with your brothers. I'll be fine."

"You're too stubborn for your own good," he grumbled, opening the side drawer beside the fridge and grabbing a set of keys. "Take the Mercedes. It's parked right out front."

Shaking her head, she waved her hands frantically in the air. "No way! You just bought it a few weeks ago and the rims costs more than my car!"

"Don't argue. Just take it. It's yours until your car is fixed."

Jariah hesitated. "Are you sure?"

"I'm positive." Nicco pressed the keys into her palm. "I'll walk you out."

Ignoring the shell-shocked expressions on his brothers' faces, he led Jariah out of the kitchen.

Outside, seconds later, he crouched down beside the driver's-side door, and gave her a rundown of the controls.

"I hate to see you go," Nicco said, stroking her long, silky brown legs. He could hear the desperation in his voice, but he wanted her to stay, and wasn't too proud to beg. "Why don't you pick up Ava and come back here? I'll fire up the grill, put on some Taylor Swift and we'll have a grand time."

Jariah laughed. "Ava would love that! She's obsessed with that girl!"

"I know, last Sunday when Richie and I were over for dinner, she sang us a bunch of Taylor's songs." Nicco smiled at the memory, wondering when the spunky six-year-old had captured his heart. "Every time I think of Ava using the remote as a microphone, I crack up."

"Maybe we can barbecue another time, though," Jariah said. "I'm taking Ava to the museum this afternoon, and I have to teach a self-defense class at five o'clock."

"Then I'll swing by later, and take you lovely ladies out for gelato."

"Aren't you going to hang out with your brothers tonight?"

"My fridge is stocked. They can survive without me for an hour or two."

Her eyes brightened. "All right, I accept."

"Great. I'll pick you ladies up at seven o'clock."

Nicco cupped her chin and hungrily devoured her mouth. Minutes passed as they feasted on each other's lips. Jariah finally pulled away, but when Nicco saw the time on the dashboard clock, he stood and closed the driver's-side door. "Drive safe, beautiful. I'll see you later."

"Definitely." She put on her sunglasses and waved. "Thanks for everything, Nicco."

Nicco stood in the driveway, watching Jariah cruise down the street in his new Mercedes.

"What the hell has gotten into you?"

"I should be asking you the same question." Nicco turned around and stared down his older brother. "You were way out of line, and I don't like the way you spoke to my girl."

"Son of a bitch!" Rafael shouted, throwing his hands up in the air. "Didn't you learn anything from the incident with Gracie?"

"Yeah, I did," he shot back. "I learned that you think I'm the scum of the earth."

"I never said that."

"You didn't have to. The minute Gracie cried sexual harassment you convinced dad to pay her off. You never once asked me if the allegations were true."

"That's because you have a track record of thinking with your dick *instead* of your head."

Nicco flinched as if he'd been slapped. His brother's words stung, cut him to the quick. "Not this time. Jariah isn't just any girl."

"What makes her so special?"

"Everything. She's honest, smart as hell and she's not afraid to call me out when I mess up. Hell, sometimes I think it's her favorite pastime!"

Nicco chuckled, but noticed his brother remained stoic. But he didn't care if Rafael believed him. He'd finally met his dream woman, and he wasn't going to let anyone ever come between them.

"Who's Ava?" Raphael asked.

"Jariah's six-year-old daughter."

"When did you start dating single moms?"

On the surface, Nicco remained calm, but inside he was doing a slow burn. Anger surged through his veins, and his hands balled into tight fits. He wanted to pummel Rafael's face into the ground, but he cracked his knuckles instead.

"You have no business dating a woman with a kid."

The veins in his neck twitched and throbbed uncontrollably.

"You're an adrenaline junky who gets off on breaking the rules. It's just a matter of time before you get bored and move on to greener pastures."

Nicco shot his brother a disgusted look.

"Does she know about Gracie?"

"No, not yet. I'm waiting for the right time to tell her."

"There's never a right time to tell a woman you were accused of sexual harassment," he said. "I'm going to keep my mouth shut for now, but you better hope dad doesn't find out about your office affair."

"Don't worry, I plan to introduce Jariah to mom and dad as soon as they get to town."

"Well, I'll be damned." Rafael whistled. "I can't believe you're actually serious about this girl. Hell, next you'll be telling me you're ready to tie the knot!"

A grin overwhelmed his mouth, one that caused him to feel like a kid again. "Think mom and dad will mind if I pop the question next Saturday at their anniversary bash?"

"Next Saturday!" Rafael shouted, his eyes bulging straight out of his head. "Slow your roll. You guys just met. You hardly know each other."

"I want Jariah to know that I love her, and I'm ready to commit—"

"Then buy her a promise ring."

"A promise ring isn't going to cut it. She's twenty-seven, not sixteen."

"This is too much drama to deal with on an empty stomach," Rafael grumbled, scowling. "I'm going inside. I need a shot of Patrón."

Chapter 17

"Are you ready to make our grand entrance, Mrs. Nicco Morretti-to-be?"

A giggle tickled Jariah's throat. She glanced up from her compact mirror, saw Nicco watching her and dropped it back inside her purse. "Don't you think you're getting ahead of yourself?" she asked, meeting his gaze head-on. "We haven't known each other long."

"When a man knows, he knows, and I knew the moment I laid eyes on you that you were the only woman for me."

"Was that before or after I insulted you?"

Nicco chuckled. The sound of his thick, husky laugh made Jariah feel downright giddy. He knew just what to say to make her melt, and sitting alone with him in the close quarters of the Rolls Royce limousine was wreaking havoc on her mind and body.

Staring down at her hands, Jariah admired her bright, multicolored nails. Ava had selected the design, and as she thought about the mother-daughter manicures they'd received that afternoon at Glamour Girlz, a smile warmed her heart. After they left the salon, they'd met Nicco for lunch. Every time Jariah thought about what Ava had told him during dessert she giggled.

"I like you," she'd announced, shoveling chocolate ice-cream into her mouth. "You're sweet and funny, and you always make my mommy laugh."

"Thanks, Ava. I think you're pretty cool, too."

"You can live with us if you want."

Nicco had cocked an eyebrow. "I can?"

"Yes, but only if you bring Richie. He's my new BFF!"

Car horns honked, drawing Jariah's gaze outside. The limousine was parked in front of Dolce Vita and dozens of couples, decked out in ball gowns, designer suits and top hats flocked inside the five-star restaurant. A red carpet scattered with rose petals flowed down the sidewalk, and waiters offered each new arrival a glass of champagne.

Peering out the tinted windows, Jariah spotted several Morretti Incorporated employees walking up the street arm-in-arm. The female interns looked young and stylish in their colorful dresses. The sound of their girlish laughter carried on the evening breeze.

"I'm so nervous, I'm shaking," Jariah confessed, fiddling with the three-stone diamond pendant at her neck. Nicco had given it to her hours earlier, and it was still hard to believe he'd spent thousands of dollars on her at the Cartier boutique. It was the most beautiful piece of jewelry Jariah had ever seen, and she was deeply touched by the sweet, unexpected gift. "What if my coworkers turn against me for being your date?" she asked, giving voice to her fears. "What if Mrs. Reddick causes a scene during cocktail hour? Or fires me on the spot?"

"Jariah, you have nothing to worry about. I won't leave your side."

"Can I get that in writing?" she joked, using his favorite line.

"You don't need to. You have my word."

To calm her nerves, Jariah took a long, deep breath. It didn't help, and the more she tried to relax, the harder her legs shook. The raspberry-colored, one-shoulder gown she'd eagerly purchased weeks earlier at Macy's now felt tight enough to choke her. "Do I look okay? Are you sure my dress isn't too tight?"

"You look incredible, and I can't wait to show you off to my family and friends." Touching her face, he sprayed kisses across her nose and cheeks. His voice was intimate, as gentle as a feather along her spine. "We're going to celebrate this joyous occasion with my parents, and after the party wraps up I'm taking you back to my place for dessert."

His grin was her weakness, his touch her Kryptonite. And when his gaze slid down her hips Jariah knew exactly what he had on his mind. They desperately wanted the same thing. But she played coy and teased him with a wink and a salacious look. "What's on the menu?"

"You'll have to wait and see."

The back door swung open, and a spicy, piquant fragrance flooded the limousine. Stars specked the night sky, the evening breeze whipped wildly through the trees, and music blared from the fleet of luxury cars parked along Biscayne Boulevard.

Nicco stepped out of the limousine and offered his right hand. He drew her into his arms, and pressed his mouth against hers. Their eyes connected, and when he smiled at her—one of his slow, easy, grins—Jariah felt a deep sense of peace. And just like that, her body quit shaking and her ears stopped throbbing. Being in Nicco's arms would never grow old. She gloried in their newfound love, relished every minute they spent together, and was hopeful about their future. Who cared what anyone else had to say? Why did it matter? She was in a committed relationship with a wonderful man who adored her daughter, and she wasn't going to let anyone come between them.

"Sei una bellezza vivace, e io sono completamente e irrimediabilmente colpita con voi."

His words caused her fears to dissipate and her confidence to soar. "You're right. I *am* a vivacious beauty." Feeling playful and sexy, she raised her chin, arched her shoulders and struck pose. "You're one *very* lucky man, Nicco Morretti!"

Flashing his trademark grin, he slid his hands down her back, and squeezed her butt. "I couldn't have said it better myself, now, let's go party!"

The Dolce Vita dining room was a scene of gaiety and excitement. And when Jariah saw the satin-draped ceilings, towering flower vases overflowing with long-stemmed roses and the eight-tiered wedding cake covered in sparkling gems she knew Nicco and his brothers had spared no expense for their parents' twenty-fifth wedding anniversary.

Round tables draped with silver tablecloths were covered with fine china and floating candles that showered the room with a sultry, golden hue. Backed by a ten-piece orchestra, a blue-eyed, soul crooner entertained guests as they sipped champagne, and feasted on imported caviar. The silver and red decor was striking, the music was enchanting and the air was filled with an appetizing aroma.

"What do you think?" Nicco asked as they entered the dining room.

"I've never seen anything like this. It's incredible, but a little over-the-top."

"That's what I was hoping you'd say!" Chuckling, he pecked her on the cheek. "My mom loves throwing big parties, so I told Claudia to go all-out, and she delivered big-time."

"You can say that again," Jariah agreed. "I don't know what you're paying her, but she's worth every penny."

He dropped his mouth to her ear. "Maybe we should hire her to plan our wedding."

"Don't we have to get engaged first?"

"How does tonight sound?"

Jariah tried not to faint, but just the thought of marrying Nicco and becoming his lawfully wedded wife made her feel light-headed. "I don't need a party planner. I just want a simple, elegant wedding with my friends and family."

"That's it? You don't want a lavish venue or a five-page guest list?"

"Nicco, if you're by my side, I'll have everything I'll ever need."

He pressed a kiss to her lips, and she snuggled against his chest. Deep inside, Jariah could feel herself changing, growing and becoming a stronger, more confident woman. It was hard to believe that one man could change her, but the Italian-born businessman had. In Nicco, she'd found what she'd been looking for her whole life. Their personalities meshed well, they always had a blast together and they shared the same values and beliefs. Feeling content for the first time in months, she slid her arms around his waist and returned his kiss.

During cocktail hour, they socialized with guests, posed for pictures in front of the ice sculpture and fed each other oysters and tropical fruit. Walking around the restaurant on Nicco's arm was an intoxicating feeling. He introduced her to his relatives, proudly showed her off to his business associates and kept a protective arm around her waist. Meeting the mayor was a treat, but nothing topped slow-dancing with Nicco to her favorite Michael Bublé song.

At seven o'clock, the lights dimmed, and guests donned elaborate party masks and colored beads in honor of the couple's New Orleans wedding ceremony twenty-five years earlier.

"Our guests of honor will be here in twenty minutes," Claudia Jeffries-Medina announced, clapping her hands together to capture the attention of the audience. A hush fell over the dining area, and all heads turned to the bubbly party planner. "I just received word that Mr. and Mrs. Morretti have left Country Club Miami, so everyone, please get in place…"

Gerald appeared, spoke quietly to Nicco and took off like a thief in the night.

"I have a surprise for you," Nicco said, draping an arm around her shoulder.

"Again? But we had a quickie in the office ten minutes ago."

He grinned. "I know *you're* not complaining. You begged for more!"

Nicco led Jariah through the dining room and out into the waiting area. And there, standing beside the aquarium, were her parents. They were dressed in formal designer threads, which made them look years younger.

"Mom, Dad, oh, my goodness, it's so great to see you!" Jariah threw her arms around her parents and held them tight. Her dad kissed her on the forehead, and her eyes stung and burned. Feeling his love caused the tears she'd been holding inside for the past eight months to finally break free. "I've missed you guys so much."

"Honey, don't cry. You're going to ruin your makeup, and you look so pretty." Mrs. Brooks snatched the handkerchief out of her husband's jacket pocket and cleaned her daughter's tear-stained cheeks. "We didn't want to stand in the way of your happiness, so after you sent that email we decided to stay away—"

Jariah cut in. "Mom, what are you talking about? What email?"

Mrs. Brooks spoke openly about how hurtful the message was, and confessed that she'd cried herself to sleep for weeks afterward.

"What? That's crazy. I never sent that message."

"You didn't?" Mrs. Brooks asked.

"Never. Someone must have hacked into my email."

Mr. Brooks frowned and stroked his freshly trimmed black beard. "But the message was full of personal, private details only you would know."

Or, someone close to me, Jariah thought, her brain switching into overdrive. Her heart beat raced, pounded with anger. The truth came to her, hit her like a ton of bricks. She thought back to months earlier to the day she'd dumped Wesley, and as his insults played in her mind. She knew he'd to have been the one to send the bogus email to her parents. He knew her email password, had access to her laptop and had never hid his dislike for her mom and dad.

Emotion clogged Jariah's throat, making it impossible for her to speak. Later, when they were alone, she'd share her suspicions with her parents, but now was neither the time nor the place. Not with Nicco standing behind her, listening in. The less he knew about her ex the better.

"I know we've had our differences in the past, and haven't always see eye-to-eye, but I would never intentionally hurt you. I love you guys, and not being able to see you has been torture."

"That's what Nicco said when he came by the house yesterday."

Bewildered, Jariah eyed Nicco. "You went to Overtown to meet my parents?"

"I had to. I wanted them here to celebrate with us tonight."

"Honey, we're so proud of you," Mrs. Brooks said, beaming from ear-to-ear. "Nicco told us you're the best executive assistant he's ever had!"

"You're proud of me? Really? Even though I've made so many mistakes?"

Mr. Brooks rested a hand on his daughter's shoulder. "Mistakes are what make us human. We haven't always agreed with your decisions, but we have never stopped loving you."

Jariah's vision blurred with tears, but she told herself not to cry. In that moment, standing beside Nicco and her parents, something inside her lifted. And as she listened to her father praise her accomplishments, she couldn't wipe the smile off her face.

"You're an outstanding mother and a thoughtful daughter," he continued.

"I still can't believe you booked us the penthouse suite at the Shore Club. We have our own butler *and* a free mini bar!" Mrs. Brooks exclaimed. "And the Macy's shopping spree this afternoon was amazing!"

Jariah turned to Nicco and mouthed the words *Thank you*. She realized she couldn't love him more. He walked as if he owned the world, but beneath the cocky attitude was a sensitive, loving man with a heart of gold. And Jariah loved him, mind, body and soul.

The front doors swung open, and hot air blew inside the waiting area.

"I thought this was a classy, sophisticated party. What are *you* doing here?"

Jariah heard Stella Covington's haughty voice and spun around with a stinging retort on her lips. But before she could get the words out, Nicco gave Mrs. Covington a hug, and kissed her on both cheeks. "Mr. and Mrs. Covington, I'm glad you made it, and just in time, my parents should be arriving any minute…"

Nicco knows The Covingtons? Her stomach lurched violently from left to right. Of course he did. They were a powerhouse couple, one of the wealthiest in Miami. Seeing Nicco with them reminded Jariah that he was *way* out of her league.

With her pulse pounding, she watched as Nicco laughed and chatted with the Covingtons. It was sweltering outside, easily ninety degrees, but Stella was wearing a fur shawl, a vintage lace floor-length dress, and what had to be a million dollars in diamonds.

"What are you doing here?" Mrs. Covington demanded, flipping her hair over her shoulders. "Shouldn't you be at home caring for Ava?"

Nicco stepped forward, and draped an arm possessively around her waist. "Baby, you never told me you knew the Covingtons."

"Y-y-you're dating?" Mrs. Covington's face was as pale as her gown. "Why doesn't that surprise me? You've always had a penchant for wealthy men, haven't you, Jariah?"

The silence was so awkward, Jariah imagined herself crashing through the emergency exit and diving back inside the Rolls Royce. Her impulse was to run, but before she could make a break for it, Nicco tightened his hold, so close she couldn't move. She expected him to question her, to ask her if the accusations were true, but he didn't. He only smiled and gave her a peck on the lips.

"Let's head back inside. My parents should be here any minute."

"Nicco, you don't know that girl like I do. She's sneaky and conniving—"

"Who the hell are you calling conniving?" Mrs. Brooks demanded, placing a hand to her broad hips. "Mind your tongue, Stella, or I'll slap you into next week!"

Tempers flared, insults flew, and all hell broke loose. The couples were arguing so loudly, no one saw Mr. and Mrs. Morretti enter the waiting area. "What is going on here?"

Jariah winced and hung her head. Mr. and Mrs. Morretti looked shell-shocked, like the sole survivors of a ship wreck, and worse, her mom had kicked off her high heels, and was taking off her clip-on earrings.

"Nicco, answer me, what is going on?" Though short and stout, with a full head of gray hair, Mr. Morretti had an air of authority and a commanding presence.

"Arturo, I'll tell you what's going on." Mrs. Covington used one hand to smooth her disheveled hair, and the other to adjust her gown. "That *girl* has been cheating on my Wesley with your son, and had the nerve to show up here with her vulgar, ill-mannered parents!"

"Vulgar?" Mrs. Brooks wagged a finger in the socialite's face. "I'll show you vulgar!"

Mrs. Brooks lunged at Mrs. Covington, but Mr. Brooks grabbed her around the waist and whisked her over to the black leather couch before she could land a single blow. "That's enough," he snapped. "You've said your peace, now let it go. You're embarrassing Jariah..."

"I refuse to break bread with uncouth factory workers from Overtown," Mrs. Covington spat, folding her arms across her chest. "If they don't leave, then I will."

Mrs. Morretti shook her head, and linked arms with Mrs. Covington. "You're not going anywhere, Stella. I haven't seen you in ages, and we have tons of catching up to do."

Mrs. Covington wore a victorious smile.

"Put this ugly incident behind you, and join me inside for cocktails." Mrs. Morretti glared at Jariah. Anger showed on her face, and her dark eyes were filled with disgust. "You and your parents aren't welcome here, so please leave, or I will call the police."

"She's not going anywhere." Nicco clasped Jariah's hand. "Jariah's my date, and I personally invited her parents—"

Arturo frowned. "Your date for what? And why is the restaurant in complete darkness?"

"Deborah, let's go. I don't want to stay where I'm not welcome, and if we hurry I can catch the second half of the baseball game." Mr. Brooks took his car keys out of his jacket pocket. "Baby girl, are you coming with us?"

Jariah's mouth dried, and her temples throbbed. Time stood still for what seemed like an eternity. Her throat was so sore, it hurt to swallow. Everyone was staring at her. She could sense it, feel it, knew they all were watching her every move. Shifting from one foot to the next, she struggled with what to do.

"Jariah, si prega di rimanere. Ho bisogno di te al mio fianco questa sera."

Her stomach did a triple back flip into her throat, but when Nicco stroked her forearm her heart melted. His voice was octaves lower, and his gaze was a light caress across her face. Jariah wanted to spend the rest of the night dancing with Nicco and stealing kisses inside the vintage photo booth, but she couldn't risk hurting her parents again.

"Have a great time with your family, Nicco, and thanks for everything."

"Baby, don't go. You have as much right to be here as anyone else."

Her sadness sat on her chest like a fifty-pound boulder. In a perfect world, it wouldn't matter where she was from, or that she'd had a child out of wedlock, but tonight it did. Especially to people like Stella Covington. Jariah would rather go home with her parents than spend another minute in the socialite's ugly presence. "Good night."

Her mind made up, she turned away from Nicco and linked arms with her mom and dad. As they exited Dolce Vita, tears coursed down Jariah's cheeks, staining her designer gown.

Chapter 18

"What are you doing up so early? On Sundays, you never crawl out of bed before noon, and when you do it's usually kicking and screaming!"

Nicco chuckled, but he didn't find anything funny about his dad cracking jokes on him at six in the morning. He was surprised—shocked actually—to see his mom cleaning the microwave, and his dad sitting at the table reading the newspaper. The very table he and Jariah had made love on just days earlier. Images of her naked, curvy body bombarded his mind, causing an erection to swell inside his jeans. He could still hear her moans, smell the perfume of her sex, and he wondered if he'd ever be able to look at Jariah and not want to make love to her.

Changing the channel in his mind, he joined his dad at the kitchen table and dropped down into the nearest chair. Nicco knew what was coming next, but was determined not to lose his temper. His parents always stayed at his Coral Gables estate when they were in Miami, but this was the first time they'd ever taken over his kitchen. They jokingly referred to his guest quarters as their "love shack," and would stay cooped up inside the plush, all-white suite for days on end. So seeing them in his space put Nicco on high alert. They were up to something. No doubt about it. Last night, during dinner, gossip-loving Stella Covington had probably filled his mother's head with filthy lies about Jariah, and now, armed with misinformation, she was anxious to talk. And so was he.

At the thought of Jariah, he felt an overpowering rush of emotion. He couldn't stop smiling or thinking about her, and he looked forward to seeing her that afternoon. Last night, after the anniversary bash ended, he'd driven over to Jariah's townhome. Inside the living room, they'd had an open, honest conversation. One that lasted for hours.

He told her about what happened with Gracie, and she told him about her tumultuous relationship with Wesley, and her ongoing struggle to keep the peace for their daughter's sake. Sharing their past pain and disappointments made Nicco feel even closer to Jariah. He was not only prepared to defend her, he was ready to propose to her. But first, he had to set the record straight with his parents.

Right on cue, his mother closed the microwave, and dropped her dishrag on the counter. Mr. Morretti lowered his newspaper and stared at Nicco over the rim of his Armani eyeglasses.

The tension in the room was suffocating.

"Thanks for making breakfast, Ma. Everything looks good," Nicco said, admiring the delicious spread. Helping himself to a plate, he loaded it with all of his favorites. "Ma, why do you look so glum? Didn't you have a good time at your anniversary bash last night?"

Her brown eyes filled with gratitude. "I had a wonderful time, but that altercation with that girl and her parents is still weighing on my mind."

"Altercation? You make it sound like they assaulted you." Nicco took a healthy bite of his panini and chewed slowly. "Mrs. Brooks's anger was directed at Mrs. Cov-

ington, not you. They have a sordid history, and if everything Jariah told me is true, Mrs. Covington has made
their lives a living hell."

"I find that very hard to believe. I've known Stella and
Lee Covington for years, and they're one of the most charitable and generous couples I know."

Mr. Morretti folded his newspaper and set it aside. "Listen to your mother, son. She knows what she's talking
about."

"And I know Jariah. She's loyal, honest and I trust her
completely."

"Is that why you gave the little tart your Mercedes?"

He took offence to his mother's quip, but didn't speak
on it. "Jariah needed a car, and I have plenty, so I insisted
she take one. Ask Rafael and Demetri. I had to practically
force the keys into her hands."

"Right, good one." His father gave a harsh, bitter laugh.
"Who would want to drive around town in a brand-new,
custom-designed Mercedes? I know I wouldn't!"

"What if she damages your car? Or sells it to a chop-
shop?" Mrs. Morretti questioned, her voice full of fear and
fret. "What then? Could you imagine the scandal? We'd be
the laughingstock of the country club and Miami's High
Society league."

"Jariah would never do that. She's not that kind of person."

"How the hell do you know? You've only known her
for five minutes!" Mr. Morretti struck his fist on the table.
The noise reverberated around the room, causing the plates
and utensils to rattle. "I knew this was going to happen.
That's why I told Mrs. Reddick to hire a male assistant to
work with you. If that girl goes to the tabloids or screams
rape it will ruin us, and I've worked too damn hard and
too damn long to watch everything I've worked tirelessly
for go up in smoke."

Shaking his head, he refuted his father's claim. "Dad, you have nothing to worry about. Jariah would never do anything to hurt me or to betray my trust. She loves me and I love her."

"Open your eyes, son, it's all an act. You're her meal ticket to a better future, and if you're not careful she'll betray you just like Gracie did, and Tye…"

Too tired to argue, he blocked out their voices and finished eating his breakfast. He snuck a glance at the clock, saw that it was ten o'clock, and took a swig of his orange juice. It was time to go. He was taking Ava and Richie to the movies, and he didn't want to be late.

"So, how long have you been screwing Mrs. Brooks?"

Nicco winced, as if he had a sore tooth, and dropped his fork on his plate. He glared at his father, staring him dead in the eye. His dad looked amused. Out of his two brothers, he looked the most like Arturo, and if that wasn't bad enough he'd also inherited his father's sharp tongue, and pessimistic nature. Before meeting Jariah, he'd thought the worst of people, and didn't trust anyone outside of his inner circle. But he didn't feel that way anymore. He'd finally found his better half, the woman he was destined to grow old with and he wasn't going to let his father reduce their relationship to meaningless sex. "I love Jariah with all my heart and I'm going to marry her."

"Nicco, you will not marry that girl. I forbid it."

"Ma, quit calling her *that girl*," he snapped, finally reaching his breaking point. "Her name is Jariah, and I'm going to propose on her birthday, so you better get on board fast."

"But she's from Overtown, and—"

Disappointed, Nicco hung his head and dragged a hand down the length of his face. "Ma, not you, too. I thought you were better than that."

"Son, I just want what's best for you."

"Then you'll accept Jariah and Ava into this family with open arms. She's the one, Ma, and I'm not going to lose her. Not for anything."

"Nicco, you can't be serious. She's Wesley's baby mother for goodness sake!"

"So what? They broke up almost a year ago, and she doesn't love him."

"But Wesley's your friend," she argued. "Sleeping with the mother of his child is...wrong."

Nicco cursed in Italian under his breath. "We went to the same high school and hit the clubs back in the day, but it's been years since we talked."

"I still don't like the idea of you dating his ex. There's something unnatural about it—"

"Ma, I'm a grown man. I can date whoever I want."

Mrs. Morretti opened her mouth to speak and then quickly closed it.

"You're so whipped, you can't think straight." Mr. Morretti stood, stalked over to the breakfast bar and scooped up the file folder beside the fruit bowl. "I had Gerald do a background check on Mrs. Brooks, and she isn't as squeaky clean as you think."

Nicco tried to conceal his anger, but inside he was seething with rage.

"Did you know that she's a registered member on over a half dozen dating sites?" He held the file up high in the air, waved it around, like a prosecutor wielding the proverbial smoking gun. "She's up to her neck in debt, so she's actively and aggressively looking for a rich, successful man to take care of her and her young daughter."

"Those profiles were created months ago, long before we ever met, and she deleted them weeks ago." Nicco picked up his plate, dumped his food into the garbage and put it in the sink. "Dad, there's nothing you can say to break us up, so save your breath."

"Read Gerald's report before making any hasty decisions."

"I don't need to. I know everything about Jariah that I need to know."

Mr. Morretti chucked the file on the kitchen table. "It's your life, do what you want, but don't come running to me when she screws you over."

Nicco wanted to lash out at his dad, but knew getting in a shouting match with Arturo would get him nowhere. Standing, he slipped on his sunglasses and took his car keys out of his pocket. "I'll see you guys later."

"Where are you going?" Mr. Morretti asked, glancing at his gold wristwatch. "We have to leave at eleven, and it's already ten fifteen. Are you packed and ready to go?"

Nicco frowned and scratched his head. "Packed and ready to go where?"

"To the airport. Our flight to Lisbon leaves at noon. We had discussed visiting Mr. Sarmento and scouting locations for our new offices, remember?"

"You mentioned it a few days ago, but you never confirmed the travel dates with me."

His eyes darkened three shades. "Mr. Sarmento was injured on *your* watch, but if you're too busy to visit one of my closest friends and associates, I'll go alone and apologize on your behalf."

"Where's Rafael? Why can't he go with you?"

"He flew to New York on the red eye. He had an urgent personal matter to deal with."

What personal matter? Rafael has no life! His brother was a workaholic with few hobbies and no close friends, so his hasty departure piqued Nicco's curiosity. Making a mental note to call him later, he said, "All right, Dad, I'll go with you to Lisbon."

Mr. Morretti sighed in relief. "I'm expecting you to come through for me in Lisbon, so stay focused. I don't have to tell you how important this visit is with Mr. Sarmento. He has been a client for years and pays big bucks for our services."

"Dad, I understand, but I can't stay in Portugal all week. I have a business meeting in L.A. on Friday that I can't afford to miss."

"Very well, we'll leave Thursday morning. I'll call First Officer Burke right now and…"

With a pang, Nicco realized he'd have to cancel his plans with Ava and Richie. The thought saddened him, but he forced a smile and dropped a kiss on his mother's cheek. "I'm going to go pack," he said, taking his cell phone out of his pocket. "See you guys in a bit."

Chapter 19

Jariah couldn't do it. Tried, but failed miserably. Typing a letter in Italian, and eavesdropping on her colleagues required extraordinary skill, and she was determined to finish the tasks on her checklist. She blocked out the noise in the reception area and continued working. Her coworkers were yakking it up like a bunch of tween girls at a slumber party, and as usual Jariah felt excluded.

Hearing her name, she narrowed her eyes and inclined her head toward the door. Raucous laughter seeped through the stark-white walls. Jariah knew her colleagues were talking trash about her, but instead of storming out of her office and giving the trio a tongue lashing, she kept her eyes on her computer screen.

Thoughts of Nicco overwhelmed her mind. She couldn't go five minutes without thinking of him, and spent hours on end looking at the pictures of him on her cell phone. It had been four days since his parents' anniversary bash, and although she'd stressed and fretted about leaving the party, nothing had changed between them. Nicco was still as sweet and as romantic as ever.

On Sunday, he'd surprised her with two dozen roses;

the following day he arranged for dinner to be delivered to her house from The Greek Isles, and last night on the phone he'd recited her favorite Maya Angelou poem to her. After days of sexting and flirting on Skype, Jariah was desperate to be back in his arms. Work was boring without Nicco to talk and laugh with, and every time she turned around Mrs. Reddick was breathing down her neck.

A message popped up on the corner of the screen. Jariah read the sentence, minimized her document and clicked on the internet icon. Nothing was more important than talking to Nicco, and Jariah was so anxious to see him she couldn't log into her Skype account fast enough. The moment his face filled the screen, her spirits lifted.

"You're looking gorgeous as usual. I love that shade of purple on you." Flashing a boyish smile, one that made his eyes twinkle, he slowly licked his lips. "Stand up so I can see the rest of your dress, or better yet, take it off so I can see what's *underneath* it."

"You wish!" Jariah couldn't keep a straight face and burst out laughing.

"That's right, baby, I do. I miss you bad, girl."

"You've only been gone for few days."

"I know, but it feels like years since I saw you. Don't you miss me? Even a little?" he asked, wearing a puppy-dog frown.

Jariah wanted to lie, to tell Nicco that he was being silly, but her conscience wouldn't let her. She longed to see him, to kiss and caress him, and was counting down the days until he returned from Lisbon. But she didn't want Nicco to know the truth, so she downplayed how she felt. "Of course I miss you. There's no one to bring me breakfast in bed or to rub my feet at the end of the day."

An amused expression covered his handsome face. "That's not *all* I'd like to rub."

That makes two of us, she thought, marveling at how

delicious he looked in his white button-down shirt and dark slacks.

"I hope you don't have plans tonight, because I'm making you a home-cooked meal."

Jariah raised an eyebrow. "That's going to be mighty hard to do from Portugal."

"I'll be back in Miami by eight."

"Tonight? But you're supposed to be heading straight from Lisbon to L.A."

"That was the plan, but I'm going crazy without you. I *have* to see you."

"So you're going to fly home for six hours, then fly back out? That's insane!"

"Not to me. As long as I can hold you in my arms, and kiss your beautiful face the trip will be worth it." He grinned, and his eyes lit up like a star. "I died laughing when I heard the message Ava left for me this morning. She is hilarious!"

The memory of her daughter singing her favorite pop song on Nicco's voice mail forced Jariah to laugh, as well. "That was very sweet of you to send Ava a gift box from Lisbon. She loved the souvenirs, devoured the chocolate seashells in one sitting and danced around the house for hours in her new Taylor Swift tour jacket!"

"I just wanted Ava to know that I was thinking about her, too."

And I love you for that.

"How are things going in Lisbon?" Jariah noted the dark lines under his eyes and wondered if he'd had a good night's sleep since arriving in Portugal four days earlier. "Did you visit with Mr. Sarmento yesterday?"

"Yeah, he was real happy to see us, and was even able to tell us more about the gunman."

"Did you finally close the deal with Sea Freight Shipping?" she asked.

"No. They're playing hard ball, so we rescinded our offer and shut down talks."

"I'm sorry to hear that. Are you disappointed?"

Nicco shrugged a shoulder and raked a hand through his hair. "Not really. There's plenty of money to be made in Lisbon, and Sea Freight Shipping is just one of many companies trying to break into the international market," he explained, loosening the knot in his burgundy tie. "On the upside, I found the perfect location for Dolce Vita Lisbon."

"That's great, baby. Congratulations! I'm so happy for you."

"We should celebrate at The Four Seasons," he proposed. "We can have dinner on the terrace and slow dance under the stars."

"That sounds wonderful Nicco, especially the part about us slow dancing."

"I thought you might like that." His gaze was full of longing and heat. "And when we get to the penthouse suite, I'm going to show you *just* how much I missed you."

Jariah was so excited she feared her heart would burst right out of her chest, but she faked a scowl and pretended to be upset. "Do you ever think of anything besides sex?"

"Yes, you, and when I'm not thinking about you, I'm dreaming about you."

Licking her lips, she fanned her hands to her face. *God help me.*

"I can't wait to see you," he said, leaning forward in his chair. "We might have to forgo dinner and spend the entire night in bed. Sound good to you?"

"Quit flirting and get off the phone." She blushed. "You have a plane to catch, and I'll kill you if you miss that flight!"

Chuckling, he threw his hands in the air like a crook surrendering to the police. "All right, all right, I'm leaving, take it easy, baby. I'll call you when I land at Miami International…"

Jariah heard a knock on the door, and reluctantly tore her gaze away from the computer screen. Fear knotted inside her chest, and panic gripped her heart. Standing in the doorway, wearing a fitted red business suit and a dark hostile glare was Vivica Morretti.

"Baby, what's wrong? Is everything okay?"

"Yes, of course," she lied, regaining the use of her mouth. "Have a safe flight."

Quickly, Jariah logged out of Skype and closed her monthly planner. She couldn't risk Mrs. Morretti seeing the love notes Nicco had given her, so she dropped it in her bottom drawer and jumped to her feet. Her stomach was twisted in knots, but she didn't let her fear show. If she did, Nicco's mother would eat her alive. "It's wonderful seeing you again, Mrs. Morretti. How are you?"

"Was that my son?" she asked, pointing at the computer. "He called you from Lisbon?"

"Yes, of course, we were talking about work, and—"

"Sex, right?"

A gasp fell from Jariah's lips.

"You used sex to entice and seduce my son, but I'm here to tell you the jig is up."

The temperature in the office shot through the roof.

"I know all about how you trapped Wesley Covington by willfully getting pregnant." Her tone was matter-of-fact, and her voice was patronizing. "You have several online dating profiles. I wouldn't be surprised if my son was just one of many wealthy, influential men supporting you."

"Is that what you think? That I'm after Nicco's money?"

"I don't think, Ms. Brooks. I know."

"If Nicco lost everything tomorrow, it wouldn't change how I feel about him. I love him because of who he is, not because of what he has. He's the man for me, and I plan to be in his life for many years to come."

"I have a hair appointment at noon, so I'm going to get right to the point." Mrs. Morretti flicked her thick, auburn locks over her shoulders. The former Broadway actress had a slender frame, a perfectly sculptured nose and radiant brown skin. She didn't have a crease or wrinkle in sight, and carried herself with the grace of a prima ballerina. "As of four o'clock today, you no longer work for Morretti Incorporated. You are not the right fit for this company or my son, and I expect you out of here by the end of the workday."

"With all due respect, you didn't hire me, and I don't work for you."

Her eyes were sharp, lethal daggers. "I'm a company stakeholder, and also one of the founding members. I have the power to make decisions just like anyone else on the board."

The news came as a shock and sent Jariah's heartbeat into an erratic tailspin. It took everything she had not to cry, and supreme effort not to argue. Mrs. Morretti spoke in a polite, quiet manner, and never once raised her voice. But her hatred was evident, as clear as the clouds in the morning sky.

Mrs. Morretti opened her Louis Vuitton purse and took out a white envelope. "Here's your termination letter and your severance pay," she said. "I understand the plight of single mothers, so I ensured that your settlement was more than generous."

A sickening wave of nausea bubbled up inside Jariah's throat. She didn't care what was inside the envelope, and dropped it on the desk.

"Open it," she instructed.

With her heart in her throat, Jariah took the envelope, ripped it open and cast a critical eye over the termination contract. It was a standard letter, legally binding, and there was nothing she could do to fight it. Staring at the check, she was sure the accounting department had made another mistake. Then, it hit her. *Is this severance pay or a bribe?* Jariah did the math in her head, and knew without a doubt that it was the latter.

"You have your money, so be on your way." Her features darkened, and her tone was sharp. "I'm not going to warn you again, Mrs. Brooks. Stay away from Nicco or you'll be sorry."

"Are you threatening me?"

"Keep your money-hungry paws off my son," she spat, "and concentrate on raising your daughter. She doesn't need a rich new stepfather."

Her words were a slap in the face. "I'm a good mother."

"That's not what I heard."

Anger surged through Jariah's veins. "You don't know anything about me—"

"Oh, yes, I do. You're as devious and as calculating as Nicco's last assistant, and I'm not going to sit back and let you hurt my son. He deserves the best, and you my dear, are not it."

Her vision blurred, grew thick with unshed tears, but through the haze Jariah saw Mrs. Morretti spin around and storm out of the office. In her mind, she replayed their conversation, and the more she thought about it, the more depressed she felt.

Wiping her eyes, she took a long, hard look at her severance check. Twenty-five thousand dollars was nothing to laugh at. It was enough to buy a new car and put a down payment on a house with a big backyard for Ava. And there would be some left over for a rainy day.

And you're going to need it, her conscience pointed out, *because as of four o'clock today you won't have a job...or a man.*

Chapter 20

"Welcome home, boss." Gerald opened the back door of the white stretch Hummer parked along the curb at Miami International Airport. "It's good to see you."

"Thanks, Gerald. Sorry for delay. I got held up in customs."

Exhausted, Nicco slid inside the car and dropped his brown leather briefcase at his feet.

Back behind the wheel, Gerald checked his rearview mirror and joined the slow-moving traffic on Airport Road. The walkways were clogged with travelers hailing taxicabs, dragging luggage and yapping on their cell phones. "How was your flight?"

"Terrible." Nicco unbuttoned his suit jacket and loosened the knot in his pinstripe tie. "Reminded me to never fly commercial again. Everyone in first-class was a mess!"

"It couldn't have been that bad."

"The turbulence was horrendous, and the soap star sitting beside me kept cooing in my ear and rubbing her fake boobs against my shoulder."

"You're right. It sounds horrible." Gerald chuckled and

tossed a glance over his right shoulder. "Six months ago you would have taken her to the lavatory for a quickie."

"I was stupid and reckless back then."

"And now?"

And now, I'm anxious to marry Jariah and start a family. The thought caused his chest to swell with pride. He'd been enamored with her from the day they'd met, and over the summer his feelings had developed into the real thing. With Jariah, he knew exactly where he stood, and never second-guessed her feelings. She proved her love and devotion to him every day, and always put their relationship first. He loved that about her, and knew without a doubt that she'd never betray his trust.

"Where to, boss?"

"Morretti Inc.," Nicco said, surfacing from his thoughts. Fatigued by the fourteen-hour flight from Lisbon, he settled into his seat and closed his tired eyes. "I have to pick up some files for my trip to L.A. tomorrow, but I won't be at the office long, so stay close by."

Rock music and the scent of seawater flooded the car through the open sunroof. Stars glimmered in the sky, fashionably dressed couples streamed in and out of upscale restaurants and nightclubs, and police officers mounted on horseback patrolled the crowded downtown streets.

Nicco spotted a girl with pigtails playing hopscotch in front of Dairy Queen and broke into a broad grin. Images of Ava filled his mind. The young girl had grabbed a hold of his heart from the onset and had been squeezing it ever since. Thinking about the afternoon he'd taken Ava and Richie to play miniature golf at Boomers made Nicco chuckle to himself.

"I think my mom has a crush on you," Ava had announced.

"What makes you so sure?"

"I heard her talking outside to our next-door neighbors, Sadie and Felicia, and she had a lot to say about you."

"Really?" he'd questioned, his curiosity getting the best of him. "What did she say?"

Ava had stuck out her left hand and wiggled her fingers. "It's gonna cost you."

Like a fool, he'd opened his wallet and took out ten dollars.

"Really? That's the best you can do? If you want me to spill the beans, you're going to have to do *much* better than that."

"Yeah," Richie had agreed. "Dig deep, Uncle Nicco! We need that money to buy candy!"

An hour later, Nicco was fifty dollars poorer, but felt ten feet tall. The next day, on his way home from work, he'd dropped by Tiffany & Co. and bought the most expensive engagement ring in the store. Nicco patted the front of his suit pocket to ensure the diamond solitaire was still safe and sound. He was ready to spend the rest of his life with Jariah and couldn't wait to see the look on her face when he popped the question at dinner later that evening. He didn't want to live without her, couldn't do it, and would be proud to call Ava his stepdaughter.

Nicco heard his cell phone ring and retrieved it from his briefcase. He slid his index finger across the screen and put his iPhone to his ear. "Nicco Morretti."

"This is Detective Katsu from the Miami Police Department," said a gruff voice. "We found your Mercedes. It's on fire."

Ice spread through Nicco's veins. At a loss for words, his thoughts spun out-of-control. He slumped against his seat, stunned and confused by the news. Panic and fear drenched his body in a cold, chilling sweat. Why hadn't Jariah called? Was she hurt? Was Ava okay?

"Do you know a woman by the name of Jariah Brooks?"

Nicco blinked, came to his senses. "Yes, of course," he said, raking a hand through his hair. "What happened? Where is she? Can I speak to her?"

"I'd rather not talk over the phone. Can you meet me at Ms. Brooks's residence? I'm in the process of taking her fiancé's statement and—"

"Fiancé!" Nicco shouted, his pulse pounding erratically in his ears. "What fiancé?"

There was a profound silence, and the distant wail of a police siren.

"When I arrived on the scene Ms. Brooks was standing outside of her residence with a man by the name of Wesley Covington," the detective explained. "He identified himself as her fiancé, led her back inside the house, and hasn't left her side since."

Slow, sensuous music penetrated Jariah's consciousness, but the stench of burnt rubber and smoke killed the romantic mood. Moistening her lips with her tongue, she opened her eyes, fully expecting to see Nicco lying beside her. He wasn't, but Wesley was.

All at once, everything came rushing back—her heated argument with Mrs. Morretti that morning, returning home to an empty house, primping and prepping for her late-night date with Nicco. Less than an hour later, Wesley and her neighbor Mr. Regula were banging on her door, imploring her to get out of the house. Outside, Nicco's Mercedes Benz S350 was engulfed in flames, and her complex was jam-packed with news trucks, fire engines and police cars. Jariah had never seen anything like it, and hours later, she still couldn't believe someone had brazenly set a car on fire in a neighborhood overrun with small children and young families.

Jariah yawned and rubbed the sleep from her eyes. She must have dozed off, because her head was on Wesley's chest, and his arms were wrapped around her shoulders.

Straightening, she noticed he was watching music videos and playing Scrabble on his iPhone. Once the police had taken her statement and left the house following a brief look around, they'd sat on the living-room couch and had a blunt conversation. Her first question? Whether or not he'd sent that bogus email message to her parents. He'd coughed like a smoker on his death bed and then fervently denied being involved. Jariah didn't believe him, but decided to put the whole ugly incident behind her. Her parents were back in her life, and that was all that mattered to Jariah.

"How was your nap? Feeling better?"

"A little." Knowing she looked a mess, she straightened her sundress and combed a hand through her curly disheveled hair. "Thanks for sticking around, Wesley. If not for you, the police would have hauled me to jail and thrown away the key."

"I'm glad I could help." He moved closer and draped an arm around her shoulder. "Jariah, you mean the world to me, and I've never stopped loving you."

Biting the inside of her cheek, she glanced away from his piercing gaze.

"I'm ready to step up to the plate, and to be the man you need me to be." His voice was filled with sincerity. He placed a hand on her thigh. "I almost lost you tonight, and I don't want to lose you again."

"That's too bad. You're too late."

At the sound of Nicco's curt, brisk voice, Jariah felt a turbulent rush of panic. By now, he knew about his car, and the fire that had destroyed it. Inwardly, she feared he'd blow up at her or blame her for what happened, and that had her on edge. Taking in a deep breath, Jariah stood and prepared to learn her fate.

"You've said you're peace. Now leave."

Wesley surged to his feet. "Make me." His nostrils flared and his jaw clenched.

Nicco wanted to sock in the man in the face, but he didn't want the police, who were standing outside in the parking lot, to arrest him for assault. He couldn't stomach seeing Jariah with her ex, so he crossed the room and draped a hand around her waist. "I need to talk to my girlfriend alone, so you can show yourself out."

"You're never going to last," he sneered, a scowl staining his lips. "When you get sick of playing second fiddle to his career, and all of his *other* women, give me a call."

Nicco chided himself to keep his temper in check, but the moment he heard the front door slam he exploded in anger. "What the hell is going on?" he demanded, dropping his hands from around her waist. "Are you out of your damn mind?"

Jariah tried to touch him, but Nicco stepped back, out of reach. "Baby, I am so sorry about your car, but I swear, I had nothing to do with the fire—"

"I don't give a shit about the Mercedes."

"Then why are you so mad? Why are you shouting?"

"Because I flew over four thousand miles to see you, only to find you hugged up on the couch with your no-good ex," he growled through clenched teeth. "Why was Wesley here? And don't tell me he came to see Ava, because I called your parents after I got off the phone with Detective Katsu, and they told me she's spending the weekend with them."

"Wesley had a bad day at work, and needed someone to talk to."

"Then he should call a shrink, not you."

"Nicco, we dated for five years, and we have a child together—"

"I don't like seeing him here."

"Too bad," she snapped, growing frustrated with his attitude. "He's Ava's father."

"Yeah, he's Ava's father, *not* your man, so remember that the next time he's rubbing your knee and whispering bullshit lines in your ear."

Nicco saw her face harden like stone and knew he'd crossed the line. In three short strides, he was at her side, pulling her to his chest. Slowly and tenderly, he stroked her hair and neck. "Damn, I'm sorry. I shouldn't have said that."

"You're right. You shouldn't have. You're acting like a jealous lover, and you have no reason to be. I've never given you a reason to doubt my love and fidelity, and I never will."

"I know, but I can't help it. I lose my head whenever I see you with another guy."

Jariah poked him in the chest. "Now you know how I felt when Estelle tried to jump your bones!"

"Baby, you're the only woman I want. You know that."

His gaze met hers, weakening the hard, impenetrable shell around her heart.

"Did you see the person who set the fire?"

Jariah shook her head and wore an apologetic smile. "No, unfortunately, I didn't. I was upstairs in the shower, and the next thing I know, Wesley and my neighbor Mr. Regula were banging on the front door, yelling at me to get out of the house."

"You must have been terrified."

"Yeah, mostly of them breaking in and finding me in my birthday suit!"

The thought of her naked, curvy body glistening with

water sent a shiver down his spine. Nicco wanted to make love to Jariah more than anything, but didn't act on his impulse. It wasn't the right time. Not with cops, firefighters and reporters roaming around her complex.

"It wasn't as dramatic as it sounds." Jariah snuggled against him. "By the time I got dressed and went outside the firefighters had the fire contained, and the police were interviewing witnesses."

"I spoke to the lead detective on the case, and he had a lot of interesting information to share," Nicco said as his gaze drifted to the front window. "I'm going to call a family meeting next week so Detective Katsu can bring everyone up to speed."

"But you're leaving for L.A. tomorrow and won't be back for two weeks."

"Once I learned about the fire, I called the VP of the Childs Corporation and rescheduled our meeting for October." Nicco gave her a serious no-nonsense look. "And this time you're coming with me. No excuses."

"I'm there. Spending time with you at a world-famous resort sounds like heaven."

Wrapping her up in his arms, he lifted her chin and covered her mouth with a deep, passionate kiss. "I'm going outside to wait for the tow truck, and you're going upstairs to pack an overnight bag. I'm taking you back to my place."

"But your parents are staying with you."

"Baby, my estate is over fifteen thousand square feet, and they have their own private wing," he said, patting her affectionately on the hips. "Besides, they'll be too busy watching, *Italia's Got Talent* to pay us any mind!"

As Jariah reflected on her conversation with Nicco's mother she felt a nervous flutter in her belly. Her head throbbed, and her heart ached at the memory of Vivica's viscous words. *You're devious, and calculating... My son deserves the best, and, you're not it.* The thought of being without Nicco—of not seeing him or hearing his voice or feeling the warmth of his touch—was killing her inside. But she'd rather lose him than put a wedge between him and his parents. He'd find love with someone else, and she had Ava, and a healthy, renewed relationship with her mom and dad to be thankful for.

You deserve to have it all, whispered her inner voice.

Encouraged by her thoughts, she swallowed the lump in her throat and told Nicco about her unexpected visit that morning from his mom. "After she fired me, she made it very clear that I'm not good enough for you, and that she'll never welcome me or Ava into your family."

"To be honest, I'm not surprised. Ma's always been overprotective, and it takes her a while for her warm up to people, *especially* women dating her sons." Nicco gave Jariah a peck on the cheek and told her not to worry. "Ma will come around. I know it."

"That's it? That's all you have to say?" Incredulous, Jariah folded her arms across her chest and gave him a pointed look. "I've been a basket case all day, and all you can say is, 'Ma will come around'?"

His grin, though tinged with amusement, didn't cheer her. And neither did the hand he placed on her shoulder. "Leave Ma to me. I can handle her."

"Fine, but until you do, I won't be sleeping at your place or traveling out of town with you."

"Really?"

"I'm afraid so," she said.

"You leave me no choice then." Nicco whipped his iPhone out of his pocket, punched in a number and put it to his ear. "Hello, yes, this is Nicco Morretti... I'd like to book the penthouse suite for the rest of the week..."

Moments later, he ended the call and pointed at the staircase. "Go pack and hurry up or there'll be hell to pay when we get to The Four Seasons."

Jariah shot him a lusty smile. "Promise?"

Chapter 21

"Now that everyone's here, and the kids ran off to play, let's get down to business."

Everyone gathered inside the living room in Nicco's Coral Gables mansion turned toward the two, gray-haired detectives standing beside the fireplace. To calm her nerves, Jariah snuggled closer to Nicco, drawing comfort from his touch. Designer fragrances and the spicy aromas drifting out of the kitchen created a delicious scent. Chef Gambo and his team were preparing a feast, and every few minutes Jariah heard the flamboyant chef shouting instructions in Italian. Laughter penetrated the windows and the sound of Ava's and Richie's high-pitched giggles lightened the bleak mood.

Sitting beside Nicco on the couch should have quieted her troubled mind, but Jariah couldn't stop thinking about what happened on Friday night. Three days had passed since the fire, and although the police had cleared her as a suspect, she knew it would take a lot longer than seventy-two hours to win over Arturo and Vivica Morretti.

Her thoughts wandered to last night. At dinner, she'd sensed the couple's displeasure, their unhappiness, and if it were not for Ava sitting beside her eating happily, she would have left the five-star restaurant and returned home. Nicco insisted that things would get better in time, but Jariah suspected his parents would never accept her.

Casting her gaze around the spacious, sun-drenched room, she marveled at just how good-looking the Morretti men were. It didn't seem fair that they were all attractive, successful and filthy rich. Demetri, a baseball superstar with dreamy eyes and a chiseled physique was soft-spoken, great with kids and wholly devoted to his fiancée, Angela Kelly. The couple sat cuddled up on the sofa, his arm draped around her shoulders, and they shared kisses when they thought no one was looking. Rafael, the firstborn and heir to the Morretti shipping empire, had a somber disposition but on the rare occasion that he smiled, he could give any Hollywood heartthrob a serious run for their money.

"We've interviewed several witnesses, and have generated some strong leads, but we still have a lot of holes in our investigation," Detective Katsu explained. "We were hoping you could fill in some of the holes for us."

"What do you want to know?" Arturo glanced between the detectives. "I have nothing to hide and I want the bastard responsible for the fire brought to justice."

Detective Katsu took a pen out of his shirt pocket and flipped open his blue spiral notebook. "I'd like to start with Demetri," he announced. "Why did you file a restraining order against your former publicist, Nichola Caruso?"

"Because she kept dropping by my estate unannounced. My lawyer said filing a restraining order would be in my best interest, so I filed the paper work with the court last week."

"I've seen this happen a million times." Detective Bueschler stroked his broad chin, regarded Demetri closely. "You had a fling with Ms. Caruso that went south, didn't you?"

"Our relationship was strictly platonic. Nothing inappropriate ever happened. Nichola was like a kid sister to me, and I viewed her as nothing more than a great friend."

Detective Katsu nodded, and then flipped to the next page in his notebook. "Why did Tye Caldwell resign from Morretti Incorporated? Was the decision of his own free will?"

Jariah felt Nicco's body tense and she squeezed his right hand to offer her support. His shoulders stiffened, and the veins in his neck were twitching, but his voice didn't betray his emotions. "It was a mutual decision between all parties involved."

Detective Bueschler barked a cold, bitter laugh. "Mr. Caldwell's Facebook and Twitter posts tell a *very* different story. He hates your family, and it sounds like he's out for revenge."

"Tye would never do anything to hurt us," Nicco argued, rising from his seat.

"I can't prove it, but I have a feeling my former assistant, Gracie O'Conner, is involved."

"That petite brunette with the braces?" Detective Bueschler doubled over, chuckled as if he was at a comedy club. "Right!"

"Tye didn't vandalize my restaurant, and he damn sure didn't set my car on fire. He isn't even in Miami. He's been backpacking in Europe for months."

"So you've been in contact with him then?"

"No," Nicco said in an exasperated tone of voice, "but my security team monitors his movements, and his ex-wife does a great job of keeping me in the loop."

Detective Katsu closed his notebook. "If Tye's out of the country, then we're back to square one, because I thought for sure he was our guy."

"Arturo, can you think of anyone who would want to

harm you and your family?" Detective Bueschler asked, stroking the length of his jaw. "Anyone at all?"

Rafael gave a wry laugh. "Pull up a seat detectives. This could take a while."

Eyebrows raised, the detectives exchanged a curious look.

Silence plagued the living room, causing the tension in the air to rise.

"Non voglio farti del male, Nicco, ma questo deve essere detto," Mrs. Morretti said, her voice matter-of-fact. *"Jariah ha datato un sacco di uomini. Come fai a sapere uno dei suoi amanti online non ha definito le Mercedes in fiamme in una rabbia gelosa..."*

A crippling pain racked Jariah's body. Tears pricked her eyes, and it hurt to swallow. She couldn't believe what she was hearing, couldn't believe the lies coming out of Mrs. Morretti's mouth. *You think one of my online boyfriends set Nicco's car on fire in a jealous rage? What online boyfriends? I don't have time to play the field; I'm a single mother, and my daughter is my number one priority!* Something inside Jariah snapped, causing her pulse to go haywire, and her temperature to spike. Her fast, heavy breathing filled the air, and her heart was beating so loud she knew everyone inside the living room could hear it.

Straightening her spine, she pinned back her shoulders and openly glared at Mrs. Morretti. Her stomach muscles clenched and contracted, but she spoke in a clear, confident voice. *"Perché, Nicco è l'unico uomo che io sono uscito e stato intimo con da quando ho rotto con il mio ex. Non ci sono gelosi ex-fidanzati, e non ho alcuna intenzione di datazione chiunque altro. Nicco è tutto l'uomo che mi serve, e non ho mai amato nessuno più di quanto ami tuo figlio."*

To Jariah's surprise, Vivica cooed, Demetri and Rafael

wore matching ear-to-ear grins and Mr. Morretti nodded his head in approval.

"Y-y-you speak Italian," Mrs. Morretti stammered, her face as pale as her white, cashmere scarf. "I had no idea... That means you understood what I said last night at dinner."

"Sì, l'ho fatto, ma io non ho intenzione di lasciare che tu o chiunque vieni tra me e l'uomo che amo. Nicco è la mia anima gemella, e non sarò mai lasciare la sua parte."

"Baby, that's beautiful." Nicco's tone was soft, a soothing caress, and happiness shone in his eyes. "I love you, too, more than you will ever know."

His words comforted Jariah, made her feel incredibly special, but she turned to Detective Katsu and asked the question on the tip of her tongue. "Is it safe for me to go home? The Sheraton is great, but I'm sick of eating room service, and my daughter misses her friends."

"Absolutely not. The lunatic who started that fire is still out there," Nicco said, furiously shaking his head. "You and Ava will move in here for the time being."

"We're going to stay here? Yahoo!" Ava raced into the living room with Richie in tow.

"I appreciate your very generous offer, but we can't live here. I don't want to set the wrong example for my daughter."

"The wrong example?" Nicco repeated, folding his arms. "What are you saying?"

"That I won't shack up with you. I made that mistake once, and I won't do it again."

Their eyes aligned, and an awkward silence fell over the room.

"Then," Nicco said, with a grin, "I guess this is the perfect time, Ava."

"For what?" Richie stopped and scratched his head.

Jariah shot Nicco a what-are-you-talking-about gaze.

And she watched him reach into his pocket and pull out a small turquoise box. He presented it to Ava, and she burst out laughing.

"Nicco, I can't marry you," she said, cupping a hand over her mouth to stifle her giggles. "I'm only six, and you're *super* old!"

Everyone smiled and chuckled.

"Ava, I bought this ring for you as a sign of my love," Nicco said.

"Wow, it's pretty." Ava snatched the heart-shaped diamond out of the box and slid it on her finger. "Thank you, Nicco. I'll never take it off. Not even when I go to bed!"

"I promise to take care of you, and to do everything I can to make you happy."

Glancing around, Ava shielded her mouth with the back of her hand. "Are you going to help me do my homework and sneak me chocolate cookies when my mom's not looking?"

Nicco winked. "Yup, *and* I'll take you to Chuck E. Cheese's on Fridays so you can beat Richie at 'Western Wrangler.'"

"Yahoo!" Ava threw her arms around Nicco's neck, and kissed him on the cheek. "And I promise to be the best stepdaughter ever!"

"Is it okay if I propose to your mom now?" Nicco asked. "Is that okay with you?"

Nodding, Ava scooted behind Jariah and shoved her into his open arms.

"Mom, it's your turn!" she said excitedly. "I think Nicco has a ring for you, too!"

Tears flowed freely down Jariah's cheeks, and the living room became a big, white blur. Her heart was pounding, and her breathing was so shallow she feared her next breath could be her last.

"Baby, I can't imagine my life without you in it. You're

smart, vivacious and fiesty as hell, and knowing you has made me a better man."

Jariah sniffed, willed herself not to sob. There was nothing cute about her cry, and she didn't want to ruin the moment by slobbering all over herself.

"You are the best thing that has ever happened to me, and I want to spend the rest of my life with you." Nicco took her hand, and pressed it flat against his chest. "You're my life, my oxygen, the very air I breathe, and I want you to marry you more than anything in the world."

It was the biggest surprise of Jariah's life, a moment she would never forget, and she couldn't contain the excitement bubbling up inside her. *"Ti amo così tanto! Certo che ti sposo! Tu sei tutto quello che potevo desiderare in un uomo e molto di più!"*

"Baby, you're jumping the gun," Nicco whispered. "Say yes *after* I propose."

Jariah giggled, felt happier than she'd ever been. Out of the corner of her eye, she spotted Mrs. Morretti dabbing her cheeks with a pink hankerchief and wondered if she was crying tears of joy or grief. Deciding it didn't matter, Jariah returned her gaze to the man she loved, her heart so full of love and affection she felt like she was going to burst.

Nicco took another turquoise box out of his back pocket.

"Dang, bro, just how big *is* your pocket? What are you going to pull out next? A brand-new car!" Rafael laughed at his own joke. But when Nicco dropped to one knee and clasped Jariah's left hand, he was the first one to whip out his iPhone and start snapping pictures.

"Jariah Brooks, will you marry me?"

The engagement ring was a stunner, a rose-gold sparkler that twinkled and shined, but it was the loving expression on Nicco's face that took Jariah's breath away. They had a lot of obstacles to contend with, and his mother would probably never accept her into the family, but Jariah chose to focus on the positives. As long as she had Nicco's unconditional love and support nothing else mattered.

Jariah wanted to dive into Nicco's arms and plant a sexy, red-hot kiss on him, but decided to have a little fun with him first. "I don't know. I'm, ah, having second thoughts."

His face fell, and the grin slid off his mouth. "You are?"

"The ring is *so* big, and look at all the sparkling baguette diamonds. It's *so* not me."

Nicco tossed his head back and erupted in laughter. Chuckling, he scooped Jariah up in his arms and spun her around until she begged in English *and* Italian for him to stop. "That's what you get for teasing me. I almost had a heart attack!"

Laughing, cheering and applauding, the Morretti family surrounded the newly engaged couple, offering hugs, kisses and well-wishes.

"Welcome to the family." Arturo kissed Jariah on both cheeks and whispered in her ear, "You're the perfect woman for my son, and likely the only person who can keep him in check. I'm thrilled, and I can't wait for you guys to fill this big, empty mansion with children."

Me, too, Mr. Morretti. Me, too.

It was a beautiful moment, but Jariah wished her parents had been there to witness it.

Later, after Nicco's family left, they'd drive over to her mom and dad's house to share the wonderful news.

"Congratulations," Detective Katsu said. "We're leaving, but we'll be in touch."

"Thanks for stopping by." Nicco shook hands with the detectives. "Take care."

"Isn't it great? Now I have three grandmas instead of two!" Ava wrapped her arms around Mrs. Morretti. "I love you, Nicco's mom. You make the best peanut butter cookies ever!"

It was the first time Jariah had ever seen Mrs. Morretti smile, and when she bent down and kissed Ava's forehead Jariah wanted to weep for joy. "I know we got off to a rocky start, but I hope one day we can be friends," she said, choking back tears.

"I'd like that, and from now on please call me Vivica. You're going to marry my son, and one day give me grandchildren. Mrs. Morretti is *way* too formal!"

Jazz music flowed through the sound system, and waiters appeared holding trays filled with artichoke brushetta, crab beignets and rose champagne. Toasts were made, laughter abounded and the appetizers were devoured in the blink of an eye. Richie told knock-knock jokes with the skill of a seasoned comic, and Ava wowed everyone with her Taylor Swift impression.

Alone in the corner of the room, Nicco and Jariah kissed and laughed like teenagers inside a parked car at Lover's Lane. Boldly capturing her around the waist, he took her in his arms and tenderly stroked her cheeks with the back of his hand.

"You're the sexiest, most captivating woman I have ever seen, Mrs. Nicco Morretti-to-be." Nicco's mouth moved over her forehead and across her cheeks, teased and tickled her warm flesh. His lips continued to arouse and entice her, caused waves of pleasure to consume her body. "Think we should kick everyone out so we can have engagement sex?"

Jariah swatted his forearm. "Nicco, you're terrible. I swear sex is all you ever think about."

"Don't *Nicco* me. You were thinking the *exact* same thing."

A giggle fell out of her mouth. "You know me so well."

"Of course I do. We were made for each other."

Their eyes aligned, made an unspoken vow, a promise. "You've made me a very happy man, Jariah." Nicco bowed his head and murmured into her ear in a voice rife with hunger and need. "I love you, baby, always and forever."

"I love you with all my heart, Nicco, for as long as we both shall live."

Nicco kissed her eyelids, the tip of her nose, brushed his lips gently against her earlobes, and when their lips touched, Jariah knew all of her dreams had finally come true. He kissed her slowly, thoughtfully, like a man hopelessly in love, and his touch warmed her all over.

"I can't wait for you and Ava to move in," he said, burying his hands into her hair. "The three of us are going to have a blast together."

"And now that I'm unemployed, I'll have plenty of time to cook for you."

"Don't even try it. I expect you at the office bright and early Monday morning."

Jariah pouted, made a face. "Can I at least keep the severance check?"

"No, but if you're a good girl I'll let you drive the Lambo when we go see your parents."

"Wow," she gushed, widening her eyes. "You really *do* love me!"

They cracked up, and the warmth and beauty of their unbridled laughter made everyone around them smile.

* * * * *

LET'S TALK

Romance

For exclusive extracts, competitions
and special offers, find us online: